ARIEL

ⱬ

ESSAYS ON THE ARTS
AND THE HISTORY AND PHILOSOPHY OF MEDICINE

ARIEL

ESSAYS ON THE ARTS
AND THE HISTORY AND PHILOSOPHY
OF MEDICINE

félix martí-ibáñez / m.d.

Editor-in-Chief of MD, the Medical Newsmagazine
New York

Former Professor and Director of the
Department of the History of Medicine
New York Medical College
Flower and Fifth Avenue Hospitals

MD PUBLICATIONS / INC.

NEW YORK

To my good and wonderful mother,
Josefina Ibáñez de Martí Alpera,
and to the inspiring memory of my father,
Professor Félix Martí Alpera
a paragon of goodness, courage,
wisdom, and integrity.

TABLE OF CONTENTS

Introduction
UNDER THE SIGN OF THE ANGEL

Born under the sign of Ariel, that elusive angel symbolic of "unselfish motives in actions" and of "the spirituality of culture," * this book of essays is intended to be a pensive yet smiling traveling companion to my previous work, *Centaur: Essays on the History of Medical Ideas,* which, thanks to the kindly welcome accorded it by my colleagues, is still prancing across the evergreen prairies of American medical thought.

The root from which these essays spring is twofold: one, the concern of a wandering, restless physician in the fragment of space and

* The Spaniard Clarin, in his prologue to the book, *Ariel,* by José Enrique Rodó (Editorial Sopena Argentina, Buenos Aires, 1949), wrote:
"It is called *Ariel* perhaps because it is reminiscent of, yet antithetical to, Renan's Caliban. As is known, Ariel is the elusive jinni—"an ayrie spirit"— who obeys Prospero's commands in Shakespeare's *The Tempest,* while Caliban is a savage and deformed slave. . . . In Rodó's book, the venerable teacher, standing next to a statue of Ariel in the study hall, bids his pupils farewell, which represents the final scene of *The Tempest,* when the magician Prospero sets free the ayrie spirit.
"Rodó incites American youth to abandon Caliban's ways, utilitarianism and blind sensualism, and to follow those of Ariel, the ayrie spirit: a spirituality that cherishes intelligence for its own sake, beauty, grace, and the unalloyed mysteries of the infinite."
Rodó himself refers to Ariel in the following terms: "Ariel, the jinni of the air, represents, in the symbolism of Shakespeare's work, the noble and winged side of the spirit. Ariel symbolizes the mastery of reason and feeling over the base urgings of irrationality; Ariel is also generous enthusiasm, highminded, unselfish motives in action, the spirituality of culture, the grace and liveliness of intelligence, the ideal goal toward which mankind strives, rectifying in the superior man, with the unrelenting chisel of life, the stubborn vestiges of Caliban, symbol of torpidity and sensuality."

the instant of time—the world and history—in which he has the privilege to live; and two, his dream that life—the miniature history of each man—and history—the mighty life of nations—should harmonize, so that every individual life may be tinged with history, and history in turn may never lose the humaneness of life.

The essays, articles, and lectures collected here in greatly expanded and revised versions were exposed beforehand to the eyes or ears of audiences, who generously granted them their recognition. This is a good way for a book to be born: to experience first, while in transitory form, its "moment of truth" before an audience, and later, after having received its approval, to acquire the dignity of permanence inherent in a book.

The curtain rises on *Ariel* with a section, "Through the Magic Door of Words," designed to recall good books and to extol the art of elegant expression. The first essay in this section crystallizes a concept, a practical philosophy of action, a journalistic ideal, all applied to the conception and development of my dream, the medical newsmagazine *MD,* that became a thrilling reality. Other essays deal with books I have reread with increasing pleasure and admiration, which, I trust, will be shared by my colleagues. This is followed by a section devoted to symbols and symbolism, so important in the world of today, where the symbolic equation $E = mc^2$ formulated by Albert Einstein has been transformed, through the atomic energy derived from it, into an omen for a future of technological perfection or for an apocalyptic nuclear holocaust.

The section "The March of Medical History" contains essays portraying the panorama of the history of medicine, both the history recorded in the clay tablets of Babylon and the yellowing parchments of the Middle Ages and that which is being made today by contemporary physicians and surgeons. This section concludes with an essay on the marvelous mind of one man, Henry Sigerist, in whose mental domains, as in the terrestrial domains of Philip II, the sun never set. In Sigerist's case, the sun was his love of man and his curiosity about history.

The section "The Epic of Medicine" includes my editorials, considerably expanded, originally published in the issues of *MD,* the medical newsmagazine, dedicated to The Epic of Medicine. The purpose of these editorials was to present a succinct but poetic view of the history of medicine, by way of introducing the reader to the fascinating world of medicine as it evolved in relation to the history of civilization. These editorials therefore are like that light, soft prelude played by the orchestra before the curtain rises.

Travels and people occupy the section entitled "Journeys, Ports, Peoples." Every man's mind changes perforce after he has made a number of journeys round the world and has witnessed the problems, labors, ideals, anxieties, and triumphs of people of races alien to us, but who, like us, struggle, suffer, and hope with all their heart and soul. This section includes essays on the human family throughout the world, the connection between medicine and travel, the witchery of the sea, exploration and medicine, the meaning of sports, the magic of great cities, and the profound meaning of a medical friendship in Japan. There will be more about travel in my forthcoming book on my trip around the world entitled *Journey Around Myself.*

The art of love, exemplified in normal love, and hypertrophied in the erotic marathon of Casanova, and female psychology as mirrored in letters written by women comprise "Love, Lust, and Letters."

It would have been inexcusable to ignore in this volume some of the wonders of the human being, wonders that, unfortunately, we physicians often forget through being too close to them, even as the curator of a fine painting, or a precious statue, or a historical shrine may eventually forget its value, and even its beauty, from seeing at all times of the day the blisters on the painting, the cracks on the statue, or the stains of time on the shrine. The face, the hand, the eye therefore receive their due in various essays, intended to relate and extol the glory and marvel of the human organs.

Medicine is art, but it is also science and, always, philosophy. The spirit of scientific inquiry inherent in the investigator, the nature and history—body and life—of the human being, and the physicians' duty to report and communicate their knowledge form a section assigned to the philosophy of medicine.

And since philosophy cannot survive without religion, be this confessional or spiritual, in the final section, "Religio Medici," I define my credo as to what it really means to be a physician and to be a student of medicine, and I set forth the heritage left by St. Luke the "beloved physician" to his descendants.

Thus, in *Ariel,* I again support the concept that the history of medicine must be a sociological instead of an iatrocentric history. I also support the idea that instead of the present-day "fire brigade" therapies, which through shocks to its organs destroy so much of the human being, just as firemen destroy so much in order to extinguish a fire, medicine must really become medical anthropology, must become more universal and comprehensive, less "shocking" and more whole, more humane and less technological.

In brief, this volume, in which the angel Ariel comes down to earth to tread lightly side by side with the restless Centaur, is an impassioned plea for the physician to remember constantly that to be a good doctor he must before all else know how to be a man.

Félix Martí-Ibáñez, MD.

I. through the magic door of words

THE FABRIC AND CREATION OF A DREAM

On the Genesis and Growth of a New Concept in Medical Journalism
as Exemplified by the Medical Newsmagazine, *MD*

I. THE SYMBOL OF THE SAILBOAT

I shall not make a formal eulogy of this meeting of the American
Medical Writers' Association. The speaker's supreme happiness
is to be enamored of a fine work such as yours and to sprinkle
his praises here and there, with the same delicious abandon of a lover
who, when kissing a pretty woman, is as likely to commence with the
crown of her head as the tip of her nose, for to him all of her is perfection.

I shall confine myself here to saying that your ideal of bringing together all who are dedicated to the cultivation of good writing in
medicine is one of the most dynamic and fruitful of any now in action.

But to speak of writing to professionals like yourselves would be
like carrying oranges to Valencia. Instead, allow me to tell you the
story of the medical newsmagazine *MD,* which I created. You may
find my experiences a little more interesting and possibly more rewarding.

A magazine, like a sailboat, requires the concerted action of three
elements to be able to navigate. The sailboat needs wind to propel
its sails, a blind driving force, without which, however, no motion
is possible; a compass to mark its course; and a pilot to combine wind
and compass into effective navigation toward the desired port.

Likewise *MD* has a philosophy, which, like the wind to the sailboat,
was the force that started it going; a journalistic concept, which, like
the compass, marked its literary course; and a team of pilots with a
unique editorial technique.

From *Mississippi Valley Medical Journal 82:* January, 1960. An abridged
version of this address was presented at the Annual Meeting of the American
Medical Writers' Association, October 2, 1959, St. Louis.

The Three Lives of the Physician

Let me tell you first how *MD* was born. *MD* is the crystallization of a dream that was born beneath the azure skies of Spain, while I was still a medical student, and that was to be fulfilled many years later beneath the silver-and-smoke skies of Manhattan.

Even as a student I already realized the strange paradox that is the physician. He is an intellectual, yet, unlike the "pure" intellectual, he is also and above all a man of action, concerned far more with occupation than with *pre*occupation, exactly the opposite of the pure intellectual, whose life is mainly one of preoccupation and whose mind flourishes far more brilliantly the more devoid his life is of action. The physician, luckily, lacks the spiritual apraxia of the pure intellectual. Instead, his life is constantly shaken by swift, vibrant professional reflexes. Yet, as an intellectual, the physician perforce has intellectual needs that his time-consuming work does not allow him to satisfy. He is thus forced to anesthetize his inner vocations, to stifle his intellectual yearnings, to let his artistic gifts grow rusty, to bury in his daily work his "unlived lives." The physician often lives in an enclosure of mirrored walls that reflect only the never-changing images of his professional interests; yet what he really needs is not mirrors but wide-open windows, allowing him to see the sweeping vistas that stretch beyond his office or hospital.

Thus began my dream of integrating the lived and "unlived" lives of the physician, of wedding his three personalities—as a human being, as a professional, as a member of society—into one single concept, consisting basically in adopting a *total perspective* of people, things, and world events, and of that living history we call "our times."

Such was my dream. The years passed. Tragic events in my native country drove me to strange lands. The urgency of mere living prevailed. But my dream was never forgotten. Like a restless little bee it continued to assail me from the deep recesses of my mind. Even as I performed my duties of the moment, I mentally worked out my concept, and slowly it evolved through the years of adaptation to a new country, a new people, and a new language.

A Magazine with "Garbo"

It became evident that the logical vehicle for this concept was a magazine that, like a castle atop a hill with windows open to all breezes, would offer the physician information both on medicine and on all aspects of life, so that he might then look at life with the eyes of a scientist and at medicine with the eyes of a man and, I would add, of an artist. For history shows that the physician and the artist were originally one and the same person and that art and medicine were carved from the same quarry of civilization.

Yes, to bring my concept home to physicians, *communication* with them on the widest scale possible was imperative. The most important moment in creating is possibly the moment of communication. Only when a work passes from one mind to another does it become a work of art.

Communication, furthermore, had to be done with "a judicious amount of levity," a decision prompted by the psychology of my native people, with whom persuasion must always be preceded by a little seduction. To put across the exactness of an idea, it is indispensable to express it with a certain undefinable charm, that magic quality that bullfighters call *garbo*. Unquestionably, a magazine expressing a concept like mine had to be done with charm and humor, or it would turn out to be—to borrow Brillat-Savarin's description of a wonderful meal without cheese—like a beautiful woman with only one eye.

And thus it was that *MD* was born.

The "Bewitchers of the Night"

The next step in my musings was how this concept of integrating medicine, society, and humanity was to be translated editorially into a magazine of medical culture and cultural medicine.

I then recalled that in old Canton there once abounded a type of magician called "bewitchers of the night," who, with the help of lanterns and Bengal lights, cymbal music, burning incense, sweet nectars, and balls of jade, which spectators were asked to rub between their fingers, played on the five human senses until they succeeded in casting their audience into a dream world that turned an ordinary evening into a night of fantasy and revelry. But, barring the fleeting sensation, so pleasant to some, of the touch of paper, the smell of ink, and the rustle of pages, a magazine can appeal to only one sense, the visual, and to do this it disposes of only two tools, words and images, which in medical journals have always been technical and factual, since scientific prose, like a greyhound, should have only lean flesh and quick bones, this being adequate enough for conveying information, but certainly not for bewitching anyone. And *MD* had to "bewitch the night" of the physician, opening for him the treasure chest of life, conjuring around him with words and images a polychrome screen of Coromandel.

Words and Images

This, I figured, could be done with three things. First, with an original approach to the people, ideas, and events that would parade through the pages of *MD*. And what could be better than an approach that combined both the past and the living philosophy and *history* of medicine, in order to attain a perspective in time of the subject dealt with, and *geography,* in order to add to that a perspective in space. Second, with colorful *words,* a luminous style unafraid of metaphors or paradoxes, rich in humor and color, in salt and sun. The language of science, like the distant stars, sheds frosty light but not warmth. *MD* had to shed both the light and the warmth of the flame. And third, with captivating *images,* revealing the strange in the familiar, the exotic in the commonplace, relating it to time and space, to its historical roots and to people and things from exotic distant times and lands.

Presentation of subjects, therefore, would be approached with such tools and would be developed using the same technique that is used by a storyteller to enthrall his audience, whether he be a ragged spinner of yarns in the Zoco Chico of Tangier or a sleek raconteur in a theatre of the Champs Élysées.

Greatness and Romance

Greatness in its editorial policy was another longing of *MD*. The longing to be great, not big but great, is one of the noblest human aspirations. There is greatness in the yearning to do things, to translate dynamic ideas into daring deeds that may have a salutary influence on the life of many people, and in doing this with simplicity, for greatness is simplicity.

To *MD*'s longing for greatness was added the desire to restore to medicine some of its old romanticism. We should not be ashamed of being romantic, for, since a romantic is a man whose heart has gone to his head, only by letting our hearts go to our heads can we perceive that the world is filled with beauty. There is no romanticism in things themselves, but in *how* we do them; not in the world itself, but in how we *look* at the world.

Today we live in a perennial haste that turns men and things into robot-like creatures in an endless frantic procession, remindful of the telegraph poles that whiz past the windows of an express train. Romanticism consists in halting in front of people and things, in detaching them for a moment from the group and seeking out their inner music and color. The mere act of setting a single person or thing apart from the crowd, even as a fine florist displays a single rose or a good jeweler a single gem, invests that object with a singular charm.

Thus, I thought, *MD* should be focused, restoring drama and poetry to medicine, transforming what seemed a prosaic task into an epic saga, the seemingly mechanized professional man into a quixotic crusader, and his apparently materialistic aims into the quest for a Holy Grail.

Courage Against Statistics

The dream was now fully developed, but life, always slower than dreams, delayed fulfillment for many years. And then came the day when *MD* was finally launched. Allow me to say that it was an act of poetic courage. For the unanimous opinion was that the editorial principles of *MD* foredoomed it to failure. Everyone I consulted— publishers and businessmen alike, bless their souls!—made the same reply. *MD* could not succeed. Its spirit was "too romantic," its character "contrary to what the American physician needed and wanted to read." The enormous rate of failure and mortality among magazines in this country, even of an eminently practical nature, was statistically demonstrated to me. In fact, they were all as negative as those people who specialize in ordering from a restaurant menu the only dish that is not available.

Fortunately, the flood of negative statistics only served to strengthen my positive decision. For—I admit it—all my life I have felt an unconquerable shyness toward statistics. They are necessary, I know, and as a physician I have often used them, but always with the same distaste with which I use an umbrella on a rainy day. Statistics are useful for confirming something, but they must never rule the making of a decision. Had statistics been the deciding factor in the chances of success of many a visionary enterprise, the pyramids would never have been built, America discovered, *Don Quixote* written, antibiotics developed, or rockets launched to the moon. Statistics will never take the place of the strength of a decision founded on the power of an idea.

If all this is romantic, then let no one say that American physicians are not romantic. For their reception of *MD* could not have been more affectionate or enthusiastic. For nearly three years now they have unstintingly given *MD* their warmest praises. Thanks to their great humanistic sense and to their kind encouragement of head and heart, the dream of a medical student in Spain has been fulfilled in their bountiful and generous land.

III. THE MD CONCEPT

The *MD* concept therefore is to help the physician satisfy his innate curiosity in the vast, rich tapestry of medicine *and of life*.

For a physician is not only a professional, interested exclusively in science and the art of healing; he is also an individual who feels the need to increase his cultural knowledge, and a member of society who, besides health problems, wants to understand also the political, economic, and sociologic problems of his community, his country, and the world at large. The physician who thinks that he knows all about disease because he knows medicine is as presumptuous as he who thinks that he knows all about the fires of Hell because he knows all about matches. A physician is not only a social person; he is also a *historical* person. He must be not only an individual but also a *person,* that is, an individual as an active factor of society, even as a people are a nation only when they are an active factor of universality. The interests of the world therefore are his interests.

The physician's mind is often like a series of rooms filled with knowledge but lacking communication among themselves. *MD* attempts to link the diversified knowledge in the modern medical mind as a corridor in a hospital links all rooms without interfering with their privacy.

The Need for History

Whichever may be the "royal road" of medicine chosen by the physician—practice, research, teaching—he must have a thorough knowledge of the history of the world and of the society in which he lives, and he must also know the links between the past and his present duties. For without history nothing has a full meaning. Proof of the value of this historical approach is that the most important medical document has always been the clinical case *history,* whether of unusual or ordinary cases, that "small change" of medicine which constitutes the real capital of the physician's experience.

History is vital, for everything of importance was said by the Greek philosophers more than 2000 years ago. No wonder a "secret Greece" beats in the heart of all men! To what the Greeks said about the awakening of man's conscience, the nature of the universe, and the dignity of man, we can only add the results of scientific research, the achievements of art, and the records of history.

Against the excessive current specialization, *MD* also endeavors to stimulate all those "reserve" occupations—writing, gardening, art, chess, sports, or travel—without which the physician, slaving at his professional occupation, would become a technical automaton. Even as the organic reserves of fat and sugar protect the body against the dangers of fasting, reserve occupations help the physician to protect his mind muscles from becoming atrophied.

MD tries to help the physician in that search for wisdom which has been defined, from Spinoza to Will Durant, as a search for a *total perspective,* that is, a universal vision, integrated in time and space, of persons, things, and events in view of eternity.

IV. MD'S EDITORIAL TECHNIQUE

Selection and Correlation

Let us now talk about the technique of *MD*.

Our technique is based on maintaining a total perspective when developing each subject, correlating its present aspects, which is *life,* with its dimension in time, which is *history,* and integrating these two components—life and history—into *living history* through the magic of words.

The theme of each article is extensively and objectively studied and interpreted in the light of its correlation with other facts. This is done not only to acquire an exhaustive documentation on each subject, but, above all, to develop original *ideas* on the subject.

MD's chief capital is the wealth of ideas and correlations we establish between the subjects studied and others that seemingly are unrelated.

Countless examples could be adduced to illustrate this thesis. The study of bull fighting reveals that the preponderance of fine *toreros* in Mexico today is related to the frequency of violent revolutions in that country's past, both these activities having a common root in a supreme personal contempt for death, whether of oneself or of another.

The traditional uncomfortable professor's chair in most colleges bears a relation to the uncomfortable royal throne of yesteryear. The chair was a symbol of authority, so much so that rulers used to carry their chairs with them on their travels, just as we today carry our valises. The more uncomfortable the chair, the more stiffly did the king or master sit in it, in court or in class. For rigid immobility was and still is a symbol of authority, in contrast to the informality of a slouched posture, and from the Byzantine icons to our modern sculpture, no statue of a king, a leader, or a master is more impressive than that which shows him rigid, as though holding back his wisdom and power.

Another example of correlation between entirely different subjects is the discovery of the circulation of the blood in the seventeenth century, at a time when art was governed by the same principles of *motion* and *emotion* that inspired Harvey's research, and Shakespeare was producing plays that put the words "blood" and "heart" on the lips of actors as frequently as they were in the mind of the great English physician. And while Leeuwenhoek in the city of Delft was investigating the world of minute animalcules, only a block away from him the painter Vermeer was busy portraying the same world of the infinitesimally small in his exquisite miniatures.

Once a subject has been selected, *MD* seeks out the concept latent in it and then examines such concept from all angles, so that it may reflect—"as the image of a dandy surrounded by mirrors in his dressing room is reflected"—all the human, social, and medical facets of the subject in both their vertical dimension of time and their horizontal dimension of space. Thus, history lies hidden in the article, impregnating it subtly with its flavor, just as invisible spices flavor a dish.

The selection of subjects is guided strictly by the criterion that they must above all be interesting, informative, useful, and topical. Of course, by "topical" we also mean universal and historical, for events that occurred hundreds of years ago can be of enormous topical interest today, as, for instance, the "prophecies" of Nostradamus. The current rise of the Asiatic nations on the political horizon seems to confirm his alarming prediction made four centuries ago that "before the end of the twentieth century, yellow men will fly over Paris."

Approach to Subject: Life, Environment, Situation, Work, Ideas

Once the subject has been selected, our *approach* to it is then determined. The same subject can be looked at from many different points of view and the reader's satisfaction depends on our choosing the most dramatic one. The important thing is to follow—as our brilliant writers and editors do—Gustave Flaubert's precept: *"Il faut intéresser."*

Take, for instance, our section devoted to literature. We never follow the usual cradle-to-grave approach in a biography. This is fine when everything in a man's life is interesting, but this is rare indeed. For human life, like the soldier's in war, consists of long periods of tedious waiting interpolated between brief moments of intense dramatic action.

Instead, we approach an artist's biography from that angle which appears the most interesting. Sometimes it is his *life,* because it was even more interesting than his work. This is the case with Alexandre Dumas or T. E. Lawrence, whose lives contained even more action than their books.

At other times we focus our article on the *environment* or the place where a man lived, because it had a decisive effect on his work. Such was the case with El Greco, for whom Toledo was not only the canvas on which he painted his pictures, but also his leading theme. Toledo, rising from a gigantic rock against which the romantic and knightly river Tagus sharpens itself like a Toledan sword, provided the inspiration for El Greco's best works. Even the inmates of Toledo's insane asylums served as models for El Greco's saints.

On occasion we prefer to select a *situation*. For an article on Goethe, I would choose his stay at the court in Weimar, which marks a conflict between his vocation as a writer and his inclinations as a courtier, particularly the masked ball of January 1, 1800, celebrating the dawn of the nineteenth century, at which Goethe appeared crowned as Jupiter Olympus.

For a biography of Pablo Casals, I would choose his first concert, when, scorning the concert halls resplendent with ladies in shimmering satins and diamonds, he preferred to play in the little village of Prades, lost somewhere in the Pyrenees, for a group of destitute exiles and modestly dressed women on whose cheeks sparkled the diamonds of tears far more beautiful than the jewelers' diamonds.

If a man's *life and work* are equally interesting, our approach embraces them both. This would be the case with Cervantes, whose roving life was as interesting as that of his own Don Quixote, or with Vesalius, whose life was as rich in adventures as the "muscle-men" of his *Fabrica* are in drama.

In other cases we find that the important elements in a man's life were his *ideas*. An excellent example is the Spanish philosopher José Ortega y Gasset, who led the sedentary, unchanging life of a professor and writer, yet, while philosophizing amid the magical blue smoke from his cigar, experienced entirely in his mind, like a Marco Polo of the spirit, perhaps the greatest adventure in universality in the twentieth century.

Research

Any theme accepted by *MD* undergoes the most exhaustive research, even though most of the labor done for each article remains buried in our files. Our patient and skillful researchers leave no stone unturned, no possibility untouched, though they know that, like an iceberg, nine tenths of their labors will remain submerged in the files and only the remaining tenth will be visible to all. With the completed bibliographic research in his hands, the writer begins his task.

Literary Cuisine: The Arroz a Banda

There are in each article a thousand invisible ingredients that impart its flavor and quality. The brilliant ballet of human life can be interpreted only when all the ingredients that give it color and music are distilled into prose, with no one but the author knowing that they are there. This culinary-like literary process is comparable to that followed in Valencia, Spain, in preparing a rice dish known as *arroz a banda*. This dish borrows freely from the polychrome encyclopedia of the *paella* and the watercolor of the *arroz con pollo,* and winds up being far superior to both. The fish and seafood of the *paella* and the chicken of the *arroz con pollo* are simmered together until they have released all their juices. The rice is then boiled in the rich broth and set on the table without a single morsel of fish or fowl to mar the glossy nudity of the grains of rice. Yet each tiny grain of rice contains all the flavor and essence of the Mediterranean. Similarly, in preparing an article we try to combine the choicest morsels of information with the most imaginative seasoning, so that it may reach the reader free of all pedantry, clad in tasteful simplicity, like a literary *arroz a banda.*

Style

What is the *style* adopted in *MD?*

Style should be like the spices that season a salad. We like our prose to be simple, yet we are not afraid of images, symbols, contrasts, or metaphors. If dogma, we feel, is the leaden ballast on the wings of theology, metaphor is the tail wind on the wings of science. Nor do we flinch at scientific neologisms, for these are unavoidable in an age when science marches forward with greater speed than the semantic progress of language. But our prose has to be simple, and, for it to be so, it is necessary to hammer it fine, as an artist hammers the metal for a work of art.

Medical journals shy away from literary quotations, poetic images, and humoristic turns of phrase. *MD* uses all of them. A train or an airplane, we believe, is no less powerful or speedy because its engines are garlanded with roses.

The Magic of Words

I have spoken elsewhere of the "magic of words" in illustration of our editorial approach in *MD.**

I remember an animal tamer in a circus that used to come to my native town every year. The tamer had a sorry-looking menagerie of what was optimistically featured as "wild beasts," with which he struggled patiently to make them leap and cavort at the crack of his whip. The years and hunger eventually killed off his troupe, until one year, to everyone's amazement, the tamer stepped into the ring with only the decaying hides of the dead beasts. Yet, so eloquently did he speak about the poor beasts and their experiences while he rustled and crackled each skin that the crowd, fascinated, forgot that they were not wild animals but only battered hides, and wildly applauded the golden-tongued trainer, who proved that words could be far more

* About this subject, see my editorial "More Magic in Words," page 17.

enthralling than the roar of beasts. The same magic of words is essential in a magazine.

Images

Images in *MD* are molded to its guiding concept, just as the pictures in a mansion bear witness to the artistic tastes of the owner.

We attach enormous importance to the illustrations we choose for our articles, because they strengthen the background and "climate" of the theme by adding color, atmosphere, or humor to the article.

The Face of Nefertete and a Snowflake Crystal

With *MD*'s covers we take particular pains. The purpose of the cover is to create the atmosphere and thematic setting for each issue. We therefore prefer the symbolic and romantic to the literal. For instance, for our cover story on helio- and hydrotherapy (*Sun and Water* *), instead of using, say, a sun-and-water still life for the cover, we chose the bust of Nefertete, the beautiful Sun Queen, sister and spouse of Akhenaton, the daring Pharaoh who initiated the cult of the sun disk in Egypt, establishing not only monotheism in a polytheistic land, but also the first "official" heliotherapy in history.

For the cover of our 1957 Christmas issue, devoted to *Christmas and Medicine,* we chose a photomicrograph of the simplest and purest symbol of Christmas: a snowflake crystal. Its white and green colors embodied the emerald green of the pine and the virgin white of the snow, the colors of the Nativity, while the enlarged crystalline structure of the snowflake revealed that the snow crystals naturally adopted the shape of Christmas trees! This was a most surprising revelation of how poetic nature can be.

The Biography of an Idea

Under no circumstances, however, does our preference for the original and the dramatic deflect us from a strict adherence to the facts pertinent to the basic theme of the issue. Pictorially, this concept has been translated into the incorporation in each issue of pictorial sections that bear a collateral connection with the basic theme, for instance, the development in photographs and illustrations of the "biography" not of a person, but of an idea, tracing its birth, growth, and maturity. We have already done this with antibiosis, ataraxia, anesthesia, analgesia, antisepsis, opotherapy, and others.

We also use a novel approach to the photography of current events.

---

* *MD,* the Medical Newsmagazine, 2:67, May, 1958.

The Fabric and Creation of a Dream 13

For instance, during the 1959 American Medical Association Convention, we sent a photographer to Atlantic City to capture such things as the pictorial drama of inanimate objects at the convention: the silent rows of empty seats; motionless skeletons awaiting the call to their ghostly dance in the early morning hours before the meetings; the lonely objects—a handkerchief, a glove, a hat, a flower—left behind on benches and chairs; the convention considered as a gigantic body with fifteen thousand heads.

The Epic of Medicine

The technique we follow to integrate so many complex elements is best illustrated in our most ambitious project, the series on *The Epic of Medicine*. In this series we do not quote historical references on each period, but embody what we have learned from these in the narrative. In this way, the reader will learn about Mesopotamian medicine without more than a passing reference to the Babylonian clay tablets or the Code of Hammurabi, although what was contained in them is incorporated in the text. The contents of the Edwin Smith and Ebers papyri were transformed into data for the narrative, and those of the *Corpus Hippocraticum* into descriptions of the working methods of the Hippocratic physicians. In other words, the source of information no longer appears in awesome academic dress but is turned into living, pulsating history.

Illustrations follow the same criterion, and so, next to the text of each episode of the "Epic" we include a pictorial section showing what has survived from each historical period and each great civilization, and their similarities and contrasts as compared with present-day medicine in each country. On the other hand, the illustrations in the narrative text itself are kinetic in character, portraying facts and persons *in action* rather than inanimate objects, and showing places and monuments not as dead, dusty ruins but as a dynamic part of the physician's daily life in each country and period. The result is not a dry and dusty chronological, academic, exhaustive history, but a selective, literary, and, above all, *living* story of the past.

To Navigate, the Essential Thing

I have told you practically the whole story of *MD*. There only remains now for me to say something about the spirit of *MD* for the future. We harbor the same hopes of the navigator who, guided by the silvery caravan of stars, sets out to new lands of promise. We believe implicitly in the byword of the daring Greek Argonauts: "The essential thing is not to live; the essential thing is to navigate."

Our future work is simple and clear. Above all, *MD* wishes to continue enriching the leisure of the physician. It also wishes the doors of the physician's often isolated mental compartments—professional, social, and human—to open to one unifying corridor: a historical purpose in life.

Thus the physician may come to replace the twentieth-century cult of anguish by a happy and serene equanimity. A life culturally enriched is the best way to attain ataraxia. Not the ataraxia that meant to the Stoics and Epicureans "tranquility through absence of perturbation," but that which twenty-five centuries ago the physician Democritus defined as calm alertness and happiness of soul. In modern terms this can be translated into self-control and presence of mind in any emergency, akin to that supreme quality of the physician that Osler called *aequanimitas*.

In our world of atoms and Sputniks, equanimity and ataraxia signify wisdom and total perspective. These things *MD* endeavors to stimulate by feeding the cultural stream of the physician's personality.

Our magazine aspires to be an educational tool at the service of medicine. It is already used to stir in students the romantic ambition to be better physicians by being better men, and to realize that to be a good physician he must first be a good and kind man.

The beloved G. K. Chesterton paid a great tribute to journals when he said: "The roar of the printing wheels weaving the destiny of another day. . . . Here is the school of labor, and of some rough humility, the largest work published anonymously since the great Christian cathedrals." I myself would say that only by listening to its beats—the medical journals—is it possible to know the condition of the heart of Medicine.

V. EULOGY OF THE WRITTEN WORD

MD therefore is trying to revive the lost romance of Medicine, the greatness of its ideals, the enthralling adventure of its endeavors, the glory and sublimity of its triumphs. For this, *words* are our foremost implement. In the other fine arts the artist needs brushes, canvases, marble, chisels, musical instruments, models, studios, or workshops, but *literature requires only a pencil stub and some sheets of paper.* The melody of music, the light and color of painting, the beautiful forms of sculpture, the gracile poetry of dancing, the stately strength of architecture—all these the writer can convey with such humble tools and that frailest vehicle of all, the written word.

The reservoir of language is a treasure chest replete with the most flexible and ductile but also the toughest and most rigid working material—words. Words, fine and common, wise and vain, musical and coarse, erudite and popular, sublime and profane, are within everyone's reach, like copper, silver, and gold coins overflowing from the open chest of language. Anyone can use words to his own fancy and discretion, to construct or destroy, to seed or devastate, to spread vulgarity or to create beauty.

The only way the writer can properly use words, which are the same for everybody, is by knowing how to *select* them—for their precision, originality, euphony, and beauty—and, above all, how to *combine* them into images, symbols, paradoxes, metaphors, and concepts, imaginative and novel. On that rests the secret of greatness and elegance in writing. In journalism, the highest attainable peak is the combination of the best words in the best way possible to express the best concepts.

With words *MD* endeavors to carry the physician, as in a winged chariot, on a journey across realms of fact and fancy in time and space. *MD* is not happy to be just a magazine; it aspires to be a flying carpet.

It is in this spirit that *MD,* with the American physician's kind encouragement and the humble but sublime tools of word and image on the immaculate whiteness of the blank page, will continue giving life to the fabric of a dream.

MORE MAGIC IN WORDS

ω e all have seen it. With the wise luminous eyes that we have only as children, we have watched them—men, beasts, and wagons—marching into town with much noise and fanfare. With a few poles and some canvas, they promptly fence in a parcel of the earth exclusively reserved for illusion. It is a traveling circus. In the small magic space, defying the laws of physics, jugglers, acrobats, and magicians conjure a vast world of wonder. Time passes. We grow up and become perhaps physicians, perhaps writers. One day we realize that, like the performers in a circus, we too can create a world of illusion. Instead of poles and canvas, we use *words* to fence in a fragment of world, wherein illusion, like the acrobats in a circus, joyously swings through the air.

Animals use sound and motion to communicate. Only man uses sounds and signs—words—as symbols of things, events, and ideas. Words are the most precious "tools with which to make other tools." To know how to use them is man's greatest attribute. Words are the most dynamic force in medicine. Words are an instrument of healing, of creation, and of communication; of healing, because down the ages they have constituted a powerful curative agent, from the Hippocratic catharses to present-day psychoanalytical dialogue; of creation, because one single new word—such as "pneuma," "circulation," "cell," "antibiosis," "unconscious"—has often triggered a whole new system of medical philosophy; of communication, because the spoken and the written word—those two most faithful servants of thought—are the wings that permit thought to dart from mind to mind as a bird darts from branch to branch.

From *MD,* the MEDICAL NEWSMAGAZINE, *3*:11, February, 1959.

In our profession, obscurity in expression, because of the aura of mystery it created, was in times past the anvil on which were hammered iron dogmas that, like lead in a bird's wing, hampered the flight of medical progress. Fortunately, in modern times lucidity has become imperative in scientific language. The lucid style of Osler and Ramón y Cajal only enhanced the rich content of ideas in their writings, just as the simplicity of the modern sportswoman's clothes enhances her ideal figure.

But there is another quality that is indispensable in making language not only a vehicle of thought but a captivating vehicle as well. We refer to good rhetoric, to the classical "art of good saying." The fast pace of modern life has killed the two most individual forms of word communication: the epistle and conversation, substituting instead those impersonal rockets—the telegram and the telephone call. The "art of good saying" is also too often sacrificed to the preference for stiff, prosaic, disheveled language, which clothes in drab garments or shapeless bizarre costumes the slender torso of scientific truth. But to degrade the language is to degrade the soul. Just as an empress is clad in a regal mantle, so must truth be clad in beauty.

It is imperative that we reinstate not only clarity but also beauty to scientific language. A little magic will bring no harm to accuracy; an image or two, a few metaphors, will like jewels add warmth and luster to cold bare facts. Thus can be mellowed the forbidding, the formidable, technical scientific language. Of course, we do not advocate a return to the old rhetoric, adipose and grotesque like the classical soprano, but to a new rhetoric, slim and athletic like a modern opera diva. This new rhetoric would help us to overcome that mental inertia which prevents us from seeing things the way they should be, that is, the way we saw them when we looked at them with a child's eyes, in all that hidden splendor which turns life into a bazaar of wonders.

This new style, already adopted by some publications, is afraid neither of literature nor of humor, and freely borrows from both to acquire charm and grace. Style *is* thought. One writes as one thinks. Many of our medical predecessors did not fear a style rich in imagery, and their prose was a magnificent Gobelin tapestry.

Let us try, then, to restore not only beauty but also joy to scientific language, using imagery and metaphor in the same manner as a fine jeweler uses tools to polish precious gems. The revival of taste for beautiful prose in science would augur much good to the future of the *lingua medica*. Until that revival occurs, let those of us who believe in a warm, colorful language, even in science, continue our cheerful crusade. And should anyone remark that our prose wears too bright a tie, let us gently answer that it is not a tie they see but our very spine showing through.

FRIENDS FOR THE ROAD

In these summer days of golden leisure, when there is a little more time for reading, let us talk about books.

Charles Grosvenor Osgood once suggested that the best way to withstand the stresses of modern life was to select a great poet as constant guide and companion in the daily adventure of living—a poet who would be an angel forever hovering at our shoulder, a Vergil capable of transporting us to the paradise where Beatrice waited for Dante. Such a poet had to be a source of inspiration, a teacher, a synthesis of intellect and spirit, humaneness and encyclopedism.

Years before I read Osgood's advice, I had already "adopted" several authors—Cervantes, Ortega y Gasset, Montaigne, Goethe, Dickens, Romain Rolland, Vivekananda, and others—as faithful companions on the road of life. My choice was guided by the affinity I felt toward these men and by the conviction that their minds were vast regions to be endlessly and passionately explored. For the spiritual reward in reading again and again the authors of one's choice is that one keeps on discovering new values in them, just as he who devotes himself to knowing one city alone keeps on discovering new attractions that are missed by the globetrotter, who knows the world with the same skin-deep superficiality with which Don Juan knew his women, while their inner beauty completely escaped him.

But here I wish only to answer a question put to me by some colleagues. Which ten *recreational* books would I take with me on a vacation? The question is irresistible, for books are the tapestry with which I have decorated my spirit.

From *MD*, the MEDICAL NEWSMAGAZINE, 3:11, August, 1959.

I shall begin by eliminating all recent books, bearing in mind Emerson's counsel not to read a book less than a year old. Where choice is of the essence, it is well to heed such advice. Besides, most of the latest literature is ephemeral and deserves no more attention than any common pastime. Most "best-sellers" are forgotten as soon as they become outmoded. For of all the fashions, the most old-fashioned, in literature as in clothes, are not those that are centuries old but those of yesterday.

The first book I would select would be that inseparable companion of my life, *Don Quixote*. As a child they made me detest it in school, just as children in schools here learn to detest Shakespeare. How fortunate I was to rediscover it later! For *Don Quixote* is a perennial garden, each page abloom with gorgeous flowers. It is Aladdin's cave overflowing with priceless treasures. It is perhaps the greatest novel ever written and no other book has exerted so much influence on human ideals. One is at once amused and touched by the adventures of the romantic knight who, mad in mind and pure in thought, sought to transfigure, before reforming it, the world; and one also takes great delight in the style, of biblical simplicity. This is a human comedy, a vast landscape drenched in the sun of life, peopled by beings rich in color and drama. Every year I reread *Don Quixote,* and my soul gains moral weight and is enriched with ounces of sunlight.

Next is Montaigne's *Essays*. A pirate's coffer could hold no greater variety of unexpected treasures. Sitting by the fire in his castle, the author, shaking with cold, finds warmth in his own thoughts. He is not gentle and kind like Cervantes, but he is wise and understanding. His work, like a *poularde au demi-deuil,* is encrusted with savory truffles—anecdotes, commentaries, ironies, witticisms, and wise sayings—and his prose has a sober musicality.

To nourish the yearning to travel in time instead of space, I would choose the two best historical novels I have ever read: *The Cloister and the Hearth,* by Charles Reade, and *The Romance of Leonardo da Vinci,* by Dmitri Merezhkovski. This preference compels me to pass up with much regret Dumas' musketeers, for while I can hardly think of a more delightful friend than D'Artagnan in *Twenty Years After* and *The Viscount of Bragelonne* (a feeling shared by Robert Louis Stevenson), in historical value and literary style Dumas' books cannot compete with the two novels mentioned.

The Cloister and the Hearth was called by our famous colleague, Arthur Conan Doyle, "the greatest English novel." Let Dr. Conan Doyle himself tell what Charles Reade did:

> He takes the reader by the hand, and he leads him away into the Middle Ages, and not a conventional study-built Middle Age, but a period quivering with life, full of folk who are as human and real as a 'bus-load in Oxford

Street. He takes him through Holland, he shows him the painters, the dykes, the life. He leads him down the long line of the Rhine, the spinal marrow of Mediæval Europe. He shows him the dawn of printing, the beginnings of freedom, the life of the great mercantile cities of South Germany, the state of Italy, the artist-life of Rome, the monastic institutions on the eve of the Reformation. And all this between the covers of one book, so naturally introduced, too, and told with such vividness and spirit. Apart from the huge scope of it, the mere study of Gerard's own nature, his rise, his fall, his regeneration, the whole pitiable tragedy at the end, make the book a great one. It contains, I think, a blending of knowledge with imagination, which makes it stand alone in our literature.

Little more could be added to this brilliant description made by Conan Doyle in his *Through the Magic Door,* a piece of writing itself as precious as a rare gem and, unfortunately, as little known as many of the Amazon's mysterious tributaries.

Merezhkovski's *The Romance of Leonardo da Vinci* could easily make today's historical best-sellers blush with shame. Its pages sparkle and glitter with the robust polychrome world of the Renaissance. Not only da Vinci but his times spring to life in this vivid portrayal of the most extraordinary period in history, when, after the long medieval night, a brilliant rainbowed dawn heralded a wondrous new world. In my opinion, these two novels are superior even to Tolstoi's *War and Peace,* another formidable contender.

From a man of encyclopedic knowledge like Leonardo, let us turn to a man encyclopedic in love: Giovanni Jacopo Casanova. Do not be alarmed, but I consider Casanova's *Memoirs* (not the cheap abridged editions, but the great eight-volume French edition of which there is an excellent English translation) one of the most dazzling paintings of his times and a fascinating portrait of a unique man, as devoted to collecting women as an entomologist is to collecting bugs. Written in beautiful terse French, the *Memoirs* reveal extraordinary descriptive powers. Characters and scenes succeed one another in a Mardi Gras crescendo. It is interesting to observe that the landscape did not exist for Casanova. Strictly a man of action, he devoted numerous pages to describing in detail one single amorous encounter, while dismissing in a few words the lovely cities that sheltered his love affairs. The *Memoirs* are a human document of extraordinary interest from a psychopathological viewpoint. To physicians they represent, besides, a window opened wide to the medicine—the great physicians and the quacks, Casanova among them—of the eighteenth century.

We now turn from the diabolical to the angelical. A physician who never became famous as such but who gained immortality as an author, Dr. Oliver Goldsmith wrote *The Vicar of Wakefield,* which Goethe considered the greatest novel of the eighteenth century and which Dickens took to bed and reread every night. Goldsmith studied medicine in

Edinburgh and Padua, but he failed professionally in England and died owing 2000 pounds. *The Vicar of Wakefield,* his most famous novel, which moved Walter Scott to say: "We read it in youth and age; we return to it again and again," and Samuel Johnson: "Goldsmith writes like an angel," is the biography of a pure, kind man. Through its pages there flows a stream of limpid, graceful prose, charm, and humor. Upon reading such pages one's soul becomes decked with sweetness and tenderness.

A sister to this last novel in the purity, simplicity, and generosity of the hero is the *Pickwick Papers,* by Charles Dickens. This book sings and dances. Its pages ring with the clangor of hunting horns and the jingle of bells on stagecoach mules. No other novel illustrates so well the fact that our predecessors walked when they strolled and ran when they wrote, whereas today we run when we stroll and we creep when we write. The *Pickwick Papers* are all action and enterprise steeped in tender sentimentalism and sharp humor. The world in this book, sun-sparkled and gay, teeming with stagecoaches jogging along frosted roads, inns with blazing fireplaces, storybook Christmases, and romantic loves—this world of Dickens—is an eiderdown quilt to warm all cold hearts.

A beautiful contrast to this last book is Voltaire's *Candide,* which describes the adventures of a young man who travels the world in search of love, fortune, and the meaning of life. *Candide*'s greatest charms are its profound satire on the philosophy that we live "in the best of worlds" and its magnificent crystalline prose. Read *Candide* if you crave to write with diaphanous clarity. Its pages vibrate with lights and shadows, with subtle sensualities and poignant yearnings.

An altogether different hero is that of *Jean Christophe,* by Romain Rolland, published in French in ten volumes and in English in one volume. Originally, Romain Rolland intended to write the life story of Beethoven, but he ended by writing a masterpiece wherein is resumed the author's life creed as action and service. This is the book, together with *The Universal Gospel* by the same author, that has most influenced my life. *Jean Christophe* is a symphony of words and the bible of humanity. Here is a universal message (completed in the author's other novel, *The Enchanted Soul*) symbolized in a river, on whose banks the hero dreamed as a child.

Source of mental peace, inspiration, and beauty—such is Thoreau's *Walden,* another faithful companion of many years. In this sensitive book we can live step by step the author's voluntary exile at Walden Pond, witness and feel the change of seasons in his Robinsonian isolation: the silver petals of the snow silently drifting to the ground, the quiet clamor of spring bursting into tiny green tendrils and shy many-hued blossoms, the glowing fires of autumn, the summer's golden peace; and, enveloped in the fresh aromas imprisoned between the pages, we can listen to the stirring inner music of the author, who finally found peace facing the placid waters of Walden Pond.

I should be most happy if I could top this delectable parfait of ten great books with the eleven adventures of John Buchan's hero, Richard Hannay; John Steinbeck's stories of the *paisanos* of Monterey; the historical novels of Conan Doyle; the great major novels of R. L. Stevenson; and my two favorite and often read novels by the physician-author, W. Somerset Maugham, *Cakes and Ale,* a technical masterpiece, and *The Narrow Corner,* a marvelous narrative.

But as Conan Doyle would say, the moment has come to close the magic door to the library and open another door far more magical: the cover to any of these books, all of them passports to the paradise of reading, the most beautiful, peaceful, and eternal of all paradises.

NO BOOKS ON THE FERRY FROM HONG KONG

O ne hot April morning last year, in Hong Kong, for the fourth consecutive time I paid the four cent fare and took the ferry-boat that plies between Victoria and Kowloon.

The ferry was crowded. Small slender Chinese chattered noisily, the women as colorful in their sam foos and cheong-sams as parakeets in a sunlit cage. White-clad Britons, who were absorbed in their *Hong Kong Times,* spread with their pipes an isolating curtain of smoke around their heads. The gun-metal waters of the bay lay prostrate under the heat, sweating light. Junks with membranous sails like the wings of a bat, slender sampans, tugboats belching smoke, passenger ships like huge hammocks for hundreds of people rocked lazily on the slumbering waters. On the pale blue sky, so pale a blue that it appeared almost white, the sun was like a strawberry mark on the ivory bosom of a young girl. The noises of the bay mingled with the smell of engine oil and boiled rice.

But after four consecutive crossings even the Hong Kong bay loses some of its attraction, and soon my thoughts drifted to other matters. One of my suitcases had gone astray at Kai Tak airport. The mishap raised the problem of reading matter, not of clothing, which in any case would be no problem in Hong Kong, where one can have a new suit made to measure in three days (not in one day, as so many people think). All my books were in the missing bag, and for my around-the-world tour I had provided myself with a stock of literature even larger than my never modest usual quota. I agonizingly remembered

From *MD,* the MEDICAL NEWSMAGAZINE, 5:11, September, 1961.

Somerset Maugham's predicament (described in his short story "The Book Bag") when he became ill unexpectedly on a Pacific Ocean island, and for several weeks had no reading matter other than a few schoolbooks, introducing Racine, Molière, and other classic French authors to children, which by a miracle he had discovered in the local general store. After that grim experience, Maugham resolved always to travel with the largest laundry sack made filled to the brim with books to suit every possible occasion and every mood.

To distract myself from worrying about the missing books, I retreated into the kaleidoscopic book of the mind. Before I left New York, several of my colleagues, commenting on one of my editorials in *MD* ("Friends for the Road," page 19) wherein I spoke of the ten books I would most like to take with me on a vacation, had suggested that I devote another editorial to the books from which I had derived the most pleasure in recent years. Picking up a discarded Chinese newspaper at my feet, I began to jot a few notes in the margins. This article is the outcome.

Reading is so personal an experience that it is almost nontransferable. Yet my sole purpose here is to try to share this experience with my colleagues. The books I mention have been chosen solely because of their appeal to me *personally,* because I have enjoyed them so much that I have read them at least two or three times, and some of them even five or six times, during the last two decades. I have read and reread them for one or more reasons: the spiritual pleasure they afforded me each time I read them; the beauty of their literary style; their inspirational message; or the complexity of the author's technique. Not all of them deal with pleasant subjects, but nearly all of them deal with daring, restless, adventure-seeking men and women. Quixotes, rascals, and mystics, plus a villain here and there, comprise the literary fauna in these books. I have included an autobiography and one volume of verse because these two books are eminently novelistic in character. Any one of these books, even the least interesting of them, would induce me to ignore the best television program.

Do not misunderstand me. I like television and wish I had more time to watch it. What I miss in television, what it needs, in my opinion, is more vision. There is too much talk—radio caters perfectly well to that—and too little imagery and action. I also believe that, contrary to common opinion, television is not only an art for the masses. (Not that there would be any harm in its being a mass art. Medieval cathedrals, the most formidable expression of mass art, are still the most exquisitely individual form of art.) Television has wrought the miracle of turning an art for the masses that comprises collective art in all its forms—theatre, painting, cinema, oratory, ballet, singing—into an eminently *individual* experience, which one can savor in the privacy of his own home. That is why television could be a perfect vehicle for entertainment and education. But, let us get back to books.

The exploits of Johnny Pym, at once the most engaging and exasperating hero in modern literature, are the theme of Gerald Kersh's *The Song of the Flea*. Kersh is one of those daring Englishmen, with the bearing of a duke and a beard like the tail of a baby fox, who love a life of rough-and-tumble Bohemia. In the sordid, motley, shifty environment of Soho, Johnny Pym, a writer with a facile pen and lofty principles, dreams of and fights for love and fame, always yielding and surrendering, even accepting defeat and humiliation, in small matters, just like Don Quixote, but, again like Don Quixote, always rebellious and defiant, fighting with pride and dignity in matters of ideals and in impossible undertakings.

Johnny Pym's precarious daily life, his financial straits, his ups and downs with money and glory, are depicted with Goyaesque brush strokes against the picturesque nocturnal scene of Soho, with its smoke-filled saloons and hangouts, its fearsome back alleys and fog-shrouded dawns, its prostitutes and roughnecks, pimps and mobsters, all of it conjuring a fascinating Dickensian tapestry. Several of these characters reappear in the same author's *Night and the City,* a rhapsodic nocturnal symphony of London's dregs.

Another quixotic Englishman is the hero of John Buchan's *Greenmantle*. Richard Hannay and other comrades-in-arms are the heroes of this and eleven other tales by Scotland's greatest modern novelist, John Buchan (Lord Tweedsmuir), a wizard of the written word— excelled only by Robert Louis Stevenson—and rhapsodist of friendship between honest men.

Forsaking the comforts of their London club, the heroes of *Greenmantle,* traveling a peril-fraught path across the Europe of forty years ago, arrive at Constantinople on the trail of a cryptic message. In Turkey, Sandy Arbuthnot, like a Lawrence of Arabia, leads an Arab revolt very like the one actually organized by his romantic counterpart in real life. The style of this book is magnificent in its Stevensonian crispness, the plot is romantic and highly colored, with mysterious meetings in Constantinople cafés, mounted charges across the plains of Anatolia, journeys on the Danube and Bosphorus, a hopeless love between the hero and an enigmatic *femme fatale*. Always battling the impossible, with quixotic flamboyancy, this novel is a splendid demonstration of the storytelling ability of its Scottish author, whose books sing the praises of rugged outdoor life and dangerous treasure hunts, with a friend's embrace as sole reward, or violent death beneath the stars as the possible outcome.

Concerning exotic environments, these have never been so spectacularly described as in a book that uses travels and geography as a painter uses light and color: *The Asiatics,* by the American author, Frederic Prokosch. Praised by great writers like Thomas Mann, this book tells of the journey—from Beirut to Hanoi, en route to Hong Kong—by a young man whose personality is never fully explained but is left shrouded in an aura of mystery. Its author wrote *The Asiatics* in the British Museum in London, drawing his material solely from reference works, never having visited any of the countries he so marvelously described.

Prokosch's latest work was an enormous disappointment, but this one, his first, is an enthralling poetic vision of Asia and her peoples and of a man's search for love and happiness among men. Levantine merchants, Buddhist monks, Indian princes, Turkish adventurers people this book, a veritable Coromandel screen brought to life and a hymn of praise to the brotherhood of man.

Still considering the exotic, I must mention two more books. One is *The Narrow Corner* by Somerset Maugham, the greatest physician-writer of our age. Of all Maugham's novels, I consider *Cakes and Ale* to be his major achievement in craftsmanship, and I have read it over and over again, seeking to learn literary technique. Its first chapter is a masterpiece, endowed in its telling with that "difficult simplicity" of which Cervantes spoke. But *The Narrow Corner* is the most enchanting of all Maugham's novels, because of its exotic setting—the Dutch East Indies—and because there is magic in the way the author acquaints the reader with his charming characters. Dr. Saunders' meditations during an opium bout, Captain Nichols' eternal diatribes, the delicate love theme in this story, are never-to-be-forgotten arpeggios of literature. Never has Maugham been so masterly in narration and so romantic in imagination as in this novel, whose beauty recalls that of the island canals traveled by the hero's boat, so exquisitely described by the author himself: "The virgin forest on each side of them still held the night, but then insensibly the grey of the sea was shot with the soft hues of a pigeon's breast."

Pre-eminent in my corner of exotic selections is Pierre Benoit's *La Châtelaine du Liban.* Benoit, I believe, is the best French novelist of our time. His latest books—I have read all his forty works—have greatly deteriorated, but the earlier ones, with their background of jungles, seas, deserts, and islands, are masterpieces of realism within an exotic frame. His narrative technique is a marvel of literary magic, forever plunging the reader into and then dragging him away from the action of the plot, which appears to be reflected in multiple mirrors, showing its every facet. *The Chatelaine of Lebanon* is set in Beirut and its environs. I have visited the castle Kala'at el-Tahara in Beirut where lived the heroine, Athelstana, a Marlene Dietrich-like woman. This novel is a tale of love, passion, and espionage, of the fall and rebirth of a man, who loses himself in the impassioned embrace of an all-consuming woman, but finds himself again in the vast immensity of the desert, close to his comrades-in-arms and the warm proximity of the camel camp beneath the distant stars.

Another man goes astray in a "patriotic" betrayal of a friend, only to find his true self, indifferent and cynical, but human, in the arms of a Vietnamese woman, in *The Quiet American* by Graham Greene, one of the greatest contemporary writers of intense, dramatic stories, which, for lack of a better term, we call "thrillers." Of all his books— all so fascinating that I have read them more than once—I think this one is technically the best, as well as the richest in human and social, political and historical depth, and the truest in atmosphere. The drama of an American idealist, who destroys himself through excessive innocence, and of a British journalist, cynical, atheistic, and sensual, but humane, in hot, danger-fraught Saigon during the war, is marvelously captured in this novel.

I do not consider this book in the least "anti" anything; it is, however, a protest against the collective and individual stupidity of war. As background decoration there is a magnificent figure of a woman, Phuong, a Vietnamese with the soul of a savage, who, as in a Greek tragedy, helps to drive one of her lovers to his death and the other to a life of quiet desperation.

The seventh exotic novel in this group is James Ramsey Ullman's *The Sands of Karakorum*. Once read, it is impossible ever to forget the spellbinding caravan journey to Karakorum (Genghis Khan's fabulous capital in the heart of the Gobi desert) made by the hero and the wife of a missing missionary, a journey in which they seek not so much the missing man as their own destiny. The black sands of Karakorum, the Mongolian villages, the inscrutable Chinese soul appear in this book like an awesome vast canvas, on which all-dominant are the gray and black of the desert, the sensation of vast mysteries, slumbering secrets, and concealed mysticism, all of it enveloped by a curtain of desert sand as infinite as the mind of man.

The Chinese Revolution is the background for *Man's Fate* by André Malraux, the learned author of so many excellent novels and creative works, to whom the anonymous supreme powers behind the Nobel Prize have most unfairly denied an award up to the present, just as they have denied it to Somerset Maugham, Aldous Huxley, and André Maurois, and as they did to the late Pío Baroja and Ortega y Gasset.

This is an excellent book, reflecting the author's experience as a "professional" revolutionary (professional in revolutionary idealism, of course) in China, even as later he went to Spain. The revolution here is simply a backdrop on which are projected man's innermost conflicts, his secret aspirations, his fears and hopes, in that nervous prose of Malraux (it would be almost journalistic were it not so literary), the creation of which, one can sense, is constantly punctuated by puffs at a cigarette and continuous interruptions by telephone calls, for he is not only a great writer but also a busy man whose life combines countless tempestuous occupations.

From adventurers let us pass to the quiet ones. Thomas Mann is the most architectonic of modern novelists. His book *The Magic Mountain* is one of the greatest novels of our time. What impressed me most in this work was the author's technical audacity in devoting almost half the book to describing a single day in the life of the hero, Hans Castorp, whereas in the other half, depicting the long months of Hans' sojourn at Berghof sanatorium, one day meant nothing. Each day was so like the day before and the day after that they all formed a unit in time that finally merged into the island in space represented by the sanatorium.

During Hans' treatment for tuberculosis at the sanatorium, he has a unique spiritual experience in which he finds love and himself and discovers the drama of love and death. There are pages in this novel closely packed but limpid, written with the serene freshness of an Alpine snowscape. Nothing so original has appeared in the love literature of our age as the hero's famous anatomical declaration to the Junoesque patient, Clavdia Chauchat, in which he praises: ". . . *la luxuriance double et fraîche des fesses, et les grandes branches des vases et des nerfs . . . Oh, les douces régions de la jointure intérieure du coude et du jarret, avec leur abondance de délicatesses organiques sous leurs coussins de chair! . . Laisse-moi toucher dévotement de ma bouche l'Arteria femoralis . . ."*

Erich Maria Remarque has written several excellent novels, the best of which are *All Quiet on the Western Front, Arch of Triumph,* and his latest, *Heaven Has No Favorites. Arch of Triumph* is, in my opinion, one of the greatest novels of our century. This will be challenged, no doubt. But I feel that the atmosphere of Paris has never been so vividly captured, the loneliness of an exiled man never so poignantly conveyed, the love of man for woman never so touchingly mirrored, as in this book. This novel, all loneliness, love, and Paris, is the novel I would love to have written. *Heaven Has No Favorites* (see MD 5:93, June, 1961), is a great novel written in the grand style in the best European tradition.

There is a very special place in my heart for my friends, the *paisanos* of John Steinbeck's books. The picaresque novel, which reached its peak in Spain with Quevedo and in England with Dr. Tobias Smollett, is resurrected in Steinbeck's three books on the *paisanos* of Monterey: *Tortilla Flat, Cannery Row,* and the novel he originally intended to call *Palace Flophouse,* but which later, unfortunately, was called *Sweet Thursday.*

Of these three novels, which contain practically the same characters in spirit if not in name, my favorite is the first, which I know almost by heart. The misadventures of Danny and his friends, especially the crafty Pilon, who in order to get their paws around the neck of a bottle or a woman's waist would promptly sell to the devil not their own soul but those of their bosom pals, make a masterpiece of humor and affection. For behind the laughter one can sense the tears for man's problems and especially for his loneliness.

This novel, with all its rascality and drollery, is a song to comradeship and brotherhood such as prevailed among the knights of the Round Table. The *paisanos,* rags, ruses, and all, are *bons vivants* and "gentlemen" at heart, chasing young maidens and old wines, ever teaching us that honors and great wealth are not worth so much as a friend's handclasp, a spot of sun on the porch, a glass of wine, or a woman's tender caress.

Another class of rascality is that depicted in Evelyn Waugh's *A Handful of Dust,* wherein the author shakes out the dust—making us sneeze but from so much laughter—from the time-worn tapestry of the life of a provincial English gentleman (not unlike "the country squire in the green topcoat" in Cervantes' *Don Quixote,* but more modern and worldly), his amorous and social adventures, and his weird and tragic aftermath in the Amazon jungle, reading Dickens aloud to a psychotic autocrat.

Evelyn Waugh is a master of satire. His *Decline and Fall* and *Vile Bodies* are satirical novels comparable to the finest works of the great age of satire in English literature. His prose is as fine and clear as a stalactite, and just as sharp. He has a keen perception of human psychology and an extraordinary sense of humor. Laughter is your constant companion when reading *A Handful of Dust,* but so is the unpleasant sensation that one is seeing himself in many of the pages—so perceptive are the characterizations.

From among the many marvelous works of G. K. Chesterton, I choose *Tales of the Long Bow* because in it as in none other perhaps are combined the elements of Chestertonian wizardry never found in any other author: paradox and metaphor, symbolism and mysticism, humor and ardor, wit in expression and depth in thought, originality in creativeness and imagination in narration. These tales, which (like R. L. Stevenson's *New Arabian Nights,* another of my favorite works by one of my favorite novelists) are actually tales within tales, all linked with other tales, like those sets of Chinese boxes fitted one inside the other, portray the amazing exploits of a group of men to whom nothing was impossible. They wear a cabbage for a hat, set the Thames on fire, cause colossal pigs to fly in featherlined para-chutes, turn castles into flying carpets, and fight the whole world with bow and arrow.

At every point the Chestertonian genius for paradox bursts through like a wild boar from ambush, and Chesterton's style, full of sun and salt, love and humor, light and beauty, like a Levantine morning radiant with sun (has anyone made sure that Chesterton was not born under the Mediterranean sun of Valencia?), sets every page aglow and fires the soul. After reading this book, one feels oneself to be a better and kinder person because one has learned again to laugh and to dream.

A more modern, realistic, and sophisticated sense of humor prevails in Christopher Isherwood's *Goodbye to Berlin,* which contains two *novelle* (the second one is entitled *The Last of Mr. Norris*) about a small group of people, their lives and loves, in the last days of the Republic before Hitler's rise to power.

This is one of the great books of our time. The historic crumbling of a nation appears only as a background for a few squalid creatures —the masochistic Mr. Norris, the nymphomaniac Sally Bowles, and the passive *voyeur* who narrates the story—who are more attentive to the beatings of their own selfish hearts than to the extrasystoles of a desperate nation on the verge of losing its freedom.

Sally, so tellingly brought to life on stage and screen by that out-standing actress Julie Harris, is one of the most adorable, wanton, hypocritical, superficial, frivolous, sensuous, selfish females in all lit-erature. She is immensely superior to two other similar, though less complex and therefore less interesting, characters of the same stripe: the dance-hall girl Villai in the excellent *A Woman from Bangkok* by Jack Reynolds, and Suzy Wong of Richard Mason's highly over-rated *The World of Suzy Wong.*

Christopher Isherwood is a magnificent writer. In his latest novel, *The World in the Evening,* the first chapter, a most devastating criti-cism of life in Hollywood, is a fine piece of work, all the more extraor-dinary since the author earns his living in Hollywood.

In another remarkable book, *Vagabond's Trilogy,* its Norwegian author, Knut Hamsun, who was awarded the Nobel Prize in literature in 1920, presents the fascinating panorama of a man who relishes with bitter delight the hazardous free life of a romantic vagabond.

It is practically impossible to choose one book from among the hundreds written by Georges Simenon, one of the most remarkable writers of the twentieth century.

Simenon is the Balzac of our day, and it is time the American public took greater note of him. His works are a vast mosaic present-ing in themes of singular violence and unique insight the conflicts of twentieth century man with himself, his past, his fellow men, his family, his amours, and his own life.

In his novel *Le Temps d'Anais* (*The Girl in His Past*), which is a prodigy of literary technique and descriptive realism, Simenon explores one of his favorite themes, the recurrence of similar situations in human life (like the repetition of the same pathological episodes in a patient, which ought to interest a lover of medicine like Simenon). The erotic experiences of Anais as an adolescent drive the hero, who had admired and wanted her from afar, to commit a crime after he marries a woman very like Anais in her nymphomania, a crime for which he is no more responsible than Anais was for her sexual experiences as a girl. I have read more than three hundred of Simenon's novels, including the extraordinary adventures of Inspector Maigret, my favorite contemporary detective, and I consider Simenon the best psychological writer of our day and, of them all, the most typical of the twentieth century. For Simenon in his books charts those still unexplored areas that are like a Gobi desert of the emotions in the human soul.

Time and space are running short, but not my subject. I should like to mention Richard Aldington's *All Men Are Enemies,* in which this British writer most brilliantly presented the drama of a man in the postwar period who feels his soul as prostituted as was the body of the woman he loves; *Point Counter Point* by Aldous Huxley— possibly the most brilliant twentieth century writer—a story like a music box with a thousand different tunes and one of this author's most remarkable works; *The Story of San Michele,* the autobiography of the Swedish physician, Axel Munthe, which I include here because it is more novelistic than any novel I have ever read. I have visited Dr. Munthe's former home, the Villa San Michele in Capri, and it is one of the three most beautiful villas in the world owned by physicians (two of them writers) that I have ever seen (the other two are Somerset Maugham's Villa Mauresque at Cap Ferrat, and Dr. Li Shu-Fan's villa Green Jade in Kowloon, Hong Kong). Axel Munthe's autobiography is really a novel lived by the author. Like the *Arabian Nights,* it contains all the elements for a novel that a writer could possibly dream of.

His work may be controversial, but I think that Henry Miller's *Tropic of Cancer* and *Tropic of Capricorn* are two extraordinary books. Despite his needless and often revolting use of lavatory terminology, these two books show a literary genius with the fertility of a Thomas Wolfe (whose works I should like also to include in this list) and the humor of a Rabelais. Besides containing an excellent picture of contemporary Paris in our time, these books are like fireworks of passion and hope.

I am also including Stefan Zweig's works, for though they actually are biographies, from the viewpoint of plot and intrigue they are novels (his *Fouché* and *Marie Antoinette* are of unequaled literary beauty); T. E. Lawrence's *Seven Pillars of Wisdom,* an illuminating account in diamantine prose of his epic adventure in Arabia; and the poems of Federico García Lorca (the greatest Spanish poet of the twentieth century, who was murdered by the Guardia Civil at the outbreak of the Spanish Civil War), for each of Lorca's poems is a miniature epic of life and death, of the amorous passion and romantic yearnings of gypsy boys and girls, against the background of lemon trees and orange groves, moonlit roads, slumbering streams, and fragrant gardens, in the Andalusia of sorrow and romance.

I should like to crown this bouquet of literary blossoms with a few miniature roses, not so large, but sometimes superior in quality. Here are six of these exquisite roses: *The Servant* by Robin Maugham, Somerset Maugham's nephew, is the best modern short novel I have ever read. This story of the disintegration of a man through an excess of material comforts provided by his servant, a degenerate who ends up by becoming his lord and master, is written in adamantine prose— compact, hard, crystalline, and sparkling. Next comes *The Pledge* by Friedrich Dürrenmatt, the Swiss writer, who in a few hair-raising pages recounts the murder of a little girl by a psychopath and his capture by a determined detective, whose only clue was a psychiatrist's interpretation of a child's sketch. (Dürrenmatt's novel *The Judge and His Hangman* is, if possible, even better.) Christopher Isherwood's *Prater Violet* is the tragicomedy, exquisite and fragrant as a violet, of a Viennese film director. The fourth is *The Man of Blood* by José Luis de Vilallonga, a magnificent evocation of the Spanish Civil War and of Spanish refugees in Paris. Another short novel I must not overlook is Wenceslao Fernández Flórez' *The Man Who Bought an Automobile,* a gem of humor about what happens to a Spaniard who decides to buy a car. But one of the best of all these short novels is *The Rock Pool* by Cyril Connolly, perhaps the finest contemporary British essayist. In this short work the author portrays the degeneration of a group of British and American expatriates at Trou-sur-Mer, a little village of the Côte d'Azur. Their hates, loves, intrigues, and conflicts are described in a prose that is as lyrical and beautiful as it is cynical and cruel.

But now the Hong Kong ferry is drawing near the Kowloon pier. The rickshas approach. The Britons fold their newspapers. The chattering Chinese make haste to land. My pencil stub drops from my hand and rolls down the deck. The trip is finished, and so is my article. Could any one ask more for four cents?

TELL ME A STORY

ell me a story. . . . . Around the Christmas fireside, in the glow of crackling logs, children are pleading to be told a story. The father, perhaps a physician, may regale the children with morsels of life culled from his daily toil. But the child craves fairy tales. And when he does not get them, he then uses the magic wand of his fantasy to transmute the world around him into a glittering fairyland in which his own home becomes a luminous crystal-walled palace.

I believe in telling children fairy tales. In the past the child was considered "a little man" who had to be fed a steady diet of facts. Today we know that a child is only a child, and even when he becomes a man there still dwells in him a child, who now and then tinkles inside him as the little pebble tinkles inside a jingle bell.

All the expressions of a child are variations on the theme of his search for his own individuality, for an answer to his questions, "Who am I?" and "How can I distinguish myself from my world?" His thoughts resemble the magic thought of primitive people in the sense that he invents his own causality relations and accepts his fantasies as reality. He differentiates himself from his world not through his thinking but through his feelings and his games. Playing for him is a rehearsal of his role in real life. To the adult, play is recreation; to the child, it is hard work and serious business.

The child should be fed not only technical instruction at school but also a fantasy feast at home. The impulses that dominate childhood

From *MD*, the MEDICAL NEWSMAGAZINE, *3*:11, December, 1959.

are biologically even more important than his culture. In the child, to *wish,* which is to dream, is more important than to *want,* which involves action. Actually, the first nourishes the second. But the child confuses them both. To him, the things he desires, however unreal, are more important than real things. If the adult mind makes history, that is, reality, the child's mind makes legends, or the desirable. Myths and legends therefore are the best psychic hormones for the child.

Fairy tales appeal to the child because their fabric is similar to that of his thought. Primitive myths and legends help us to understand the infancy of mankind, just as fairy tales show us the infancy of man.

Myths once governed the creation of European culture. Later, the gods were exiled to earth, wherefrom they still rule our daily life through the image of their mythological deeds. Only artists have remained as custodians of the gods. The rest of us, in our hurried life, do not dream enough, and daydreams are important, for they are both the truest form of dreams and the modern counterpart of myths.

Like primitive man, the child identifies himself with the outer reality in the belief that to manifest his wishes is sufficient to make them come true. In his own world, as in fairy tales, the child allots magic powers to objects surrounding him. To the child the world is a jungle bristling with dangers, as the primeval forest was to primitive man. From his awareness of his disproportion and weakness in face of the gigantic outer world were born such classic tales as *Gulliver's Travels* and *Through the Looking-Glass.*

Wolves, goblins, evil genii are fairy tale symbols of the forces in the adult world that threaten to devour the child's ego. In a tale for a child lost in the fearsome darkness of the forest—which matches that of his own bedroom—the only refuge against such forces is the magic square of gold cast upon the dark forest by the illuminated window of fairy tales. In real life, though, the child may stop dreading the nocturnal darkness once he realizes—as in the story by Madeleine Gekire —that he can with his own imagination "switch on the night," "turn on" the moon and the stars, the crickets and the frogs, and all the other wonderful lights and sounds that are part of the night.

Let us, then, keep telling children tales of wonder. And let us never forget that the most wonderful tale of all was that of a Child born on that first Christmas when Mary "brought forth her firstborn son, and wrapped him in swaddling clothes, and laid him in a manger; because there was no room for them in the inn." This tale is particularly beautiful to us as it was told almost 2000 years ago, in stained-glass words in the Gospels, by a good and kind Greek colleague, St. Luke, the beloved physician.

II. the wonder-world of symbols

SYMBOLS AND MEDICINE *

ω hy from the huge bouquet of possible subjects has the Art Directors Club chosen the thorn-bristling rose of symbolism?

It is not enough to say that this is a problem of the greatest interest, for there are many others similarly worthy of your attention and even of greater importance. The selection of a subject for a conference, like the selection of a profession or a bride, is highly revealing of the chooser's psychology. In the case of a subject like symbolism, which so intensely interests our age, we must remember that every age has its own special preoccupations. As a matter of fact, no age ever chose its preoccupations; always the preoccupations chose the age. Man seldom chooses his basic preoccupations, any more than the bridegroom in old-fashioned plays "chose" his bride, whom, compromised by his amatory impatience, he was forced to marry under the shotgun of her irate parent. The choice of a preoccupation, like that of a wife, was often imposed on man against his own will.

Every age has had its overwhelming preoccupations. In the neolithic world, it was how to survive the menace of the mysterious surrounding world; in archaic Egypt, how to attain immortality of the soul; in the Medieval world, how to conquer the fear of God in Heaven and of demons and plagues on earth; in the Renaissance, how to explore the mysteries of the open space beyond the seas and of the space

* Presented at the Fourth Annual Communications Conference, on "Symbology," sponsored by the Art Directors Club of New York, April 2, 1959, New York, N. Y.

From *Symbology*, edited by Elwood Whitney, New York, Hastings House, 1960.

within the human body. In our own time, we have passed from fighting for "ideas," like Dadaism, socialism, laicism, Fauvism, and parliamentarianism, to exploring the symbols that represent them, symbols that are really ideas with a mask underneath which there burns an emotion.

WHAT IS A SYMBOL?

First, let us define the word "symbol." Etymologically, it is derived from the Greek *symballein,* "to throw together or join." A symbol is something that conveys to the mind an image of something else; it therefore "represents and conceals something else"; it conceals a much wider intrinsic meaning. Symbols have three meanings: a *conventional* meaning, or the relation between the word and the object it designates; an *accidental* meaning, that is, the emotional color the object may acquire, pleasant or unpleasant, happy or sad, depending on the individual experience to which it is related; and a *universal* meaning, for symbols are man's oldest and most international language, a "lost language" in which thoughts and emotions, many of them archaic, have become fossilized, but which can reappear in the most unexpected manner.[A]

SYMBOLS IN OUR TIME

Ours is a time of symbolism. From the moment we wake up we live in a world of symbols. The mute symbolism in the things surrounding us continually calls us to action. The water tumbler invites us with its crystal lips to drink; the Gillette blade—a tiny guillotine —bids us to eliminate our whiskers; the fried eggs—two golden suns nesting in an ivory sky—incite us to assimilate them into our metabolism; the jacket, hanging on its hanger like a fragment of ectoplasm, calls to us to fill its flapping arms with living flesh; the morning newspaper—a paper window on the universe—spurs us with words and images to think, to feel—fear, joy, anxiety, hope—and to act—travel, dress, buy, read, dance. The rest of the day is spent going from one circle of symbols to another, and, when the day comes to an end and we go to bed, we cross the misty threshold of dreams and enter a spectral world where *everything* is a symbol.

THE CAUSES FOR OUR "AGE OF SYMBOLISM"

Is ours more an "Age of Symbols" than an "Age of Anxiety"? Anxiety has been present throughout all history, but much more so in the past than now, though man may have had no name for it, just as syphilis probably existed always but lacked a name until the sixteenth-century physician Fracastoro gave it one in his beautiful poem *Syphilis sive morbus Gallicus.*

In prehistoric times, man, menaced by the cataclysms of nature, by monstrous beasts, and by fears caused by his own ignorance, must have suffered torturing anxieties; and in the Middle Ages he must have been terrified by the fearful pandemic of the Black Death, which killed one fourth of the people in Europe. Our own age has ample reasons for anxiety, but it is not *the* Age of Anxiety, though its worship of allegory and symbol might well entitle it, together with the early Middle Ages, to the name of "Age of Symbolism."

The reasons determining ours as an Age of Symbolism can be found, I believe, in the arts, science, psychology, communications, and politics of our time.

The *artistic* causes of present-day symbolism began around 1907, when Picasso started splitting up the human face in *Les Demoiselles d'Avignon.* Later, surrealist and fantastic art contributed to the creation of an art of idea-symbols, just as impressionism had been an art of emotions, and classic art one of objects.

The *scientific* reasons are to be found in the fact that atomic physics and the quantum theory not only disintegrated the universe and, following the disconcerting lines of Einstein and Planck, set it up again as a "limited and finite space-time continuum," but also used symbols to elaborate their theories. In this sense, modern science, particularly physics, is "fantasy" conditioned by real data whose basic conceptions—starting with those of the point, line, surface, and volume—are purely imaginary creations with a symbolic structure.

The *psychological* causes began to prevail about sixty years ago, when an imaginative Viennese psychiatrist and his followers taught us how to plumb, from the "Nautilus" of the psychoanalytical couch, the mysteries of the abyss of the personal and the collective unconscious. Thus the life and art of our age became colored with sexual and mystic symbols, whose meaning still influences every act of our daily life.

The causes derived from *communication* techniques are exemplified in the movies and television, which concentrate in a few symbols the whole spectrum of human emotions, bringing with songs, words, and pictures a treasure of rich imagery and symbolism to the fireside. The inevitable offspring of these techniques are the use and abuse of symbols and symbolism in publicity and advertising.

The *political* causes are based on the fact that those nondemocratic political systems of today that have most influenced—for the worse—the progress of mankind founded their propaganda techniques (many of which unfortunately have also been adopted by the democracies) on a monstrous hypertrophic worship of symbols, from the gestures, popularized in pictures, posters, and television, of political leaders, down to slogans, hymns, watchwords, and other political phraseology highly charged with emotional symbolism.

These five great groups of causes, operating on people shocked by the electrified historical climate of our time, have been the reason for the symbol's becoming an extremely important part of our thinking, our language, our dreams, and our world. So intense has been the impact of the symbol that too frequently we confuse the face with the mask, the idea with its symbol, so that the symbol instead of being a mirror of truth often becomes a mask of falsity.

THE STAGES OF MEDICINE AS SYMBOLS OF HISTORY

Symbols interest the physician because medicine is essentially the art of deciphering the secret of those subjective symbols we call *symptoms*—headache, anxiety, insomnia—or of those objective symbols we call *signs*—edema, conjunctivitis, varicosities—so as to ascertain the process hidden behind their symbolical manifestations. Every patient is a treasure chest filled with pathological symbols, and the physician must know how to reconstruct, based on such symbols, the outline of the mysterious morbid process that caused them.

Passing from the individual to the universal, just as the waters of a river reflect the different blue and silver tones of the skies above as they flow toward the sea, so has medicine, perhaps more than any other profession, symbolically reflected down the centuries the influence of the civilization of each epoch.

Thus, the physiology of ancient Egypt, which stated the existence of "conduits" in the human body to carry the blood and humors, obstructions wherein caused "floods" in some parts of the body and "droughts" in others, was symbolic of the Egyptians' daily vision of their vast sun-scorched plains through which flowed the sacred river that could fertilize the land or condemn it to drought. The ebbs and floods of the Nile were symbolized in the "floods" and "droughts" of the humors in the human body.

In classical Greece, the Hippocratic physicians accepted two theories: that of the *four humors* (blood, black bile, yellow bile, and phlegm), which explained disease as alterations of these humors; and the *pneumatic* theory, which considered disease as alterations of the pneuma or personal spirit, the counterpart of the universal spirit. Both theories were symbolic, the four-humor theory symbolizing the doctrine of the four elements of the universe, a doctrine established in the eighth century B.C. by the early Greek philosophers—Thales of Miletus, Anaximenes, Empedocles of Agrigentum, and others—and the pneumatic theory symbolizing the philosophical doctrine of the pneuma or universal spirit.

Byzantine medicine, which developed during the millennium when the golden-domed city of Byzantium, bulwark of Christianity, was besieged by Arabs, Tartars, and Ottomans, was a medicine of compilations and summaries of classical medical knowledge. It was a symbol of flight into time. Barred from traveling spatially beyond the walls of their beleaguered city, the Byzantine physicians—Oribasius, Aëtius, Paul of Aegina, and Alexander of Tralles—traveled more than a thousand years into the past, until they reached the sources of classical knowledge. This flight into time was also symbolized in the work of the Byzantine artists, who found escape from the besieged city in time-consuming stained-glass work, enamels, miniatures, and illuminated manuscripts.

Renaissance medicine, which explored the wonders of the human body through dissection and sketching under Vesalius and the artist-anatomists, Verrocchio, Pollaiuolo, Donatello, and Leonardo da Vinci, was a symbol of the explorations that were then being made by the conquistadors and other navigators in the *terra incognita* of the Indies. The longing to know the open spaces overseas had its counterpart in the longing to know the still unknown inner space of man's body.

The medicine of the seventeenth century, which witnessed Harvey's discovery that the blood *moves* and does so *in a circle,* was symbolic of the then prevailing baroque art, which exalted motion and emotion, characteristics reflected also in Shakespeare's plays, which, like Harvey's scientific writings, abounded with the words "blood" and "heart."

The concern of the medicine of the Enlightenment with the infinite and the infinitesimal, as exemplified in the work of Leeuwenhoek, who with homemade lenses explored the invisible world of animalcula imprisoned in a drop of water, was symbolic of the artistic interest in the world of minute details—the "finite"—exemplified in the magnificent paintings of Vermeer, executed at the same time as Leeuwenhoek's work and beneath the same tarnished-silver sky of Delft.

Medical encyclopedism at the beginning of the eighteenth century was symbolized by the general encyclopedism of the age, just as the realism of Claude Bernard's physiology was symbolized in the realism of Émile Zola's work.

In our own time, advances in ophthalmology at the beginning of the century were symbolic of the new visual attitude in painting reflected in Seurat's pointillism; the new physics of light and form—so important in medical refractometric apparatus—was symbolized in the impressionistic trends of Manet, Monet, and Pissarro; exploration of the unconscious by Sigmund Freud was symbolized by van Gogh's psychological expressionism; fragmentation of the human figure into new planes by Roentgen's radiology was symbolized by the multiplane cubism of Braque and Picasso; the atomic disintegration of the universe was symbolized by levitation in Dali's work; and the creation of a physical space-time continuum was symbolized by Picasso's portrayal of figures standing simultaneously full-face and in profile, which introduced the dimension of time into the spatial world of painting.

In other words, in the history of medicine, the physician's inquiring attitude has always been symbolically parallel with the attitudes of human thought in other fields of civilization. Hence, the symbolism of medicine is of interest not only to the physician but also to all those—writers, artists, publicists—who need symbols for inspiration and in creation or communication.

A GLANCE AT THE ORIGIN OF SYMBOLS

Medicine has helped us to understand the anthropological origin of symbols. Whether innate or acquired, symbols have been mankind's secret code, a universal language that may have preceded all others. The most ancient concepts have been perpetuated in symbols, so that some of them have become fossils of human thought.

When, at some memorable hour, primitive man lengthened his arm and increased its reach by means of eoliths or stone axes, he began to carve all around him psychic shapes that existed only in his mind. First he made magic drawings, then esthetic ones. Sometimes his drawings were of natural objects (the origin of surrealist art); at other times he produced geometrical shapes (the origin of cubist and abstract art). Art was followed by pictographic and ideographic writing, pictorial representation preceding the phonetic representation of sounds. With the development of symbolic and hieroglyphic writing, such images, emotions, and concepts as were inexpressible in words became incrusted in these two forms of writing and became symbols. These symbols are today of great value to the psychiatrist in interpreting the fragments of broken mirror that dreams are, and the hallucinations of psychotics, in the light of the symbolism of the universal unconscious of mankind.

Symbols are also of great value in understanding ourselves and our fellow men, in the appreciation of art, and in human communication.[B]

THE MEANING OF THREE SYMBOLS OF MEDICAL MYTHOLOGY: THE EYE OF HORUS, THE CENTAUR, AND THE CADUCEUS

To tell the story of all the symbols that have played an important

44

role in the history of medicine would be an unending task. Instead, by way of illustration, I shall deal with the meaning of three symbols directly connected with the history of the healing art, after which I shall tell how medicine helped to unravel the secret of three other symbols that exerted a deep influence in various periods of medical history.

The first three symbols are: the Eye of Horus, the centaur, and the caduceus.

The symbol of the *Eye of Horus* (fig. 1) appeared in history more than 5000 years ago. When speaking of the history of medicine, one is frequently inclined to think that it began with Hippocrates, but actually Hippocrates marks the chronological *halfway* point in the history of medicine. We shall have an accurate idea of the antiquity of medicine only when we realize that the first medical figure identifiable as an individual in history was the physician, architect, statesman, and musician Imhotep, who lived about 2950 B.C. and who built, not far from Cairo, the oldest stone structure existing today on earth, the pyramid of Sakkara. This means that Imhotep appeared in history almost twenty-five centuries before Hippocrates; more time elapsed between him and Hippocrates than between Hippocrates and Fleming!

Now, the Eye of Horus is of earlier date than Imhotep himself. Its legend is based on that of Horus, son of the goddess Isis, who lost his sight in childhood as the result of a vicious attack from the demon Set, but recovered it when his mother invoked the aid of the wise scribe Thoth. Thereafter, with their lyres made of medicinal woods, the Egyptians implored the hawk-headed god Horus to cure their ills. The Eye of Horus, portrayed in Egyptian iconography as an "R" with an eye inside the top circle, became a symbol of healing, and *udjats* or amulets made of gold, copper, wood, or wax, representing the Eye of Horus, were used as a protection against eye diseases and the Evil Eye. Later, Horus was replaced by other gods—for there have been fashions even in that—and the Eye of Horus disappeared, but it reappeared in the Middle Ages in the form of a sign similar to the number 4, which physicians and alchemists affixed to their prescriptions to invoke divine aid, thus reviving the Roman custom of writing the sign of Jupiter for similar purposes.

The sign ℞ was introduced by the physician Krinas in the time of Nero to show graphically that the physician was subject to the power of the state. In a typical swing of history's pendulum, while in Nero's time the state fought Christianity, in the Middle Ages the Church, in its struggle against medieval paganism, compelled physicians in countries like Spain to use the initials of *Responsum Raphaelis* in place of the pagan sign of Jupiter. Gradually the sign of Horus merged

FIG. 1. The Eye of Horus.

FIG. 2. Image of Hygea, the centaur Chiron, and Aesculapius
(Late Roman).

with that of Jupiter and became the ℞ sign, which we still use in the upper left corner of prescriptions.

The *centaur* symbol also played an important part in ancient medicine, so much so that the oldest symbolic representation of the healing art ought to be not Apollo or Aesculapius but Chiron, the noble, kind, and gifted centaur.

If the island of Cos was the cradle of Hippocratic naturalistic medicine, Trikka (now Trikkala) was the cradle of the psychotherapeutic medicine of the Asklepian cult and of the temples of Aesculapius. He who became the future god of medicine had a very complex mythological genealogy. To mention only one of the many legends woven around his birth, the sun god Apollo, enamored of lovely Coronis the nymph, on being informed by his talebearer, a white crow, that the nymph had betrayed him with a mortal, promptly had her slain. Coronis fell, her arrow-riddled bosom bejeweled by a necklace of rubies, and the son in her womb was delivered by Caesarean section. The infant, Aesculapius, was then sent to the mysterious mountain where dwelled a strange race of monsters, half man, half horse—the centaurs—who were related to the gods. (Figs. 2 and 3.)

To understand the psychological origin of the centaur symbol, it must be remembered that the horse played an important role in the evolution of mankind. From the times of the Pharaohs until the time when Napoleon's Grande Armée marched through the ermine-blanketed steppes of Russia, the horse was (with the sailing vessel, and later the coach or diligence) man's main means of locomotion. Man, who at first used the horse in war chariots, and only much later as a beast of burden, came to identify himself with the horse for many reasons, among which was the unconscious craving to possess its supposed sexual power. The greatest symbolic expression of the union of man and horse was the symbol of the Greek centaur, the only monster admitted among human beings. The centaurs were a wild, violent, and treacherous race, as exemplified by the centaur Eurytion and his companions. But Chiron was gentle, kind, and wise.[c]

Chiron, son of the Titan Cronus and the sea nymph Philyra, lived on Mount Pelion in Thessaly, where he taught the healing art to Aesculapius, who accompanied Jason and his Argonauts on their fabulous expedition in search of the Golden Fleece.

In the course of the centuries the symbol of the centaur became denaturalized. The horse was identified by Job and Jeremiah in the Bible as a symbol of aggression and power, an unconscious archetype of the unconquerable forces of the ego. The horseman began to be considered a unit with his horse, and the horse without a rider began to appear in dreams and fantasies, today analyzed as symbols

.ESColApivs. plato CEN TAVRVS

FIG. 3. Medieval manuscript (eleventh century) showing
Aesculapius, Plato, and the centaur Chiron.

FIG. 4. (*Above*) Detail from medieval representation of Hermes
with caduceus.

FIG. 5. (*Right*) Hygea and
Aesculapius showing staff with
serpent.

of castration and death. The Spanish conquistadores, who performed their heroic and bloody deeds on horseback, were thought by the American Indians to be centaurs. But the noble, wise, kind, healing symbolism of the centaur has slowly yielded to its other symbolism: the erotic, aggressive, and violent forces of the human unconscious.

The third great symbol of medicine is the *caduceus*. Like Aesculapius' staff, the caduceus was born of the serpent cult. Worshipped and feared, adored and destroyed ever since prehistoric times, the serpent, able to move without feet, to cast off its skin, and to be reborn each spring, has always been an object of fables and legends. The American Indians worshipped the rattlesnake; Asiatics, the cobra; Africans, the python. Temples in honor of the serpent-goddess were erected by Druids and Navajos, by Brahmans and Apaches. Because of its undulating movements, the serpent became a symbol of rain and of the flow of water, as well as of wisdom, wealth, sagacity, fortitude, health, convalescence, immortality, and longevity, that is, the most powerful symbol against disease, possibly because of the parallel between man's shaking off disease and the serpent's casting off its skin.

The two symbols derived from the serpent—the caduceus and the staff of Aesculapius—have as centerpiece a wand, which is regarded as an instrument of authority, a divining rod, a phallic symbol, or the tree of life, probably the palm tree, the *loma* of the Iranians, or the *soma* of the Vedic Hindus. The latter is the holy tree of the ancients; its sap is the oldest intoxicant of which we have record.[D]

The word "caduceus" derives from a Greek root meaning a "herald's wand" or "staff," and the root in turn derives from the Greek word *kerykeion,* meaning "to announce." Specifically, it was the wand of Mercury or Hermes, herald of the gods and protector of heralds.[E] (Fig. 4.) Mercury was also the god of dreams, magic, and commerce. Since he was born in the fourth month of the year, the numeral 4 was sacred to him and the fourth day of the week was named after him: *dies mercurii* in Latin, *mercredi* in French, *mercoledi* in Italian, and *miércoles* in Spanish. Through the centuries the caduceus reappeared in printers' watermarks, on the prows of merchant vessels, as an emblem of secret societies, and finally as a medical symbol when Sir William Butts (d. 1545), physician to Henry VIII, used it in his heraldic crest.[F]

The second symbol, the staff of Aesculapius with a single entwined serpent, head up and tail down, appeared in Homer's time (around 800 B.C.) and was used as a symbol by Aesculapius, who went about performing his cures followed by a serpent of the variety *Elaphis aesculapii.* (Fig. 5.) His staff with entwined serpent, symbol of the healing art, has been adopted by several medical societies, although

FIG. 6. Shield of the United States Army Medical Corps,
with Aesculapius' staff.

FIG. 7. Witch with broom and black cat.

the debate still continues as to which of these two symbols is the more appropriate.^G (Fig. 6.)

THE MEDICAL MEANING OF THREE FOLKLORE SYMBOLS: THE WITCH'S BROOM, APOLLO'S ARROWS, AND "COLD IRON" MAGIC

Medicine has uncovered also the secret of certain of the popular symbols that through the ages have exerted a great impact on mankind. As examples, I shall mention the broom of the witch, the arrows of Apollo, and the "cold iron" that wards off demons.

Witches are of interest in the history of medicine because in the late Middle Ages and early Renaissance some two million persons were burned in Europe on charges of witchcraft. The slightest denunciation, the least accusation of consorting with the devil or of attending a witches' Sabbath promptly brought death at the stake to the unfortunate victim.

Belief in the devil was born in the Middle Ages as a result of opposition to Christianity. In the popular mind, against God arose the Devil, and against Heaven, Hell, and many people hungry for power and protection took refuge in satanic cults. The belief spread that witches made a pact with the devil by signing the deed with their blood, kissing the devil's anus with reverential ceremony in the infamous *osculum sub cauda,* and receiving from Satan the *sigillum diaboli,* a mark resembling a mole or tiny spot, which was insensitive to pain and did not bleed when pricked by the long iron needles of the physician-inquisitors (a phenomenon frequent in hysterical persons). This horrible witch-hunting ceased when the brave Swiss physician, forerunner of modern psychiatry, Johann Weyer proved in his famous book *De praestigiis daemonum et incantationibus* that witches were nothing more than pitiable mental patients.

Now, the main symbol of witches, *the broom,* has been medically interpreted as a survival of ancient fertility rituals, which, together with mystery rituals, are possibly the oldest religions in the world. Medieval images of witches and modern pictures in fairy tales always show the witch with a broom. (Fig. 7.) However, this broom is only a relic of ancient, ritualistic, soil-fertility dances, in which men carried a wooden pitchfork and women a broom as a symbol of domesticity. The broom was symbolic of the home and the woman's role therein. Whether used for sweeping or for witchcraft, the original broom was a branch from the broom plant with a bundle of leaves at the end. This plant was supposed to possess magic and healing virtues, especially for the purpose of granting or denying fertility, and thus the broom still appears in gypsy nuptial dances. It is of interest to observe that the broom plant contained scoparium, a mild diuretic, so

Symbols and Medicine

FIG. 8. Renaissance representation of St. Sebastian
pierced by arrows.

FIG. 9. Policamus, Sebastian, Quirinus. Catacombs of
St. Calistus. Fifth century A.D.

that its infusion was of moderately beneficial effect in many illnesses. Since it was the woman who handled herbs at home, she knew their virtues, in cooking as in healing.[H]

Another symbol interpreted by medicine is that of the *arrows,* used in iconography, from the paintings of the Roman Empire down to the modern cartoons created on Madison Avenue, to illustrate the propagation of an infection. This arrow symbolism began with Apollo, god of plague in Rome, who could cause plague with plague-bearing arrows as well as stop it.

As the late beloved historian Henry Sigerist showed, when Christianity succeeded paganism, it lacked a protective saint against the plague. With the outbreak of a terrible epidemic in the sixth century, it became essential to elect a patron saint against plague, and, because of his history, St. Sebastian was chosen. As a youth, Sebastian, born in Milan, had been a captain in Diocletian's Imperial Guard. Because he later was converted to Christianity, Sebastian was shot at with arrows by Diocletian's guards until his body resembled a porcupine's. But Sebastian survived and it was necessary to execute him a second time (A.D. 303). Because arrows, symbol of infection and sudden death from the plague, had failed to kill him, which was tantamount to death and resurrection, Sebastian was chosen as patron saint against the plague, and a church was erected to him on the Palatine, over the ruins of an ancient temple to Apollo. Where centuries before people had invoked Apollo, they now prayed to St. Sebastian. (Fig. 8.)

Thereafter, St. Sebastian, who in fifth-century frescoes in the St. Calixtus catacombs in Rome appeared in tunic and pallium like the other saints, began to be portrayed by artists as a bearded soldier riddled with arrows. Later, in the Renaissance, since he had been made to assume the function of Apollo, he was portrayed not as a bearded soldier but as a handsome Apollo-like youth with his breast pierced by the arrow that could not kill him. (Fig. 9.)

The third symbol I shall cite was the subject of an excellent study by Dr. Walter Alvarez, and that is the use of "cold iron" (steel), in preference to brass, in extracting splinters embedded in the flesh or in preventing wound infections. Frazer has shown that primitive people added an iron nail to food so that demons could not infect it, and that a wounded person always kept a piece of iron nearby to drive away demons. Belief in the protective power of iron is substantiated by the custom of hanging a horseshoe atop doors or gates and iron amulets and rings on babies' cradles.

On the other hand, iron was barred from many religious ceremonies in the ancient world. Roman and Sabine priests shaved themselves not with iron but with bronze razors, the magic plant mandrake could not be cut with an iron knife, and the Druids never used iron to cut mistletoe. In order to avert disasters, many Roman temples and thrones were built without a single particle of iron.

The aversion of both the gods and the powers of evil to iron was due, according to Dr. Alvarez, to the fact that for many centuries iron was an unsuitable novelty for the gods and their priests, who since the paleolithic age were accustomed to carved stone knives and tools. Religion, always highly conservative, having used flint knives for thousands of years in sacrifices, was a long time getting accustomed to the use of iron. Though the universal religions were spreading, still many people adhered to the ancient gods and rituals in which iron was interdicted. This was due especially to the fact that the iron used prior to 1000 B.C. was of meteoric origin and people believed it was impure and demoniac and were afraid to use it.[1]

MODERN MEDICINE, A SCIENCE OF SYMBOLS

Stepping from the past to the present, one cannot help realizing that medicine is a science submerged in a world of ever-increasing symbols, which it has invented or adopted itself and the use and abuse of which threaten to destroy the clarity of medical communication.

To a certain degree, the overwhelming plethora of symbolism in medicine is the result of its historical evolution.

In its prehistoric stage, when man was his own physician, licking, sucking, and rubbing his wounds in imitation of animals, and in its neolithic stage, when the first empirical treatments began, based on what man had observed to be useful in previous similar cases—in these two stages, medicine was literal, realistic, naturalistic and needed no symbolism. Later, when herbs and empirical physical treatments were supplemented by prayers, exorcism, and magic rituals, medicine started to become symbolic. A further step in that direction was the discovery of pictographic and hieroglyphic writing, which introduced in medicine the use of symbolic signs to describe the progress of disease and its treatment.

However, for many centuries and particularly during the Golden Age of Greece, medicine was strictly an *oral* science, and it was not until the Middle Ages, when the written word came to be used increasingly for teaching and for communication with other people, that medicine plunged into an orgy of symbolism and allegory, not only in relation to natural magic and zodiacal and astrological medicine, but also in medical description and illustration. Instead of simply describing or sketching disease, medieval medicine symbolized it in often unintelligible allegories. Thus came the transition from *seeing* things to *thinking* of them, and finally to *interpreting* them symbolically.

In our time as never before, medicine has accentuated the symbolic not only in its methods and language, but in its techniques of clinical exploration and in its educational aspects as well.

Basically, the excessive use of symbolism and hieroglyphics in modern medicine is the result of its excessive technicalization. When a science progresses as rapidly as medicine has, it must increase its vocabulary at great speed also, but sometimes this does not happen. As a result, medicine has had to invent terms, apply a second meaning to other words, or borrow from the linguistic armory of other sciences words that are not always appropriate and therefore increase still further the semantic and symbolic chaos.

Moreover, the vast volume of facts, data, concepts, and discoveries added to its coffers every day has compelled medicine to simplify its idiom by abbreviation. The result has been disastrous. Physicians, and particularly we psychiatrists, use a "shorthand" jargon often unintelligible even to ourselves. The excessive use of abbreviations in scientific reports, clinical case histories, and medical books is making still more difficult a medicine that, being submerged in an ocean of symbols, is already extremely complex.

Glance at any standard clinical history from any hospital and you will see a conglomeration of cryptic laboratory data, figures, signs, abbreviations, tables, numerals, percentages, and concentrations, which reflect faithfully the state of the patient's basic humors, of his vital movements, and of his physiological functions, but not a trace is to be found anywhere of the spirit that distinguished the Hippocratic clinical history, which was above all a picture of a suffering human being, victim of disease. Fortunately, new trends in biographical and psychosomatic medicine are marking the return to the study of the *whole* patient and of his disease in relation to his whole life, his personal history, and his environment.

Until this approach is adopted by all physicians, imagination will be needed to translate the detached coldness of the tables and graphs of a clinical history into the dramatic reality of the sick man struggling for life.[J]

IMITATION, SCHEMATIZATION, AND SYMBOL

Since medicine is the science I know best, I have here approached from a medical standpoint the problem of the abuse of symbols and symbolism in our times, and the need to restore their true value to avoid the danger of their abuse.

But first let us inquire frankly: Is the symbol superior to other ways of interpreting reality? I believe that, from a purely intellectual point of view, it definitely is.

Let us imagine that we want to depict a human eye. There are three ways of doing so. The simplest and most direct method is *to imitate* reality, to draw the eye exactly as it appears to us. The second method is *to schematize* the eye in a diagram, indicating the basic ocular structure with a few clever lines. The third way is *to symbolize* the eye by means of an outline that not only conveys the anatomical reality of the eye but also interprets its function as a marvelous photographic camera in the human being.[K] The same methods could be applied in the portrayal of a face, an airplane, an eagle, a star, or a flower. In each case, the reality can be imitated, schematized, or symbolized.

From the viewpoint of intellectual quality and efficacy, neither the imitative nor the diagrammatic representation of reality has the high rank of the symbolic representation. For while literal imitation of visible reality is the work of a skillful hand, and schematization is the work of the abstractive function of reason, symbolic interpretation is the work of a constructive and symbolizing high intelligence.

In such sense, "modern" art—an art of ideas and symbols—can claim an intellectual supremacy over the naturalistic classic and imitative forms of art, since it not only schematizes but also symbolizes and *interprets*. This makes it even more imperative to protect symbols, use them properly, and avoid their "diseases."

"DISEASES" OF SYMBOLS: INTOXICATION, INFECTION,
TRAUMATISM, AND DEGENERATION

If we apply a medical criterion to the condition of symbols and symbolism in our time, we observe that symbols in our age suffer from a series of diseases that can be diagnosed medically.

Strictly for the sake of simplification, diseases may be classified in medicine into four groups: infections, intoxications, traumatisms, and degenerations—for instance, brucellosis, lead poisoning, fracture of the femur, and arteriosclerosis, respectively.

Now, in my opinion, many symbols today suffer from one or the other of these four illnesses, and, unless some treatment is promptly applied, the end will be the same and as inevitable as that of every untreated disease: aggravation, invalidism, or death of the symbol.

As examples let me cite the intoxication of the cross symbol, the infection of the swastika symbol, the traumatism of the atom symbol, and the degeneration of the symbol of ataraxia. All these diseases of symbols can be summarized as a pathological deterioration of the symbol in our own time.

Take, for instance, the symbol of the *cross* as an example of deterioration by *intoxication*. Like the majority of primitive symbols, the cross is a symbol of solar origin. Most primitive myths, symbols, and even religions are essentially solar in origin. The life of all the great Oriental religious reformers includes the birth, rise, and death of the prophet, god, apostle, or messiah, who symbolizes the dawn, noon, and setting of the sun in its journey from east to west. Another sun symbol is the inner light and mystic halo of reforming religious saints. In all mythologies the sun concept represented the conscious and elevated, and the moon and earth concepts the profound, what was submerged in the unconscious.[L]

The Christian-type cross has been found in the temples of Karnak, sometimes set up at crossroads. Egyptians, Phoenicians, and Chaldeans symbolized new life by the solar cross—originally perhaps a cross made of two crossed branches for making fire—and the cross has also been found on the breasts of statues excavated in pre-Columbian cities of Central America. In Babylon the cross was associated with water deities; in Assyria it was an emblem of creative power and eternity; in India, China, and Scandinavia it represented the heavens and immortality; and among the Mayas it was a sign of rejuvenation and freedom from physical suffering. In the Dionysian and Eleusinian mysteries in ancient Greece, the cross was placed on the initiate's breast as a symbol after his "rebirth." Universally, the cross appears to have been a symbol not of tragedy or defeat, but of strength, happiness, and eternal love. The cross of the Calvary became a symbol of miracles, able to perform healings upon whoever touched it. In Russia, *troitea* or cross trinities were put in crossroads for their miraculous powers.[M]

The cross, a symbol of sublime simplicity, changed the course of a great portion of humanity by becoming the guidance, inspiration, counsel, hope, and stronghold of millions of human beings during many centuries. But gradually, through intoxication with other meanings, the cross came to be considered a symbol of death and destruction, a negative and funereal symbol. People gradually began to see the cross as a symbol of past or imminent death, of torture and disaster. In medicine, for instance, crosses were used in laboratory reports—for example, Wassermann tests—to denote positive reactions indicative of sickness.

Hence, the cross—by a negative intoxication of the original positive symbol—became a psychologically negative, unpleasant, and sad symbol, though originally it was a positive symbol of joy and happiness and for religious people still is a pious, inspiring symbol. Perhaps because of its special geometrical structure of two strokes crossing one another negatively, the cross was condemned from the start (even without its symbolic connection with Christ's Calvary) to become a symbolic image of tragedy and death. It is sad, nonetheless,

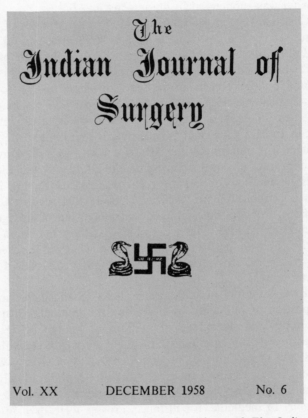

FIG. 10. Photograph of cover of an issue of *The Indian Journal of Surgery* with symbol of swastika with two snakes on the sides depicting original meaning of the symbol.

that few persons today recall the original joyous symbolism of the cross.

An example of *infection* of a symbol is the *swastika,* a cross with arms prolonged at right angles. Originally, the swastika was a symbol of wisdom and good luck, and it has been found in prehistoric burial grounds in Scandinavia, Persia, Mexico, India, Peru, Greece, Scotland, and North America, where it was always associated with sun worship. The most prevalent meaning of the word "swastika" was favorable, since it derived from the Sanskrit compound meaning "to be well." The swastika therefore was originally a sign of well-being, meaning that though the labyrinth of life is confusing, the way of light crosses through it.

The symbol of the swastika was stricken with a mortal infection when, some thirty years ago, a paranoid schizophrenic Viennese house painter succeeded, using all the resources of modern propaganda, including mass hypnosis and—why should we not say so—collective symbolism, in dominating almost all Europe on his way to mastering the whole world. The swastika, which had been a symbol of well-being and enlightenment, then became a symbol of chaos, sadism, oppression, and tyranny. Infection of its original meaning condemned this symbol to fall victim to a chronic infection, which will take centuries to heal, at least in the West, since in the East it is still used in relation to its original meaning, as on the cover of *The Indian Journal of Surgery.* (Fig. 10.)

A symbol deformed by *traumatism* is that of the *atom.* Originally, as conceived twenty-eight centuries ago in Greece by Leucippus and Democritus, this symbol was the first philosophical conception of how the universe was constructed. The atomistic theory served as the foundation not only of a philosophy but also of a curative system widely applied in Rome in treating huge masses of slaves in plantations. The atom was a symbol of the luminous and positive basis of the human being. Atoms, indivisible parts, were held to be linked together in various forms so as to produce objects, and everything, even the soul, was composed of atoms, which moved in the "void" that Democritus converted into "space." The moral ideas of Democritus begot the figure of the sage endowed with imperturbability, self-mastery, and serenity.

In our time, the atom and atomism have become the victims of traumatism, despite the concepts of Einstein and Planck, who employed them to perfect the theories that form the basis of our present atomic physics. Such has been the mental impact on the people of our time of the image of atomic and hydrogen bomb explosions with their fearful mushroom clouds, prelude to a cosmic apocalypse, that atomism, and the atoms with it, has turned into a symbol not of

FIG. 11. Three ways to "ataraxia": (*Left*) Tranquility was achieved by Eastern peoples through various methods of self-hypnosis; by intense meditation, maintenance of a difficult pose (as in this ancient Hindu painting), or through the use of narcotics.

FIG. 12. Three ways to "ataraxia": (*Above*) So-called "tranquilizing chair" used in Philadelphia in the eighteenth century by Dr. Benjamin Rush to restrain mental patients.

FIG. 13. Three ways to "ataraxia": A pleasurable feeling of languor was obtained for centuries in many countries with opium (as in this Chinese opium den), mentioned by Homer as a garden plant.

construction and planned structure, but of world destruction, and hence into a frightful menace to twentieth-century man.

Ataraxia, the last symbol that we will consider, has been the victim of *degeneration,* like that caused by the degenerative diseases, such as nephrosis or arteriosclerosis.

We are today witnessing the exaltation of anxiety and anguish by neurotics and pseudo-artists—the angry young men of England, the existentialists of Montparnasse, the beat generation in this country—but there was a time when the opposite was the rule, when ataraxia or a state of serenity was greatly sought after. This search was characteristic of the school of the Skeptics, particularly of Pyrrho (c. 360–270 B.C.) and Sextus Empiricus (second century A.D.), which defined the Skeptics' aim as imperturbability or ataraxia, later eulogized by the Epicurean and Stoic schools. Epicurean ataraxia was liberation from fear, like Seneca's impassivity, or what Democritus (460–370 B.C.) called *euthymia* and *ataraxia,* a positive, active, well-tempered emotion; the joviality, distinction, discernment, equilibrium, and moderation of a man *atarakthos* or free from commotion, worry, and perturbation, not lacking, but exercising moderation in emotions; the fearlessness preached by Aristotle; the state of alertness, serenity, and clear-sighted preparedness for action, which the philosopher Julian Marias called "a serene state of alertness ready for unexpected peril."

The affirmative form of ataraxia would be the Spanish *sosiego* of Ortega y Gasset—calmness, tranquility—derived from the same root as *asentarse* (to settle), meaning to attain stability, steadiness, security, serenity, and authenticity (according to Marias). It is what St. John of the Cross meant by "now my house being peaceful," in his "Ascent from Mount Carmel." It is the opposite of anguish and fanaticism. Such positive ataraxia was exemplified in one of Ovid's fables of the halcyon, which relates how the halcyon built her nest floating on the sea and laid her eggs in the dead of winter. Raging storms and winds promptly ceased for fourteen days so that there would be calm while the halcyon brooded.[N]

But in our days the frantic search for tranquility, the craze for freedom from anxiety has brought degeneration to ataraxia. Man, being what he is, *must* have problems and anxieties, for they are indispensable to make him strive for success in life. Excessive calm, tranquility, inertia, passivity are only penultimate to death. (Figs. 11, 12, and 13.)

The beautiful symbol of ataraxia therefore, which was no more than alert calm preparative to action, has degenerated into a foolish search for a moronic lethargy that leads to nothing. Formerly, ataraxia was sought through philosophical contemplation and, what is more important, through *action*. For example, the Oriental *karma* yoga is in a way a search for mental peace through *continued* action. Today we seek tranquility with Miltown and Perry Como! We no longer think of ataraxia as that beautiful inner peace of mind that comes when man finds fulfillment and contentment in his occupation and activities. This alert and active ataraxia of fearless, peaceful men is the symbol that, as in former times the cross opposed the eagle, must now oppose the demoniac plume of smoke that symbolizes atomism.

FOR A RESTORATION OF THE HEALTH AND JOY OF THE SYMBOL

It is therefore our duty to restore the true meaning and value of symbols if we do not wish, like the sorcerer's apprentice, to become the victims of our own creations. To do this, it should suffice to apply a few basic principles. In the first place, we must restore the true object existing behind each symbol. Second, we must not confuse the symbol with the object or idea hidden behind it. Third, we must use it adequately. Fourth, we must respect only good, honest symbols. Fifth, we must use symbols honestly. Sixth, we must make of the symbol not an end but a means toward the expression of our sentiments or ideals. And seventh, we must restore *health* and *joy* to the symbol.

The ancient world was for many centuries divided under the influence of two symbols: the cross and the eagle. Under the eagle were gathered the powerful forces of paganism, the ambitious purple- and scarlet-mantled emperors, the cruel captains with restless swords glittering in the sun, and the hordes of daring warriors hungry for pillage. Beneath the cross were gathered the forces of Christianity, the heroic saints and brave knights of the Crusades, the common people impelled by a craving for faith and adventure. For many centuries, in Byzantium, the Mediterranean, Spain, and Lepanto, the eagle and the cross relentlessly fought each other.

Today other symbols, especially political symbols, have taken the place of the cross and the eagle. The gesture of sublime simplicity of the cross, which spread like quicksilver over the entire planet even though in those days there were no fast means of communication, has been replaced by modern political gestures: the Roman salute of Fascism and the clenched fist of Marxism. More than of ideology, these are symbols of collective emotion. Their power lies not in symbolizing ideals, that is, emotions inflamed around an idea, but in being typical, imperative, and uniform. These are symbols of conduct, vehicles for imposing a discipline, uniforms of the soul that turn man into part of an organization, thereby making him renounce his individuality, his personal arrhythmic gesture, and acquire instead the symbolic, disciplined, rhythmic gesture common to an organization.[O]

Human gestures are living symbols, especially hand gestures, the first man makes when he is born and the last he makes when he is dying. The hands symbolize the heart, just as the tongue symbolizes the brain. This is why the ancients believed that special veins connected the hands to the heart, particularly the finger on which is placed the wedding ring—a symbolic surrender of the heart.

The hand, which has created almost all symbols, is the supreme vehicle of all emotion-laden human impulses. Hence, in the face of two conflicting symbols of our day—the atom and ataraxia—in their worst manifestation (the hydrogen bomb and tranquilization by melancholy drugs), it is essential to replace the mushroom-shaped smoke cloud of the atom with a stronger symbolic gesture that embodies the true meaning of ataraxia: the gesture of man's hands working, of the man who has peace of mind because he uses his hands creatively, or better still, the gesture of two hands clasped in the noblest symbol of all: universal brotherhood.

L'ENVOI

The original meaning of the word "symbol" was "emblem," or moral allegory, and "device," or the sign knights painted on their shields in the days of chivalry. And so I suggest that we return to that brave, romantic, and quixotic meaning of the symbol as emblem and device, so that we may restore health and joy to the symbol.

NOTES

A. About seventy years ago, a group of young poets in France created the "Symbolist" or "Decadent" movement. This was a rebellion against the too concrete "Naturalism" and the too restricted "Parnassianism" movements, which had failed to satisfy those poets who had adopted the sense of the Ineffable from Poe, Baudelaire, Wagner, and the pre-Raphaelites and sought a means to express it. Verlaine gave the Symbolist movement a watchword: *Pas de couleur, rien que la nuance,* and introduced the masters of the Decadents—Rimbaud, Corbière, and Mallarmé—in his book *Trois Poètes Maudits.* The movement later fell into decline and disappeared, but it left its seed in other areas of modern art.

B. Of great interest is one particular chain of symbols that shows that mankind continued to portray its repressed desires in the "lost language" of symbols. In 1909, Harold Bayley, in his book *A New Light on the Renaissance,* formulated the theory that from their beginning in 1282 until the latter half of the eighteenth century, the curious watermarks in writing paper represented a coherent and uninterrupted chain of emblematic symbols that could be fossil-thoughts. Frozen and preserved in the cryptographic sanctuary of these watermarks were the aspirations and traditions of many of the mystic and puritan sects that dominated Europe in the Middle Ages. This is why such watermarks are historico-psychological documents of great importance.

Thanks to the symbolism of watermarks, we know that the art of paper-making was introduced in Europe by Protestant sects—the Albigenses and Vaudois in France, and the Cathari or Patarini in Italy—prior to the Reformation. These heretic sects survived secretly for several centuries after having been excommunicated and proscribed by the Pope. Of identical origin are the symbolic decorations used by medieval printers, which can be explained by a similar code of interpretation. These printers, papermakers, and other artisans were precursors of the Renaissance, when symbolism was freed and began to appear openly in art.

C. "In that melancholy centaur Chiron," said J. Rof Carballo, "according to Kerenyi, incurably wounded by one of Heracles' arrows, were combined the animal or instinctive and the Apolline, the blind unconscious, and luminous reason. This figure, half theriomorphic and semihuman, became a fine physician because of his own wound, which made him more sensitive to the injuries and affections of other people, as happens with every good physician. The riddle posed in classical antiquity by the Chiron myth is clarified if we think that while the statues of Aesculapius were clothed in harmonious folds and full of tranquility, Chiron shows us his torso shaken by obscure and violent subterranean forces. Chiron is the bond between Asklepios and man's secret world—the unconscious, and one is struck with wonder at the profound intuition of the Greeks in placing Chiron at the most remote beginning of the profession of physician."

D. One of the oldest portrayals of the caduceus is on the famous green libation vase from Lagash, dedicated to the god Ningishzida by Gudea in Sumer, which is supposed to date from 4000 B.C. This caduceus has a wooden axis with two serpents coiled around it. Originally the caduceus was an olive branch with two woolen threads wrapped round it, later changed into serpents while the branch terminated in a knot with two wings. The caduceus became the symbol of Mercury, or Hermes, when he gave Apollo a lyre made of the shell of a turtle, with dried fibers for strings, and received from Apollo in return a winged staff entwined with two golden serpents: the caduceus.

E. Travelers used to pile at crossroads stones or *trivia* (whence the word "trivial") in honor of Hermes.

F. In 1856, the U. S. Marine Hospital Service used the caduceus to denote the noncombatant character of the medical corps; in 1902 it was adopted by the U. S. Army Surgeon-General for all military physicians and allied professions.

G. It seems that the one preferred by the majority is that with the *single* serpent coiled around the staff, having been adopted by the American Medical Association in 1912, by various medical battalions in the last war, by the World Health Organization, and in 1957 by the U. S. Air Force.

H. A black cat was another of the witch's symbols. In 1566, one Agnes Waterhouse was burned at Chelmsford because she owned a mottled cat. From remote antiquity the cat was supposed to possess magic powers. In Ireland, Dr. Walter Langdon-Brown has pointed out, many cats can still be seen with their tails cut off, since country people believe that its blood cures erysipelas and herpes.

Another symbol of the witches were the "flying ointments," with which they smeared their bodies. By the way, witches were not always slovenly old hags, as many people still think; often they were young women of diabolical beauty, which made them all the more dangerous. The ointments enabled witches to fly over towns, protected by the blue-black night. This symbol has been interpreted in our own time by Professor Clark, who, upon analyzing the medieval formulas for such ointments, discovered that they contained belladonna, which produces hallucinations, and aconite, which causes an irregular action of the heart with the consequent sensation of falling through space. Together, these sensations made witches and their acolytes believe that they had flown through the heavenly spaces.

I. Three thousand years before it came into general use (700 B.C.), iron was a metal of meteoric origin and as rare as gold. Iron apparently began to be produced on a large scale at Hallstatt, near present-day Salzburg in Austria, but as early as 1300 B.C. the Egyptians had been defeated by the Hittites because the latter used iron weapons.

J. A clinical case history contains only figures: temperature, pulse, respiration, blood pressure, respiratory quotient, total daily acetone rates, and daily glycosuria. But with a little imagination, by projecting the symbolism of such cold figures, we can readily see the heart-rending picture of a diabetic with acute circulatory failure and coma, intense and sharp drop in systolic volume, with the heart beating almost "dry." The columns of figures thus seen reflect a flux of matter and energy in great conflict, and the patient's life as a river of chemical, mechanical, and thermal movements, ebbing away at full speed, as the historian P. Laín Entralgo has brilliantly indicated.

K. In primitive mythology, the eye often represented the deity as a symbol of force, power, and luminosity. As J. Eduardo Cirlot recently indicated in his excellent study on this subject, the eye was often employed in mythological iconography, in which its magic powers were stressed by three processes: *displacement,* or placing eyes in places other than the anatomically normal, for instance, heterotopic eyes in the wings of romanesque angels; *diminution,* or reducing the number of eyes, as in Cyclops; and *augmentation,* or increasing the number of eyes, as with the hundred-eyed Argus of Greek mythology.

To the afore-mentioned uses must be added the use of the eye as a protective magic talisman, such as the eyes painted on Greek galleys, Oriental eye amulets, the eye painted on the faïence orbs used by Indochinese religious sects, and the eye symbolic of the Divine Providence stamped on ancient Christian Gnostic images. The eye was also used as a symbol of the powers of darkness in some medieval allegories of satanism. The eye has been considered a powerful magic symbol by artists also, and in our own times it has been used in surrealist painting (Ernst, Magritte, Dali). Cirlot in his work contrasts the symbols of the three attitudes adopted by man when, facing the Infinite, he inquires about his fate: the symbol of the *wall* (for instance, the Wailing Wall of Jerusalem), which represents a feeling of impotence in the face of the Infinite; the symbol of the *window* (the perforated jade disks of the Chinese), which represents a feeling of possible but restricted human activity; and the symbol of the *eye talisman,* which is not impotency like the first symbol, nor an opening offering escape like the second symbol, but a *mirror* that provides an answer to man, for upon looking into the eye he finds in himself the answer to his anguished queries.

L. The ancient symbols of the tree, cross, and serpent were at first identical with that of the sun saving mankind after the Flood, for they represented the same imagery of death, salvation, and resurrection. The serpent and the tree revive in spring, respectively renewing skin and leaves. In Paradise stood the tree of life, symbolized in due course by Christ on the Cross, that is, by ideas of death and salvation. The original sin was committed in the Garden of Eden, and as a punishment came the Deluge, but when the sun shone over the waters it saved mankind, a symbolic equivalent of Christ rising again to save all men.

M. In the Middle Ages there appeared a movement—which had nothing in common with that for a return to Helios vainly attempted by the Emperor Julian the Apostate—of transition to the rose symbol, expressed in the formula *per crucem ad rosam* (through the cross to the rose), which crystallized in the high Middle Ages into the *Rosenkreuz* ("Rosie Crosse") of the Rosicrucians. According to these people, the essence of the sun descended from the heavens into the flower, which was the earth's response to the kiss of the sun. This symbolism survived in the "golden flower" of Chinese alchemy. The blue flower of the Romantics was the last nostalgic representation of the rose in which was reflected the solar gold.

N. A form of ataraxia was exemplified iconographically in the ancient *mandalas* or magic circles, employed in Lamaism and yogist tantrism as *yantras* or aids to contemplation based on a quaternary system, the *quadratura circuli,* whose content, derived from lamaist dogma, is one of the most ancient religious symbols of humanity. *Mandalas* have also been found in paleolithic rock paintings in Rhodesia, and Jung discovered them as internal images in his patients' dreams. They are a psychic center in the personality not identifiable with the ego.

O. Accented by the resources of collective hypnotism and Pavlovian reflexes of emotion as described by Aldous Huxley.

BIBLIOGRAPHY

1. ALVAREZ, W.: The impact of the introduction of iron on religious thought. *In:* Essays in Biology in Honor of Herbert Evans, Berkeley and Los Angeles, University of California Press, 1943.
2. ATKINSON, D. T.: Magic, Myth and Medicine, Cleveland and New York, The World Publishing Company, 1956.
3. BAILEY, H.: The Lost Language of Symbols, New York, Barnes & Noble, 1952, 2 vol.
4. BETTMANN, O. L.: A Pictorial History of Medicine, Springfield, Ill., Charles C Thomas, 1956.
5. BRILL, A. A.: The universality of symbols, Psychoanalytic. Rev. *30*:1–18, Jan., 1943.
6. BROWN, W. L.: From Witchcraft to Chemotherapy, Cambridge, England, Cambridge University Press, 1941.
7. CIRLOT, J.-E.: Elojio en la mitologia y su simbolismo, Laboratorios del Norte de España, 1954.
8. CORIAT, I. H.: Medical magic, Ann. Med. Hist. *4*:291–301, 1922.
9. FRAZER, J. G.: The Golden Bough: A Study in Magic and Religion, New York, The Macmillan Company, 1942.
10. GESSMANN, G. W.: Die Geheimsymbole der Alchymie, Arzneikunde und Astrologie des Mittelalters (The Secret Symbols of Medieval Alchemy, Medicine and Astrology), Berlin, Karl Siegismund, 1922.
11. GOMOIU, V., AND PLATAREANU, V.: La Croix dans le folklore medical roumain (The Cross in Rumanian Medical Tradition), Bucharest, Institutul de Istoria Medicinei, 1938.
12. GRATTAN, J. H. G., AND SINGER, C.: Anglo-Saxon Magic and Medicine, London, Oxford University Press, 1952.
13. HASTINGS, T. G.: Love, Evolution and Religion, White Plains, N. Y., 1924.
14. KOCH, R.: The Book of Signs, London, First Edition Club, 1930.

15. Laín Entralgo, P.: La historia clinica, Madrid, Consejo Superior de Investigaciones Científicas, 1950.
16. Levin, S.: The evil eye and afflictions of children, South African M. J., p. 663, June 28, 1958.
17. Marias, J.: Ataraxia y alcionismo, Madrid, Ibys, 1957.
18. Marti-Ibañez, F.: Centaur: Essays on the History of Medical Ideas, New York, MD Publications, Inc., 1958.
19. Marti-Ibañez, F.: The Fabric of Medicine. In preparation.
20. Marti-Ibañez, F.: On the psychology of symbolism in Oriental rugs, Internat. Rec. Med. & G.P.C. *169*:651–662, 1956.
21. Marti-Ibañez, F.: Symbols and life, Internat. Rec. Med. *171:*116, 1958.
22. Meerloo, J. A. M.: "Infection mentale" communication archaïque et régression insensible: Contribution à l'étude psychosomatique des épidémies mentales, Med. et Hyg. *16*:57–460, 477–478, 1958.
23. Park, R.: The Evil Eye, Thanatology, and Other Essays, Boston, The Gorham Press, 1912.
24. Pettigrew, T. J.: On Superstitions connected with the History and Practice of Medicine and Surgery, London, John Churchill, 1844.
25. Potter, E. S.: Serpents in Symbolism, Art and Medicine, Santa Barbara, Calif., Privately Printed, 1937.
26. Rof Carballo, J.: Quirón el centauro, Madrid, Ibys, 1957.
27. Smith, L. P.: Symbolism and Science: A Paper Read before the Germantown Science and Art Club, Philadelphia, Privately Printed, 1885.
28. Sozinskey, T. S.: Medical Symbolism: In Connection with Historical Studies in the Arts of Healing and Hygiene, Philadelphia and London, F. A. Davis, 1891.
29. Stenn, F.: The Caduceus and the Staff of Aesculapius, Abbott-therapy, no. 169.
30. Symposium on symbolism and religion, Internat. Rec. Med. *171*:703–771, Dec., 1958.
31. Wilson, R.: The Caduceus and its symbolism, Ann. Med. Hist. *4*:301–303, 1922.
32. Wolff, W.: Structure and origin of religious symbols, Internat. Rec. Med. *171*:706–708, Dec., 1958.

ON AN ARMENIAN "FLYING CARPET" *

In his first two books on the psychological symbols buried in the knots, plaiting, colors, and images in Oriental rugs, H. M. Raphaelian, a patient and original scholar and a man of great kindness, related the enthralling tale of the secrets woven by dexterous and subtle fingers into the varicolored tapestry of rugs from many parts of the world.

Now this tireless author has produced another work, as excellent and revealing as the former two, thus completing his trilogy. But while in the previous volumes he surveyed the symbols in Oriental rugs "horizontally"—in space—he here concentrates his efforts "vertically"—in time—deciphering the secrets of the rugs of a single country, his native land, that beautiful and distant Armenia, whose towns bear names as bewitching as a romantic Oriental fable. Just as by digging deep in the soul of an individual, one may find the key to all mankind, the author, by digging deep in the roots of the art of rugmaking of a single country, has found the key to that same art throughout the world.

To reach the road to universality it is not always necessary to roam first all the roads of the earth. Likewise, in fathoming a single soul or a single nation, it is possible to encounter the problems of all humanity or of all the world. Just as the miracle of love leads one to discover the perfections of all womanhood in a single woman, so the miracle of certain authors—like Cervantes and his knight-errant, so fiercely Spanish and yet so universal—can create a figure that is

* This article is the author's Foreword to the book *Armenian Rugs* by Harry Raphaelian, New York, Anatol Sivas Publication, 1960.

supreme for all time and for all the world. Such is the case with this book, which unravels many secrets of universal art, ancient and modern, merely by looking, as the author does, with eyes filled with sympathy and wonder at the colors, designs, and figures in the rugs of Armenia.

Tragic had to be the destiny of Armenia, spread as it was, like a rug of many-hued designs, across the route of conquest-hungry empires. As on a rug, the boots of invading armies from Babylon and Assyria in the past, and from Turkey in modern times, trampled over Armenia. Like Byzantium, Armenia was a gem constantly coveted by invaders, but unlike Byzantium, Armenia had no towering walls and deep rivers to protect it, and had to fight for its historical survival not only with arms but also with souls. Armenia's longing for historical continuity was translated into its vast literary output down the centuries, especially in the fields of religion and history. It tried to win immortality through books on the grace of God and on the work of man. This longing found expression also in the development of the very ancient Oriental art of rugmaking, whose origin, evolution, and varieties are expertly and lucidly studied in this volume, which through its magnificent illustrations is itself like a multicolored paper rug.

Thanks to the wealth of illustrations in this book, we can see for ourselves the dazzling panorama of Armenian rugs, their history and technique, and their influence on the cognate art in other nations. We can peer into the mysteries of the Kohar and Heripsine rugs of Kabistan and the Caucasus, and may even unravel the secret of carpets made immortal through being incorporated into pictures, as, for instance, the rug in Holbein's portrait of Gyscze, which our author "diagnoses" as a Kuba rug, or the one in the portrait of Milton, here identified as a Kabistan rug decorated with a scarab motif. Rugmakers liked, the author explains, to show rugs as table runners in paintings because of the color they lent to them.

In like manner, the author explores the symbolism in Armenian rugs: the fig, a fruit symbolic of divine wisdom, fertility, and beauty; the horseshoe, a phallic symbol; the turtle, symbol of immortality; the serpent, a sexual symbol; the conventionalized bird designs, symbols of regal learning, power, and fertility. He also shows us the Chinese influence on the art of Armenian rugs, exemplified in tablets and carvings in Armenian churches.

In our trip over Armenia on this symbolic "flying carpet," we can observe the vast historic panorama of Armenian art in its numerous manifestations. The selection of plates in this book is as exhaustive as it is beautiful and original. Studying this volume, which is the transmutation of many years of research and meditation, we feel grateful to its author for sharing with us that magic world to which he holds the passkey.

The art of the Armenians, masters of rugmaking, might be compared with that of the Byzantines. In their thousand years of historic existence as an independent empire, the Byzantines turned their backs on the cruel world of enemies lurking beyond their golden walls and the azure waters of the Bosporus and took refuge in the exquisite world of miniatures, enamels, stained glass windows, and illuminated initials. Perhaps the same thing occurred with the Armenians. In the face of the historic threat that eternally hovered over them, they sought refuge in an art of eternity, precision, and fantasy like that of rugmaking.

In the noisy heart of Manhattan, the author, a dedicated and pensive man, performed an even greater miracle. Turning his back on the empire of smoke, steel, and concrete around him, he retreated into the fine and subtle world of the symbols in his rugs. For that alone he deserves our warmest admiration and affection.

III. the march of medical history

THE GREAT HISTORICAL CHALLENGES IN MEDICINE

CHALLENGE AND REPLY IN MEDICINE

ω hat counts in the lives of men and of nations is not so much their achievements as the challenges that cross their path and particularly the way they face them. In this sense, the history of our seven symposia is the history of the great challenges encountered by antibiotic medicine and of the way scientific investigators have faced them.

At the first great symposium of all, held more than two thousand years ago at the house of Agathon in Athens, by the light of torches that sparked the wine goblets into a myriad of rubies, Eryximachus the physician defined medicine to the other guests, among whom was Socrates, as "the study of the love affairs of the organs of the body." In like manner, we might say that at these annual symposia we have listened to the love affairs between antibiotics and germs, with the latter behaving like frivolous girls, now being vulnerable, now resisting the antibiotic onslaught.

At first sight, these symposia may appear to summarize every autumn the rich scientific harvest of the previous year. But I would say it is the other way round. Getting together here, interchanging impressions, inquiring into one another's work, dreaming together, sharing our hopes—this to a large degree is what determines the harvest of discoveries to be reaped the following year. More than an account of what you have done in the past year, this symposium each year is like the hoisting and unfurling of an inspiring banner that galvanizes you scientists to further action, to do still greater things in the year to come.

Presented at the Seventh Annual Symposium on Antibiotics, Washington, D. C., November 4, 1959.

It is fitting to inquire if the new scientific challenges uncovered at each symposium are just another facet of these our times, which, like a rose among thorns, are so full of promise and yet bristle with problems. History tells us that medicine obeys the law of action and reaction, wherein each new scientific step, each medical discovery, starts a chain reaction of challenges that the physician must resolve if he wants to ensure continuity in the history of medicine.

In mythology each new victory of Hercules during his Labors, each new exploit of Ulysses during his Odyssey across the azure waters of the Mediterranean, led only to new perils that the hero had to overcome if he wanted to reach the haven of his dreams safe, sound, and victorious. In science, each conquest engenders new menaces to itself, and the scientist must stand ready to overcome these menaces, if his progress is not to be deterred by setbacks, like the tortoise in the fable.

Thus, science, like human life, is an operation that moves forward. Like life, science also must be fiercely faithful to itself and to its vital authenticity. It must be faithful to the duty of facing its repertory of problems. In life, as in science, one cannot shelve, shirk, or evade problems. They must be confronted with a serene face and a valiant soul, since problems are wont to flee and vanish before the bold tread of the fearless fighter, just as phantoms in a haunted castle vanish before the first glow of dawn that sheds light and life upon everything.

THE SEVEN GREAT CHALLENGES IN THE HISTORY OF MEDICINE

The emergence of challenges on the road of contemporary medicine is nothing new. At every period in history the physician has been beset by tremendous problems, which he has resolved by dint of his genius and ingenuity. We could reduce to seven these great historical challenges to medicine, just as we could reduce to seven contemporary medicine's responses to such challenges, and again to seven— always the magic number—the spiritual virtues of the scientific investigator, on whose ability to respond to such challenges medical progress depends.

The first great challenge arose in the world that emerged from the neolithic world of the flint. "River civilizations" sprang up on sun-blazed steppes, and brown-skinned peoples, originally from Asia, condemned to annihilation by the scorching sun and whirling sands, struggled desperately to survive in the wildernesses. Such were archaic Egypt and Mesopotamia when man answered the challenge of the shapeless world around him, peopled by invisible presences and demons, with the sheltering geometric architecture of pyramids and ziggurats. That was also the time when medicine men tried to master the invisible forces of nature and disease by means of the first pseudo-science, magic medicine. The archaic medicine man resorted to the stars, the livers of sacrificed animals, and auguries to safeguard the life of his people against the demons that caused the spiritual possessions and fevers we now call psychoses and infections respectively.

The second great challenge came on the golden Greek peninsula and its sun-blistered lemon-and-olive groved islands, where the first great philosophies and religions of the western world were born. There, more than 2500 years ago, man for the first time in history dared to face the intellectual challenge posed by the nature of the universe, of man, and of disease. The Greek philosophers, many of them physicians, were the first to use the magnificent instrument of thought to awaken man's conscience and dignity, and to formulate the concept of disease as a natural process that could be healed by empirical and rational means.

The third great challenge was sheltered by the gloomy skies of the Middle Ages, when the Black Death and other great pandemics threatened to destroy the human race. The men who met this challenge were physician-priests, shut away in the only places where medicine could still be practiced, the monasteries, which, stationed along the great routes traveled by pilgrims, crusaders, and merchants alike, were a dynamic combination of news agencies and centers of bookish research. Theirs was strictly a "book medicine"; nevertheless, in their fight against epidemics and other manifestations of nature's destructive forces, they created hospitals, universities, and public health measures, which, together with the Gothic cathedrals and *The Divine Comedy,* were the great medieval contributions to civilization.

The fourth challenge arose in the Renaissance, a period throbbing with the parallel urges to explore the human body and the horizon stretching beyond the seas, both of which until then were *terra incognita.* The fever of the navigators to discover the lands asleep beneath the virgin stars of the western sky was matched by the fever of Renaissance surgeons and anatomists to discover with their scalpels the mysteries hidden beneath the human skin. The challenge posed by the mysterious structure of the organic fabric was answered by hands urged on by the bold and rational thought of the Renaissance surgeons and anatomists.

The fifth challenge was to decipher the secret of the physiology of the human body and its mysterious functions. This problem was unraveled in the Baroque period, when the motion and emotion characteristic of Baroque art were reflected in the concepts applied to scientific investigation, as in the discovery of the circulation of the blood, which was to make *anatomia animata* in space, just as Baroque embryology made *anatomia animata* in time. When dynamic physiology replaced the static anatomy of the past, the way was opened for a series of discoveries in circulatory, digestive, and nervous physiology, on which modern medical science is founded.

The sixth challenge was presented by disease therapy, which at the end of last century was still as empirical as it was two thousand years ago. Clinical and laboratory investigators answered this challenge with immunobiological, endocrine, chemical, and, more recently, antibiotic therapies, calling for a naturalistic and experimental criterion in the treatment of diseases.

The challenge of our own time is to decipher the nature and the biochemical substrate of disease and its natural history, the biological cycles of the pathogenic agents, the enigmas of genetics, and the secrets of ecology, and thus be able to anticipate the biological destiny of man and to make of therapeutics a subtle diagnostic key with which to unlock the last door opening to the threshold of life.

THE CONCEPT OF BIOCHEMICAL RESPONSIBILITY

We have progressed therefore from the primitive *anatomical* notion of disease, which placed all responsibility on one organ only, to the *physiological* notion, which accepted a multiple organ functional responsibility, and from there to the *biochemical* notion, which, ignoring the primitive concept of the diseased organ and the later concept of multiple alteration, concentrates instead on biochemical responsibility.

This means accepting the *totality* of the pathological disorder, which, though initially it springs from the alteration of one organ, is not limited to the boundaries of that organ, but adheres to the concept that the seat of every disease, however limited it may seem, is the *whole* body, and the disorder is therefore a *general* disturbance of all the organic humors.

We have thus returned to the original humoral notion propounded more than two thousand years ago by Hippocrates, which was later displaced to some degree by Galen's partly anatomical concepts. This is one of the paradoxes in the history of medicine. It took many centuries to agree that diseases did not float mysteriously within the body but were localized in what was successively described in the course of history as organ, texture, fiber, web, membrane, tissue, cell.

In contrast, we are nowadays reverting to the *humoral* idea of disease, but with the difference—on which rests the progress of our knowledge—that we now agree that diseases, including psychiatric disorders, are localized in organs but affect the totality of the organism due to the efficient correlation mechanisms of the body, particu-

76

larly the endocrine and neurovegetative systems, and that mysterious, pallid tissular jungle known as the diencephalon and the hypothalamus-pituitary-adrenal axis. This jungle is in our century the site of enthralling explorations which, with the aid of biochemical tools, are destined to make discoveries in the inner space of man more extraordinary than those that rocket ships may make in outer space.

MEDICINE'S SEVEN ANSWERS TO THE CHALLENGE OF OUR TIME

The challenge therefore that Medicine faces today is to protect health and prevent disease by increasing its knowledge of the processes of health and disease.

In facing this challenge, modern medicine has established the basic problems it must first solve, as follows: First, to know the biochemical substrate of health and its alterations, including that of mental processes. This knowledge, which already enables us to look into the chemistry of joy and sorrow and of the genius and the artist, will provide a dynamic tool with which to approach the promotion of health, not from afar, as in the past, but from the innermost redoubts of its formerly impregnable citadels. Second, to know thoroughly the processes of growth, convalescence, aging, and death, so as to be able to rehabilitate the diseased, to safeguard the development of the human being, and to prolong his life, if not for the purpose of realizing Faust's utopian dream of immortality, at least to ensure that man's twilight may be as bright as possible, delaying the final fall of the mist-shrouded night. And third, to know the biochemical processes underlying the etiology and pathogenesis of the three great groups of diseases: neurosis, biosis, and sclerosis, that is, functional, organic (including the infectious), and degenerative diseases, for this is the only way we can get to know them, prevent them, and cure them.

To solve these problems, contemporary medicine has already started on seven different tracks:

It is using biochemical, physiotherapeutic, and dietetic resources to strengthen normal human physiology and organic defenses as the best means of converting the body into a fortress, walled against the invasion of disease and capable of resisting all sieges or of expelling any invader that may succeed in penetrating into the human citadel.

It is applying ecology in providing man with the most suitable environment to safeguard and improve his health, his well-being, and his culture. Pursuing this end, "portable" environments with adequate food and artificial climate have already been created to enable man to travel to the polar zones, the tropics, or in cosmic space, carrying with him his most favorable ecologic environment.

It is combating the causes of disease—germs, toxins, traumas, stresses, radiation, noxious foods, noise—by trying both to prevent them and to eradicate them as they spring up. Our aerocosmic age has brought about the vertiginous development of a new discipline, space medicine, whose greatest value lies in its findings not so much about man's life in cosmic space as about man's normal physiology.

It is synthesizing new drugs to treat "new" diseases (alterations of the collagen system, the ABD syndrome, Korean icterohemorrhagic fever, radiation disease, antibiotic-resistant infections) native to our times, which are man's penalty for the progress of civilization.

It is using new drugs to treat "old" diseases, replacing the bow and arrow type of medication with weapons of "atomic" scope, such as antibiotics, ataraxics, new vaccines, and the more recent diuretics and anticholinergics.

It is discovering different techniques to study those processes of the body still unknown, in the hope of forcing the organs to reveal their secrets in that mysterious language of theirs that is translated into data, figures, microstructural images, and laboratory reactions. These new techniques have also revolutionized the teaching of medicine and medical communication by placing at their service a dazzling armory of electronic resources.

To diagnose diseases still unknown, it is seeking and investigating new substances such as the experimental cancerogenic agents, the new cholesterol solvents, and the hallucinogenic drugs that are now being used in mental diseases and that may disclose some of the secrets of schizophrenia and perhaps even the roots of artistic genius.

THE DANGER OF CREATING A MYTHOLOGY OF SCIENCE

These, then, are the historical challenges that medicine faces today, challenges that must be met not by philosophers, priests, or visionaries as in the past, but by scientific investigators, men who have been driven into *research* by their *search* for truth and for their own personal destiny.

If that brave infantryman of Medicine, the practicing physician, must daily provide prompt answers to the problems of the moment of his patients, since their lives may depend on his decisions, the medical investigator must provide more permanent answers to general medical problems, answers in which he must even anticipate the future. If clinical medicine must answer individual challenges of a temporal nature, medical research must answer universal and eternal challenges.

Never before have investigators had at their disposal so many and such good tools and equipment and so much economic aid with which to face medical problems. Even the popular support that in every period in history has invested great heroes with a golden halo is now accorded to investigators.

But the present formidable advance of science entails the danger of superimposing a mythology of science over contemporaneous scientific thought, a danger that, like a storm cloud, is soaring across the sunlit scientific panorama of our time.

What do I mean by mythology of science?

Well, we know that ancient mythology was characterized by a monstrous overestimation of the hero's powers. The mythological hero was credited with supernatural powers, superhuman energy, unparalleled bravery, and extraordinary determination, which enabled him to do anything, to overcome everything, to master all things and beings. More impressive than his exploits was the extraordinary fact that he always faced impossible enterprises with the foreknowledge that he could accomplish them.

The hero's weapons were equally overevaluated and had an importance equal to that of the hero himself. Siegfried's sword, Apollo's arrows, were considered invincible.

And finally, each individual triumph of the hero was so overestimated that his final goal was lost sight of. Each successive victorious step was confused with the accomplishment of the hero's original mission. The labors of Hercules became more important than their original motivations; Ulysses' voyage because of its epic magnitude eventually obscured its original purpose: to return to the loving arms of Penelope.

But mythology was not made only by the poetic bards in the days of Homer and classical Greece. Mythology has continued to be made all through history, even in medicine, and the result has always been the same: the myths, which are only projections of man's hopes and fears, just as legends are history distorted by the imagination, eventually supplant reality. This is what happened with the myths created around Imhotep and Aesculapius. Imhotep actually existed three thousand years before Christ, but twenty-five centuries later he was a god; and Aesculapius started as a prince of Thessaly and ended centuries later as a god of medicine venerated in hundreds of temples throughout Greece.

Man to this day continues to create mythology, because he simply must have heroes to protect himself against the tedium of life, and because he still needs to project his hopes and fears onto extraordinary beings and objects. Recently, the psychiatrist C. G. Jung demonstrated in a magnificent study that "flying saucers," whatever their physical origin, are crystallizations of a popular psychic projection of the myth that intelligent forces do exist in cosmic space. In such sense they are a "modern psychological myth."

Likewise, in medicine a dangerous mythology of science is now being created. This mythology has the same characteristics as the mythology previously mentioned, that is, overevaluation of the almost supernatural power of the hero, in our case, the scientific investigator; overevaluation of his weapons or tools, in our case, technology; and confusion of his partial triumphs—the conquests of applied science—with his final goal, which in our case is a better knowledge of nature and of man so as to be able to protect his health and prolong his life.

An example of the first characteristic is the unfortunate popular publicity nowadays given to the scientific investigator, which leads to the belief that every investigator who has developed a new substance has already conquered the disease for which it is intended, or that each new drug—ataraxic, steroid, toxoid, antibiotic—is the definitive therapy for a disease. An example of the second characteristic is the almost religious worship of all technological advances in electronic instrumentation, laboratory techniques, and the rest, while the object for which they are destined often takes second place. An example of the third characteristic is the recent overestimation of certain drugs, for instance, ataraxics, which are really only a key to unlock a few doors in the unexplored castle of the psychoses.

We must be on guard, lest this mythology of science grows roots and takes the place of reality, lest excessive faith in the investigator's invincibility and the power of his technological weapons and excessive glorification of practical scientific victories end in diverting science from its true path. The frequent sight of his countenance mirrored in the pools of technological progress might make the investigator forget to keep his eyes fixed on the broad sunny horizons that are the true objective and ideal of science. Each of the investigator's triumphs is a step forward in the march of progress, but technology, that is to say, applied science, can never replace basic science, wherefrom flows, like water from a spring, the clear philosophical stream that guides man on his way through history.

Above all, it is necessary to banish the growing tendency to experiment for the sake of experimenting, without a definite philosophical purpose. Though Claude Bernard recommended hanging up imagination with one's hat upon entering the laboratory and retrieving them both only upon leaving, he himself never failed to exercise his *scientific* imagination, a luminous and almost poetic vision of what he wished to attain by his experiments, which he wore on his brow like an invisible hat from which he was never separated.

Experimentation is the foundation of science, though it is not its *raison d'être,* as devotees of the mythology of science claim. It must at all events be guided by ideas, by hypotheses, by an intuitive vision of the ideal goal that it wishes to reach. Should it not be so guided, the now developing hypertrophy of "pure" experimentation will ultimately lead to atrophy of the investigator's imagination.

The best remedy against the danger of mythology is for all those dedicated to science continually to remind themselves with humility, as the Carthusian monks continually remind themselves of death, that both the investigator and technology have their limitations. Although the answers we have found to concrete problems up to the present have been dazzling, the greatest problems still remain unsolved after some six thousand years of written history.

The mythology of science, that is, excessive credence in what science can do for humanity, may continue to grow among the general public, but I feel sure that we scientists will try to maintain a human nonmythological attitude, because we know that without it there can be no real progress in the field of science.

I believe this because, quite apart from the dazzling mythological armor in which the public arrays the investigator, the investigator does possess certain virtues, invisible to the public, that give him inner stature and in which reside his true greatness and that of his work.

THE SEVEN VIRTUES OF THE MODERN SCIENTIFIC INVESTIGATOR

Everyone knows the technical resources today available to the investigator in accomplishing the formidable task entrusted to him. I shall not quote statistics, for though I sometimes use them I dislike them strongly, just as I hate umbrellas, yet use one when it rains. Instead, I shall mention the spiritual resources of the investigator, his seven capital virtues—as I called them in a recent study on Carlos Finlay, "The Pasteur of the Americas," discoverer of the mosquito's role in yellow fever—virtues which hold the key to his greatness and the justification for looking forward with optimism to medicine's response to the great challenges of our time.

History, including that of medicine, is made by men, and on the number of spiritual carats such men possess depends the possibility and magnitude of their triumphs.* But even in the clean, fresh climate of science, one needs a purpose, a method, a spirit. I have already spoken of the purpose and the method of contemporary medical science. Its spirit is that of the men who are today making that science. Benjamin Franklin said, "All mankind is divided into three classes: those that are immovable, those that are movable, and those that move."

---

* Science has progressed because it stepped from what was its basis in the past, that is, qualitative impression, to its present basis, which is quantitative measurement. If to make art is to create, to make science is to *measure*.

Scientific investigators are those who *move,* who do things, who express their greatness in actions of vast consequence to humanity. On their virtues depends the progress of science. The best scientific machine or instrument, the most perfect laboratory, the most advanced statistical methodology, the latest electronic advance, all these would be worth nothing without the man who, in the laboratory, clinic, office, or library, contributes his life so that the stately chariot of medicine may move forward. Without these men no history of medicine could be made, just as no good building could be erected without pillars to support its foundations.

Foremost among the investigator's virtues I place *goodness.* A castle is as strong as its foundations. Every great man, every great investigator, begins by being a good man. The humaneness of daily life must overflow into the humanism of the investigative genius. In no profession as in medicine is it so important to be a good man. "Science without conscience is nothing but baseness of the soul," said the lapidary of eternal truths, Montaigne. The true investigator is an indefatigable galley slave of medicine, who, renouncing the glitter of easy success and tempting profit, chooses the troubled seas of investigation instead of the calm harbors. Modesty is usually the inseparable companion of such goodness.

The second quality is *greatness.* Greatness is simplicity. This has been so from Hippocrates to Fleming. A greatness that is an aristocracy of the spirit is the only sovereignty people can accept without relinquishing their own sovereignty. Greatness in the true investigator is to go through life doing with a simple spirit things that may benefit his fellow-beings, building a mighty pyramid without losing his childlike innocence of soul. It is to remain indifferent in the face of indifference, to have faith in his convictions, even during the interminable night of failure, certain that the dawn will come. It is to accept life— as did El Greco in Toledo—as splendor and radiance, lighting the shadows of his laboratory with his own inner light.

Sometimes *genius* is added to these qualities. While in art knowledge is spasmodic and nonaccumulative, in science it is systematically accumulative and keeps on replacing itself. A Botticelli, a Cervantes, a Beethoven, each in himself is a complete cycle who needs no predecessors and leaves no school. Hence a work of art—symphony, statue, painting—is immortal, while the life of a scientific work— report, address, lecture, or research—is ephemeral and always liable to be superseded by a more recent work.

In art, genius is the rebel artist who creates his own universe in its entirety; in science, genius is the rebel investigator who excels his universe by applying the spark of his intuition to already existing knowledge. Genius is intuition, but it is also logic in the service of a fervent vocation, displayed at the right time and in the proper place. Besides quality, genius is also quantity, as borne out by the prolific work of Paracelsus, Harvey, Hunter, Freud, and Fleming. The true genius rarely makes a single discovery. The great investigator, generally, makes many.

Add to that the *spirit of inquiry,* in which experimenting is the indispensable complement to theorizing thought and not a means for exploding sensational intellectual fireworks. Patience in waiting and quickness in thought distinguish the investigator. Often the genius' intuition flashes suddenly, but the true investigator will, if necessary, spend years in verifying his spark of truth, reconciling noble haste—haste, eternal companion of the creator—in his endeavor with patience in its confirmation.

Lucidity is another quality indispensable in the investigator, because the style is the man, or in other words, man in his human quality is his style. In his tribute to Claude Bernard, delivered in Paris on the third of April, 1879, the great historian Ernest Renan said of Bernard's style words that could be applied today to any investigator: "Human intelligence is a whole so well united in all its parts that a great mind is always a good writer. The true method of investigation, given a firm and healthy judgment, embraces the solid qualities of style. The standard of good scientific style is lucidity, perfect adaptation to the theme, complete forgetfulness of self, absolute abnegation. But that is also the standard for writing well, whatever the subject. The best writer is the one who develops a great subject and forgets himself in order to allow his subject to speak for itself. . . . He uses words like a modest man uses his clothing, to cover himself. . . . He thinks, he feels, the words flow. . . ."

The style of the good investigator sparkles with the diamantine brilliance and limpidity typical of the man who knows certain things thoroughly and wishes to explain them so that everyone will understand. Reading great writers, like Erasmus and Juan Luis Vives, one realizes that style is like the acrobat's tights, which cover his figure without concealing it, like a close-fitting glove on the hand of thought. Fleming's reports are like a transparent window through which one can see unmarred by a single mote of dust the wide prairies of his thought. The creed of the true investigator is fidelity to the truth, and that means not only to seek it and serve it, but also to express it in language intelligible to everyone. Finlay, Ramón y Cajal, Freud, Fleming, Osler—these men allowed no hyperbole or redundancy, no exaggeration of concepts, to creep into their prose and cripple its scientific probity. Lucidity in style presupposes lucidity in thought, and this in turn implies clarity of spirit. A clear style, like a clean windowpane, indicates that the owner does not fear inquisitive eyes. The investigator's prose must be fluid, fresh, and crystalline, like the water from a mountain brook.

The investigator is a true *patriot,* because he is a living part of the historical conscience of his epoch. He can look at the problems of his country and of his time with eyes both critical and loving, for the true lover does not respond blindly to Cupid's darts but loves his beloved though his eyes are wide open to her defects. The investigator's homeland grows with each of his discoveries, until it becomes a universal homeland not to be found in any geography book. The investigator is the *homo universalis* of our time and helps to promote the health of all people on our planet. He can sometimes, without leaving his home or country, delve so deeply that he reaches universal roots, preferring vertical profundity to horizontal spread, which guarantees his universality in space and his immortality in time.

Finally, the investigator possesses *universality.* In the address already quoted, Renan said, "Glory has something homogenous and identical. Everything that vibrates produces it. There are not various types of fame, any more than there are various kinds of light." All glories derive their rays from the same source. The investigator's glory is universal and clothes with honor all who can admire an ideal and dedicate themselves selflessly to it.

L'ENVOI

In these times of atomic and cosmic terrors, it must be remembered that when all the mechanical marvels of the age have been replaced by others, the example of the selfless investigator will endure unshaken as an inspiration to man and peoples and as a memorial pillar for all time.

On such virtues is founded my optimistic readiness to believe that the mind of the investigator, like a many-colored glass dome shedding its radiance on all fields of human knowledge, guarantees the unceasing progress of human effort.

Other speakers here are better prepared than I to describe and extol the vast intricate technical resources, instruments, equipments, and institutions now at the service of science and of the investigator. I, like a flower-laden botanist emerging from the woods, would only like to pin in your lapel a sprig of seven blossoms: goodness, greatness, genius, spirit of inquiry, lucidity, patriotism, and universality. On those seven ineffably sweet-smelling flowers is founded my belief that the investigator will solve the greatest scientific challenges that humanity has ever faced by writing opposite those dark pages of technology, which record hydrogen bombs, war-provoking missiles, and other infernal machines, those glittering pages that can be written only by the spirit of man.

THE FIRST THIRTY YEARS

THE MEANING OF THIS ANNIVERSARY

*t*his Symposium coincides with the celebration of a memorable anniversary. An anniversary is a great occasion when it commemorates persons whose inventions are of immeasurable value in everyday life. Every time we switch on the electric light, pick up the telephone, or fly in a plane, we extend unconscious tribute to the persons whose genius brought comfort and efficiency into our lives, even though their names may have been lost in oblivion. But when it commemorates discoveries that save thousands of lives every day, the anniversary becomes a reverent tribute to those who, besides being standard-bearers of civilization, were also benefactors to humanity. Such is this thirtieth anniversary of that historic moment when, in a modest laboratory in London's St. Mary's Hospital, a Scottish scientist observed the remarkable effect of a spore that had accidentally landed from the dull, smoky skies of the borough of Paddington upon a *Staphylococcus* culture plate.

Thirty years ago penicillin was discovered and ten years ago broad-spectrum antibiotics were introduced. Let us note the difference between these two achievements of the Antibiotic Age. The first was accomplished by one man alone, as in the days of Pasteur; the second by a team of men dedicated to tracking down an antibiotic as persistently as safari hunters track down their quarry. This latter fact detracts nothing from the historical importance of the event, but

---

Presented at the Sixth Annual Symposium on Antibiotics, Washington, D. C., October 15, 1958.

it marks the development of a new mental and social attitude in research.

The Antibiotic Age is one more facet of our extraordinary epoch, which unquestionably deserves the appellation of "time-axis" applied by the philosopher Karl Jaspers to moments of portentous historical meaning, such as 500 B.C., when simultaneously in China, India, and Greece, fired by the words of Confucius, Buddha, and the Greek philosophers, human dignity and conscience were born and the great religions of the world began. Ours is another memorable "time-axis" because of the great discoveries made in fields of knowledge whose common-interest frontiers are as removed from one another as were in space the frontiers of the ancient cultures. So, in nuclear physics, cosmic astronautics, abstract art, depth psychology, and antibiotic research, revolutions have taken place leaving an indelible mark on the cultural face of the world of today.

Just as a mirror faithfully reflects the lines imprinted by the passing years on the human face, lines which if well earned add only to its beauty and dignity, so does this annual Symposium—the mirror of antibiotic medicine—faithfully reflect with every passing year the ever-increasing complex changes in this the most important branch of modern therapeutics.

WHAT THIS SYMPOSIUM MIGHT HAVE BEEN 3000, 300, AND 30 YEARS AGO

Nothing can give a better idea of what this Symposium represents in the light of history than the use of that winged Pegasus, swifter than the fastest jet plane, our own imagination, to compare what will be said here with what might have been said at similar symposia on infectious diseases held, let us say, 3000, 300, and 30 years ago.

Three thousand years ago this Symposium might have been a gathering of priests and magi in Babylonia, under the shadow of the majestic ziggurats, from whose summits watch was kept on the passage of the golden caravan of stars. Disease being then attributed to possession by devils or a punishment from the gods, prognosis would have been founded on auguries, divination, hepatoscopy, or horoscopes, and therapy on magico-mystic rituals or empiric remedies; and interchange of ideas would have consisted in formulating spells and praising the gods.

Three hundred years ago, in 1658, our Symposium might have taken place in Baroque Europe, in one of the academies at Bologna or Padua, which were then beginning to replace the medieval universities. The participants, clad in flowing velvet robes and starched ruffled collars, their fingers bejeweled with glittering rings, would have presented their *observationes* or biographic clinical histories, would have discussed their patients as people affected by a natural process caused not by demons but by miasmas, and would have formulated a prognosis and treatment based on empiric remedies and supplications almost as primitive as those of the symposium 3000 years ago.

Thirty years ago, in 1928, the Symposium would have been very similar in appearance to this one. In the intervening 270 years since the previous Symposium in 1658 practically all we know today about the basic concepts of infection, immunity, and natural history of certain infections had already been learned. However, pneumonia was still considered the "captain of the soldiers of Death," as Osler described it; tuberculosis and typhus were decimating the planet; malaria and plague were endemic in wide zones of the earth, and the memory of mortal pandemics, like the influenza epidemic after the First World War, still made us tremble.

This swift historical cavalcade brings us to our present Symposium, the thirtieth anniversary of the Antibiotic Age. We speak with pride of the Antibiotic Age; yet, just as such technical miracles as the airplane and television no longer excite us, so the tiny tablets and ampoules imprisoning the God-created magic discovered by man in the minute world of molds no longer even stir our thought.

It is a fact that while artistic work is intimately bound up with its creator, thus leading us to speak of Beethoven's *Ninth Symphony,* Cervantes' *Don Quixote,* or da Vinci's *Mona Lisa,* scientific work is synonymous with anonymity. Though every time we use a drug we are offering mute tribute to its discoverers, still we administer antidiphtherial serum, antismallpox vaccine, or morphine without giving a thought to Roux, Jenner, or Sertürner. It is essential therefore that we celebrate anniversaries like the present, to recall the founders of medicine, to rescue not only their work but their names also from the dust of oblivion.

THE FORGOTTEN PRECURSOR: HOMAGE TO DUCHESNE

Now is the time, therefore, to pay due honor to the memory of one of Fleming's forerunners who anticipated the discovery of penicillin by 31 years. I refer to Ernest Augustin Clement Duchesne, a French army physician who died of tuberculosis at the age of 38 years, who in 1897 published his doctoral thesis on the antibacterial action of Hyphomycetes and demonstrated experimentally that cultures of *Penicillium glaucum* decreased the virulence of highly pathogenic microbes such as *Bacillus coli* or *Eberthella typhosa* in inoculated animals. On this anniversary let us present a tribute of admiration to the genius of this forgotten French scientist, who alone in an obscure laboratory anticipated the Antibiotic Age.

ANTIBIOTICS AND HISTORY

Nothing can enlighten us so well on how antibiotics might have changed the course of history than speculating on what they could have done for humanity both collectively and individually in the past.

Collectively, antibiotics might have stopped the great pandemics that changed the course of humanity—for instance, the ten plagues of Egypt, the plague of Athens, Justinian's plague, the Black Death, the syphilis epidemics of the Renaissance, the Great Plague of London, yellow fever in the United States, typhoid in the Boer War, typhus in the Balkans, and the influenza pandemic of 1918–1919.

Individually, there are countless examples of what antibiotics might have prevented. Had Henry VIII's syphilis been treated with penicillin, his wives might have borne him an heir, instead of miscarrying every time, and would have been saved from the scaffold, while Henry himself, not needing divorce, might not have broken with the Pope nor supported the Protestant Church of England; Charles V might have been saved from syphilis and prolonged his reign, thus extending the might of the Spanish Empire; and had Lenin been cured of syphilis, he might never have reached the dizzy heights of general paresis from which he planned the Russian Revolution.

But all this belongs to the spectacular side of history. Here we are interested in appraising the changes undergone in these past 30 years by the *men,* the *research,* and the *results* of antibiotic medicine.

ANTIBIOTICS: THE WORK OF RESEARCH VETERANS

The first thing we observe on contemplating the discovery of antibiotics is that practically every discoverer was a man ripe in years. Almost all discoveries in antibiotics have been made by men between the ages of 45 and 60. This fact must please us all—the young, because it confirms that scientific creation has no age limit; the mature, because it proves that they can still do as Don Quixote, who nearing his sixties set forth on his sorry nag to seek immortality. This maturity of antibiotic scientists is a symbolic herald of our Geriatric Era.

What does this mean? First of all, it means that in medicine as in history there are "young times" and "old times." There are also branches, such as surgery, that will increasingly become fields of action for the young, just as there are branches, like psychiatry,

FACULTÉ DE MÉDECINE ET DE PHARMACIE DE LYON
Année scolaire 1897-98. — N° 59.

CONTRIBUTION A L'ÉTUDE

DE LA

CONCURRENCE VITALE

CHEZ LES MICROORGANISMES

Antagonisme entre les Moisissures et les Microbes

THESE

PRESENTEE

A LA FACULTÉ DE MÉDECINE ET DE PHARMACIE DE LYON

Et soutenne publiquement le 17 Decembre 1897

POUR OBTENIR LE GRADE DE DOCTEUR EN MÉDECINE

PAR

Ernest DUCHESNE

Né le 30 mai 1874, à Paris (Seine),
Eléve de l'École du Service de Sante Militaire.

LYON

ALEXANDRE REY, IMPRIMEUR DE LA FACULTÉ DE MÉDECINE

4, RUE GENTIL, 4

—

Décembre 1897

FIG. 1. Title page of Ernest Duchesne's thesis.

CONCLUSIONS

I. The molds (mucedines) do not develop, or at any rate disappear very rapidly in water below a certain volume, the principal reasons for which are the following: *a*) the increase in moisture itself; *b*) the movement in the liquid mass; *c*) finally, and especially, the result of the struggle for life.

II. There is, in fact, a very marked and undeniable antagonism between *molds* and *bacteria* which have been simultaneously set in water or any liquid culture medium, and more often than not such antagonism turns out to the benefit of the *bacteria*, at least as far as life and growth processes are concerned.

III. The reason the *microbes* practically always prevail over the *molds* in the struggle for life is their greater vital resistance and above all their infinitely speedier multiplication, itself due to the phenomenon of *bipartition* or *scissiparity* (*fissiparity*). It does not, however, appear that *microbial toxins* are called upon to play an active part in that struggle and its outcome.

IV. The *molds* may, however, sometimes see that struggle turn out to their advantage when the culture medium in its reaction is more clearly favorable to them than to the bacteria, if they are not absolutely immersed in it, and when in fact they are at the beginning in a really preponderating proportion.

V. Furthermore, it seems from some of our experiments, which unfortunately are too few in number and which ought to be repeated again and checked, that certain *molds* (*Penicillum glaucum*), when inoculated into an animal simultaneously with extremely virulent cultures of certain pathogenic microbes (*B. coli* and *Eberthella typhosa*), are able to attenuate the virulence of such bacterial cultures to a remarkable degree.

VI. It is to be hoped therefore that in pursuing the study of the facts of *biological competition* between *molds* and *microbes*—merely outlined by ourselves and to which we have no claim other than submitting here a very modest contribution—the discovery of further facts directly useful and applicable to prophylactic hygiene and therapy may be attained.

CONCLUSIONS

I. Les *moisissures* (mucédinées) ne se développent pas, ou disparaissent, tout au moins, très hâtivement dans l'eau, sous un certain volume, et cela pour les principales raisons suivantes : *a*) l'exagération même de l'humidité ; *b*) le mouvement de la masse liquide ; *c*) enfin et surtout le résultat de la concurrence vitale.

II. Il existe, en effet, un antagonisme très marqué et incontestable entre les *moisissures* et les *bactéries* qui ont été simultanément semées dans l'eau ou dans un liquide nutritif quelconque, et cet antagonisme tourne le plus souvent au profit des *bactéries* en ce qui concerne, tout tout au moins, les processus de vitalité et de végétalité.

III. Si les *microbes* l'emportent ainsi presque constamment sur les *moisissures*, dans la lutte pour la vie, c'est par suite d'une plus grande résistance vitale et surtout d'une pullulation infiniment plus rapide due, elle-même, au phénomène de la *bipartition* ou *scissiparité*. Mais il ne semble pas que les *toxines microbiennes* soient appelées à jouer un rôle actif dans cette lutte et dans ses résultats.

IV. Les *Moisissures*, cependant, peuvent parfois voir cette lutte tourner à leur profit lorsque le milieu de culture leur est, par sa réaction, plus nettement favorable qu'aux bactéries, qu'elles ne s'y trouvent pas absolument submergées et qu'elles sont enfin, initialement, en proportion vraiment très prépondérante.

V. Il semble, d'autre part, résulter de quelques-unes de nos expériences, malheureusement trop peu nombreuses et qu'il importera de répéter à nouveau et de contrôler, que certaines *moisissures* (*Penicillum glaucum*), inoculées à un animal en même temps que des cultures très virulentes de quelques *microbes pathogènes* (*B. coli* et *B. typhosus* d'Eberth), sont capables d'atténuer dans de très notables proportions la virulence de ces cultures bactériennes.

VI. On peut donc espérer qu'en poursuivant l'étude des faits de *concurrence biologique* entre *moisissures* et *microbes*, étude seulement ébauchée par nous et à laquelle nous n'avons d'autre prétention que d'avoir apporté ici une très modeste contribution, on arrivera, peut-être, à la découverte d'autres faits directement utiles et applicables à l'hygiène prophylactique et à la thérapeutique.

LE PRÉSIDENT DE THÈSE,
LÉPINE

Permis d'imprimer :
LE RECTEUR,
G COMPAYRE

Vu : pour le doyen,
L'ASSESSEUR,
LÉPINE

FIG. 2. Conclusions drawn by Duchesne in 1897.

where the main concepts were formulated by mature men. From the times of Pasteur, microbiology also has attracted men of maturity. Antibiotic medicine, the youngest of modern therapeutic branches, is the basic work of a team of illustrious mature veterans.

TEAMWORK AND INDUCED "LUCKY ACCIDENTS"

Antibiotic research has also changed during these thirty years. Originally there were innumerable lone investigators, but today the work is done in teams. The lone struggling scientist has been practically replaced by "commandos" in a "combined operation," just as in the Baroque the "corporative" savant of the academies replaced the lone Renaissance scholar.

Similarly, discovery as a lucky accident has been replaced by discovery as the result of planning and organization. "Lucky accidents" were almost the rule in the history of research. Archimedes accidentally discovered a law of hydrostatics while investigating the adulteration of gold in the royal crown; Scribanus, physician to the emperor Claudius, anticipated "electroshock" when he applied an electric eel to the forehead of a patient with migraine; by accident Roentgen discovered the rays now bearing his name; a milkmaid's casual remark led to Jenner's discovery of antismallpox vaccine; Pasteur's first great discovery occurred when through accidental contamination a fungus (penicillin!) developed in a solution containing the two isomers of tartaric acid; Ringer's solution, George Oliver's adrenalin, Sir Henry Dale's acetylcholine—all these were accidental discoveries. And a glorious accident befell Fleming, initiating the Antibiotic Age.

Today antibiotic research induces such accidents by experimentally producing the conditions leading to them. Likewise, we have stepped from experimental production in the laboratory to the development of gigantic research and isolation programs in the vast research departments of the pharmaceutic industry, which on another occasion I called the "scientific subconscious of a nation," where great discoveries in antibiotics are incubated.

LABORATORY AND MEDICINE

The laboratory has increasingly gained greater importance during these thirty years of the Antibiotic Age. In the Middle Ages Medicine was made by clerical physicians in monastery libraries lined with the splendored tapestry of ivory- and gold-bound tomes and deep in centuries-old dust turned iridescent by the golden sun; in the last century Medicine was made in hospitals; in our time, it is made largely in laboratories, which takes the investigation of the sick one step beyond what our own senses might reveal.

ANTIBIOTICS: FROM "HEROIC" SPECIFIC THERAPY TO UNIVERSAL MEDICATION

Antibiotic therapy is the outcome of a long historical evolution that started about 6000 years ago. Back in those days, man treated disease with spells, herbs, and metals to drive out the causal agent, which was considered to be a demon, miasma, or germ; he then passed to the use of sera and vaccines to reinforce the body's natural defenses; aimed "magic bullets" at the bacteria; arrested their development by "putting them to sleep" with sulfonamides, enabling the leukocytes to sweep them away with their magic broom; tried to interfere with the bacteria's metabolism by throwing a monkey wrench into their biological machinery; fenced in the bacteria with the "magic wall" of penicillin; and finally he employed microbial antagonisms for therapeutic purposes.

In thirty years antibiotics have progressed from a "heroic" specific therapy to universal medication. This trend is the result of the conversion of antibiotics from an emergency medication to a routine medication which on occasions takes the place of precise diagnosis. The picture of infectious nosological entities has thus been altered, and contributing further to it has been the change in the natural history of a disease and in the biological cycle of its causal agent. Other features of interest have been the increasing synthesis of antibiotics in the laboratory independent of natural sources, and the improvement of their vehicles to assure greater tissue penetration, longer effectiveness, and reduced toxicity.

THE NEW PROBLEMS: RESISTANCE, METABOLIC ATTACK, BIOLOGICAL SYMBIOSIS, AND NEW SOURCES OF ANTIBIOTICS

Antibiotic medicine has also encountered many problems. Of enormous importance is the growing resistance to antibiotics of certain microbes, as indicated by recent outbreaks of infections by antibiotic-resistant staphylococci in hospitals, which have been transformed into veritable culture foci on the living plate of the human being.

Another present-day problem is finding antibiotics that will attack the microbic forms of life still immune to them. Possibly the answer lies in discovering fresh forms of metabolic attack against such germs, in learning more about their biological cycles, or in developing a greater biological immunity in the human being. As Dubos said (thereby reviving one of Bernard Shaw's witticisms), probably the best thing would be not to destroy the germs but to learn to live with them in biological symbiosis, on a "live and let live" policy. We may also end up by reducing to the essential the drugs now being used, which recalls Osler's words: "The young physician starts life with twenty drugs for each disease, and the old physician ends life with one drug for twenty diseases."

It is also vital to develop fresh sources of antibiotics. The cure for many mortal infections may perhaps lie in the depths of the sea. Another tremendous source, despite its spatial smallness, may be the human body and its intercellular "inner sea," whose humors probably contain defensive powers as phenomenal as those of the waters of the high seas. Since Fleming investigated lysozyme, many ferments and hormones have been discovered, but a great many more remain to be discovered.

Finally, it is necessary to verify *how* and *where* the antibiotics work, and how much of their action is exerted on the microbe and how much on the surrounding cells and humors. We have to investigate the action level of antibiotics in the body, a level that may lie in the deep planes of tissular metabolism or in the circulating humors, and also whether antibiotics create a system of chain reactions involving the antibiotic, the microbe, and the humoral medium, that "internal sea" where the microbe, cell, and antibiotic lie submerged.

TOWARD A PROPHYLACTIC ANTIBIOTIC THERAPY

In the medicine of tomorrow the role of antibiotics will become increasingly more prophylactic as the interval between the discovery of a drug and its clinical application becomes shorter and shorter. For a long time mankind was deprived of the benefits of many drugs simply because it failed to use them until long after their discovery. But we have learned the lesson and are now reverting to the times of Paracelsus, when a drug was put into use as soon as it was discovered. On the other hand, in modern times, the sulfonamides, discovered in 1908, were not employed until twenty-seven years later; isoniazid, discovered in 1912, was not applied until forty years later, and penicillin, discovered in 1928, was not used until thirteen years later. These delays were often caused by fear of toxicity. It is now high time to convince ourselves that a drug's toxicity often runs parallel with its therapeutic activity, demanding not its rejection but merely greater precision in its use.

THE NEWER PHILOSOPHICAL CONCEPTS OF DISEASE

The revision of our concept of the nature of disease is of increasing importance for the future application of antibiotics.

Today we agree that man is not only Nature but History. Man is what he does, the succession of moments in his life, his passage as a spatial form through time, a form always subject to the forces of his genetic equation, his environment, his internal stresses, and his free will, all of which create his biography, of which disease is a part. Accepting clinical history as pathography or *graphia* of the *pathos,* we also accept the concept of the patient as a *whole.* The human being is regarded as a somatopsychic unit in motion, "making itself in the course of time." Disease therefore is disharmonious living, an abnormal and painful way of life, and infections are something more than a simple reaction among microorganisms, antibodies, and phagocytes. Disease is a series of interactions between an etiological cause and the patient, and infection itself is "a germ-time sequence crossing the space-time sequence."

Antibiotic therapy must take these concepts into account if besides fighting the causal microbe it also endeavors to fortify the patient's "whole person." According to Henri Laborit, it is more important to reduce the organism's total response to the morbid attack than the attack itself. The drugs of tomorrow may be used to lessen excessive organic response to microbial attack, just as those of today are used to destroy the attacking stimulus.

WORDS AND SCIENCE

On this thirtieth anniversary of the discovery of antibiotics we can do no less than acknowledge the supreme lesson in humility that antibiotics have taught us, for these, the most important drugs of our times, originally come from the humble diminutive world of molds and bacteria, thus bearing witness to the importance of the minute in this vast world of ours.

Antibiotics have also afforded us the unique pleasure of inventing new scientific concepts. Of the pleasures the scientist may have in his work, none is more satisfying than that of formulating a new concept. It is as delectable as the addition of a fresh batch of beauties to his harem was to Harun-al-Rashid in *The Thousand and One Nights.* Science also has its thousand and one nights, in which the supreme enjoyment is to feel, as Ortega y Gasset once pointed out, what the Greeks must have felt when they discovered scientific thought and discussed it in the common tongue.

Using metaphor (science's greatest semantic instrument), the Greek philosopher-physicians observed that by dressing a scientific concept in worn-out common words the latter sparkled anew, as though a brilliant gem had suddenly been pinned on their threadbare semantic form. In its new sense, the common word ceased to be a

94

workworn nag, exhausted from hard and constant use, and was transfigured into a winged Pegasus of philosophical thought. Similarly, in antibiotic medicine, we have been drawing from the bottomless sack of popular knowledge modest words which, kindled by the gemlike flame of a scientific idea, have been transformed into bright new technical terms.

However, there is one word that has not varied through the centuries and to which the ages have done nothing except add carats to its value. The word that on Hippocrates' lips meant love and kindness; on Galen's, experiment and curiosity; on Vesalius', a craving for wisdom and a passion for scientific honesty; on Harvey's, devotion and scientific ingenuity; on Pasteur's, industry and gentility; and goodness and genius on Fleming's. The word to which these thirty years of labor on antibiotics and more than six thousand years of endeavor and success in the art of healing pay tribute. The word synonymous with goodness and wisdom and the craving for service and abnegation by man for man. The word, MEDICINE.

"THAT SKILL THAT DEATH LOVES NOT"

Surgery, "that skill that death loves not" (as it was called in the thirteenth-century *Regimen sanitatis Salernitanum*), whose first example, a "costectomy," took place in the Garden of Eden, is turning from individual art into team science. In prehistory's dark millennia, surgery was born as an instinctive reaction to accidents demanding immediate and individual action, such as stopping a hemorrhage, splinting a fracture, or binding a wound. Man before he truly became a surgeon was first an operator, that is, an empirical expert in repairing with his hands and tools the effects of traumas. Many centuries ago man bored with a stone scalpel into human skulls, though the purpose of such trephining was not to penetrate *into* the skull but to let *out* the invading demon that possessed the patient. When surgery became rational in Greece and Rome, empirical purpose instead of magic ritual began to guide the use of the scalpel. But the medieval night, fraught with demons and witches, once again shrouded the scalpel's point in the cobwebs of mysticism.

In the late Middle Ages and the Renaissance a new surgery was born in the teachings of the great medical masters, whose word, skill, and example finally snatched this art from the hands of barbers, bathkeepers, and executioners. Later Ambroise Paré gave surgery the humane touch, just as John Hunter gave it science; Lord Lister, technique; and Theodor Billroth and Harvey Cushing, art.

Modern surgery began when, with the conquest of surgery's two

From *MD,* the MEDICAL NEWSMAGAZINE, 4:11, May, 1960.

most ancient enemies—hemorrhage and pain—the operating surgeon no longer had to fight against time. Later came the defeat of other fatal adversaries of surgery: postoperative infection, malnutrition, psychic trauma, and physical exhaustion. Only when hemostatics, analgesics, anesthetics, ataraxics, antibiotics, vitamins, minerals, and physiotherapeutic equipment became available, banishing the danger of bleeding, pain, shock, infection, malnutrition, and invalidism, could the surgeon truly dedicate himself to the development of surgery.

Paradoxically, it was the two World Wars and various lesser wars in the present century, and the increase in accidents owing to improvements in modern locomotion and industry, that stimulated surgical progress. The surgeon has sought in chemistry and physics new and increasingly more subtle substances and instruments for exploring the lesions of the human body. No longer compelled to watch the clock in operations or the calendar in convalescence, the surgeon can now save his energy more for brainwork than for handwork. Today, surgery is less and less a heroic emergency operation and more and more a well-thought out scheme of *physiological* repair.

Today the patient's psychological, surgical, and nutritive traumas are reduced to a minimum. The three fundamental objectives of preoperative preparation and postoperative care are now: to prevent infection, to eliminate pain and hemorrhage, and to maintain a normal metabolism. Operations are based on an accurate diagnosis, depending on clinical examination, laboratory tests, intraorganic visualization, and roentgenograms. Analgesics, from codeine to meperidine, are constantly being developed and adapted to different types of operation; antibiotics prevent infection; anticoagulants prevent unwanted blood changes; vitamins, fluids, electrolytes, and amino acids forestall dehydration and malnutrition in the patient; physiotherapy and early ambulation promote recovery and rehabilitation.

Ultrasound scalpels, "chemical scalpels" of proteolytic enzymes, such as plasmin, and other new types of steel scalpels, some smaller than a fingernail, are now employed. Special lighting arrangements, electronic and radar devices for pinpointing organic processes, radioactive tracers, and artificial lungs, kidneys, and other organs are also used. Countless are the methods and instruments, from ballistocardiography to gastroscopy, and from the dermatome to the "cyclone" knife. Daring techniques follow one another in a spectacular procession, for instance, resection of the aorta in the treatment of an aneurysm, or leukotomy to sever the thalamic centers (still the nervous tissue lair of our primitive ancestors) from the "civilized" prefrontal lobes. A neurovegetative block is obtained by means of "lytic cocktails," which send the adrenal-pituitary couple off on a "chemical holiday," while the shock of surgery is reduced by artificial hibernation. Electrical stimulation of some temporal lobe zones revives forgotten memories.

All these and many other facilities, such as blood banks and stocks of individual organs, ultraviolet rays, advances in the chemistry of gases and the physics of thoracic pressure, which have furthered progress in anesthesia, oxygen tents, hospital air conditioning to prevent the evaporation of organic humors—all these facilities moved the Surgeon-General of the United States Army to say once: "More than 96 per cent of the wounded who reached medical care in World War II lived."

Like a traveler on the march, surgery approaches a new horizon with each fresh dawn. Surgery is no longer "the failure of medicine," as someone once said, but its partner. Although medicine has wrested from surgery many fields of work (such as mastoidectomies and other otological infections, or digital and instrumental manipulation in urinary infections), surgery, on the other hand, with its successful treatment of cerebral embolisms, arteriosclerosis limited to vascular zones, coronary occlusions, valvulopathies, and even certain neurological diseases, has replaced medicine in certain affections previously susceptible only to medical treatment. The surgeon is no longer the Renaissance adventurer who set out to explore the human body with the same enthusiasm with which navigators explored the *terra incognita* beyond the seas. Nowadays he explores man's inner space with the same insight and astounding accuracy that is shown by physicists exploring outer space. The surgeon's manual skill is supplemented and guided by the light of his scientific knowledge.

The drama of the amphitheatre, however, remains unchanged. Just as the *matador,* alone with the bull in the arena in that dramatic instant that decides the *corrida,* has his "moment of truth," so must the surgeon also (the only man to use cold steel in a mission of healing and mercy) pass through the crucial moment. Now, as thousands of years ago, the surgeon, all alone with his patient on the mysterious threshold of salvation or death, depends entirely on his skill and wisdom and must also suffer his "moment of truth," from which so often his scalpel emerges, as Ambroise Paré said, like a merciful emissary of God's goodness in healing by the hand of man.

THE MIND OF A MAN

*t*his book is, by the power of the enlightening words it contains, an immortal mirror of the luminous mind of a great medical historian. But perhaps the best homage I can pay Henry E. Sigerist is to say simply that this book is a monument to a Man.

To be a man and to deserve such title is very difficult nowadays. In times when society was based on individualism, as in the Renaissance, the man who ventured to assert himself held in his hand the winning cards in the game of life. This is why geniuses like Leonardo and rogues like Casanova triumphed in the early centuries of the modern age, some through the magic of genius and others through sheer rascality, but always through their fiery individualism. Today, to try to be a man, to be faithful to Pindar's dictum, "Become what thou art," to be loyal to one's own real, personal, and inalienable destiny, is highly dangerous and, though sometimes it leads to victory, is often a road to ostracism.

Henry Sigerist was, in his own words, "a nonconformist," a *homo universalis* who even in the heyday of the empire of "the masses," whom he loved dearly and to whom he contributed so much, never renounced his personality, his ideas, or his passionate individualism, although he knew how harmful to him this could be among the Pharisees. Possibly his individualism was one of the intimate factors that resulted in his being hemmed in by adverse circumstances and prodded into seeking the peaceful environment of palm and vineyard under the azure skies of Switzerland. Over there, his dynamic spirit,

Foreword to *Henry E. Sigerist on the History of Medicine*, New York, MD Publications, Inc., 1960.

unrestrained by frontiers of time and space, blossomed freely. His mind, like Aristotle's, was a vast empire of culture incessantly lashed by gales of insatiable curiosity about the life around him.

But Sigerist's individualism was what made possible the legacy he left us, which will breathe with life as long as man remains man. His dynamic philosophy of medical history will help us, now and in the future, to face and resolve problems of health and disease by making the history of the past a key to that of the future, and the shining example he gave of courage, idealism, genius, and greatness, which, like a mountain shadow lengthening in the sunset, has grown only greater in stature since his death, will be an ever stronger inspiration to physicians the world over.

The greatness of Sigerist is manifest in the supreme humanism with which throughout his life he undertook almost superhuman enterprises. Prominent among these was the writing of his great history of medicine, which remained an unfinished symphony at his death.

Sigerist's greatness rests upon his having been a man, nothing more and nothing less, pledged to epic projects and great achievements, who never for an instant relinquished his human quality, possibly because he felt that there is no greatness higher than that of the human being who makes his life a supreme endeavor to renounce nothing, not even his simplicity. For greatness is simplicity. It is doing great things that change the life of mankind, keeping the spirit aloft in the heaven of ideals but retaining one's supreme personal simplicity, even in one's most glittering hours on the road to glory.

Physicians and students will continue far into the future to read Sigerist's works and to assimilate his ideas, as we all have done, making of his concepts a compass for navigating the broad seas of medicine. But only those who knew him personally can fully benefit from the memory of his presence and words, from that ineffable learning and feeling, thinking and working, dreaming and creating, that were his life and his example.

Elsewhere * I have recounted my memories of Sigerist during his visit to Spain and our last meeting in Rome. On these occasions, acquaintances and friends alike were amazed and charmed by this man who for years had been spiritual mentor to so many physicians and yet retained the enthusiasm and curiosity of a child, the sense of wonder, the enjoyment of life, the high spirits and strong emotions, and consequently the ability to convert the dry, faded herbarium of medical history into a sunlit garden filled with the fragrance of roses and the hum of bees.

* "Sigerist and Spain," *Journal of the History of Medicine and Allied Sciences* *13:* 244, 1958.

Sigerist was a *great* man, which is far superior to being a "big" man. This greatness of soul and mind of Sigerist moves me to say here something that to some may sound like heresy, but that I, sincerely believing it to be the truth, dare lay reverently upon his, in our memory, eternally warm ashes: the best of Sigerist would not have been a long, formal history of medicine; the best of Sigerist are the articles and papers, now scattered like flocks of restless birds, that he published in his lifetime, and that contained his heart and mind.

Many people deplore the fact that Sigerist never completed his monumental history of medicine. I do not think he would have ever finished it. Had he done so, I do not think, great though it would have been and undoubtedly the best work of its kind, that it would have been *the best* of Sigerist. Besides, I think that Sigerist *did* write such a history. One need only peruse his works to prove that. It is not a history written in the chronological order and organized form beloved by some, but in the way he himself preferred, that is, in articles varying in theme and occasion but unified by the thought that inspired them.

Sigerist's work, his articles and lectures, lead by paths full of beauty and precision to all the problems of the history of medicine. When Ortega y Gasset died, some people regretted that he did not leave a complete treatise on philosophy. Dr. Gregorio Marañón remarked at the time: "What could a circumstantial and dogmatic treatise add to that infinite curiosity and clarity that he [Ortega] put into everything?" Very true. Similarly, Sigerist did not leave a complete history of medicine possibly because there was no need to do so, just as Einstein did not need to leave a complete treatise on physics to ensure his immortality.

As a matter of fact, geniuses rarely have the patience, time, and desire to leave "complete" works on the favorite subject of their vocation. It seems as though the genius were fated to be a sublime catalytic agent that creates, inspires, and stimulates but rarely has the opportunity—denied by his life or restlessness—of devoting sufficient years to creating a definitive work on his specialty. But even if he produced such a work, it could never capture the brilliant light that the genius flashes forth in his moments of creation.

Geniuses are rarely good scholars in childhood—as witness Santiago Ramón y Cajal, a very poor student, who failed in anatomy, yet later became the genius of neurohistology—perhaps because their creative nature instinctively rejects the routine and discipline that others less gifted have no difficulty in accepting.

Sigerist's work is a scattered mosaic whose pieces his disciples will some day assemble. It would be sufficient to arrange chronologically selected fragments of his articles—some day I myself may try to do

The Mind of a Man

this—in order to have a history of medicine far more effective and inspiring than anything Sigerist might have written after taming the winged Pegasus of his spirit into the plodding plow horse that the historian perforce becomes under the burden of compulsory regimented writing. Sigerist left a great history of medicine. All one need do to find it is look for it in his writings, his words, his life.

For a medical historian makes history not only with what he says and writes but also with his person and his thought. Like a catalyst of greatness, he inspires his surroundings. Sigerist made history because life for him was all light and clarity. No one will ever again be able to make medical history uninfluenced by Sigerist's ideas, which have become integrated into the thinking of physicians all over the world, thus stamping upon the beloved absent a supreme epitaph of universality.

In this book we present a selection of Sigerist's works as made by the author himself at my request some years ago, when I suggested to him the idea of publishing an anthology, together with some other pieces selected by myself as the best examples of his work. The selection he himself made at my personal request in March of 1956 faithfully reflects his personality. He left out some important works on medieval medical bibliography, in which he so greatly excelled, yet he included several delightful articles on such subjects as how to spell his name and how to prepare a truffled turkey on Thanksgiving Day. That he chose those articles for his anthology reflects better than anything else his great simplicity, his deeply warm nature, and his enchanting sense of humor. He never affected pompous postures. He was fond of life, kind, simple, and merry even in the hours of his greatest professional renown.

Our editorial efforts on these pieces have been focused on arranging them in some "chronological" order (by periods) and by subjects, with the object of helping the reader get his bearings. Otherwise, I have preferred to let the master speak in the way he was fond of, passing from one theme to another, alternating serious statements with humorous remarks, always in that friendly conversational tone characteristic of the true master who, unimpressed by his own learning, acts more like a companion than a tutor. I have preferred to let his thought—on whose mighty wings the sun of ideas shone as fiercely as the sun on the far-reaching wings of the condor—range over time and space, continents and ages, facts, figures, things, and places of history—the history not only of medicine but also of civilization.

Sigerist's great innovation is to have made the history of medicine a facet of the history of mankind by linking it with the history of the culture, art, creeds and philosophies, economy, technology, and sociology of each period, thus binding the physician's endeavor to man's yearnings, struggles, and conquests in each historical epoch. This great contribution of Sigerist's as a historian can be compared only with the impact that his presence, speech, and example as a man made on all of us who knew him.

Sigerist considered medicine to be a science natural in its methods and social in its objectives. He placed medicine among the social sciences by making it responsible not only for preventing and healing disease but also for protecting the health and well-being of mankind.

The history of medicine was to Sigerist a powerful tool with which his mighty hands carved a statue to human well-being. His history is no mere story about a coin, a parchment, an instrument, a statue, or a building. He was a true artificer of history, in whose hands everything instantly acquired a dynamic character and was illuminated by the vivid light of our own time.

Let us emphasize that dynamic character, of *living* history, in Sigerist's work, for it illuminates all the writings contained in this volume. From the sunny sands of the island of Cos, just as from Boerhaave's Amsterdam, Harvey's London, or Paracelsus' Zurich, Sigerist knew at once how to extract an inference applicable to our own age, a lesson of enormous practical value to the present-day physician.

History with Sigerist was never a static investigation of the past, but a dynamic exploration of the present and an anticipation of the future. He made history because history to him was learning from the past how to interpret the present and anticipate the future. History never repeats itself; hence we must know it in order to re-create it at each instant with our effort. A sociologist of medicine, Sigerist always bore in his heart the longing to help every man by offering him the best that medicine could do for his health and well-being. For him medicine was not so much the healing of disease as its prevention and the promotion of health.

But what I admire most in Sigerist is his concept of the history of medicine as a facet carved on the immense quarry of the history of civilization. From his earliest works, Sigerist knew how to get away from the narrow ambit of history considered as a mere chronology of dates on a single subject, so as to link medicine with the civilization of each epoch. Without talking of philosophy, he had one of his own, properly organized, that allowed him to integrate medical knowledge with all the other endeavors of man in time and space.

Prior to Sigerist, medical historiography, the study of the activities of medicine, suffered from being neither historical nor medical enough. Sigerist established from the start that the history of medicine must be first of all *history,* but always *medicine* as well. Its objective must be to serve the physician's vocation by stimulating him, enlightening him, and serving him as a tool and a system.

At the same time, Sigerist knew how to combine in a clear and entertaining prose the three ways of making history, namely, to describe the lesser facts, to narrate the important facts, and to interpret the basic facts. In his polished and lucid style, he made pleasing and friendly history, not grave and stern like the face of a professor of the last century, but cheerful and dynamic like the face of a young sportsman of our time.

This book contains all that and more. It affords a *total* perspective of the history of medicine, requiring the reader only to fill in mentally the gaps between one section and the next in order to complete the span of the unfinished bridge that Sigerist started, and whose curve can be projected mentally to reach over to the other side of the river of history. This book also contains a philosophy and a dynamics of history, a historical methodology that can be applied to any historicomedical study. Above all, just as the breast encloses the heart, this book contains the soul of a man who, like a crusader for humanism, lived serving an ideal and died hoping for it.

IV. the epic of medicine

THE EPIC OF MEDICINE

I t is now two years since we undertook the quixotic task of integrating within the pages of *MD,* the medical newsmagazine, the three spheres of life—professional, social, and human—and the three personalities—physician, citizen, and man—of the physician, and thus attempted to help him to attain that plenitude which is attained only when man renounces nothing in life. Thanks to our colleagues' constant support and encouragement, *MD,* more than a magazine, is today a magic carpet on which the physician may soar through the blue skies of the spirit.

Our only compass has been our desire to make *living* medical history by looking with eyes filled with love and wonder at the world and age in which we live, our place in space and our point in time, and by applying to both minor and major events in Medicine and in life the delicate instrument of History—History, without which nothing has any real meaning. For only History can help man to understand the present and improve the future.

These have been two years of unremitting effort and rewarding harvest. Each month we have erected a complex editorial scaffolding from which, with words and pictures and a drop of common sense— the least common of the senses—we have tried to paint a mural of the ideas, men, events, and things of the world we live in, a mural true and realistic, but also warm and colorful, for we prefer the fresh flowers that gracefully lift their perfumed heads in a garden to the faded pressed flowers in a rare herbarium.

From *MD,* the MEDICAL NEWSMAGAZINE, 3:11, January, 1959.

Like a mountaineer on the ascent, issue by issue, *MD* has broadened its range of vision. We have also sought to dig deeper into the core of things and the essence of man. In enveloping the physician's work in the rich fabric of History, we have turned History—which is remembrance—into a dynamic instrument for the conquest of the future—which is hope.

A magazine's life, like that of a human being, must move forward, must continuously project toward the future, must keep on making new plans. Hence, in this third year of its life, *MD* will launch a new project, inspired by my forthcoming book *The Fabric of Medicine,* a monumental triptych on the History of Medicine, consisting of *The Epic of Medicine, The Physician's Saga,* and *The Patient's Progress,* which for the first time will present the History of Medicine dramatized by means of all the resources offered by the modern graphic arts. Thus we shall open a new picture window not on space but on time.

History is above all pageantry. With all the pomp and glory of pageantry, *The Epic of Medicine* will present the History of Medicine as craft, art, and science, relating it to the history of civilization, of the arts, and of science and technology. A series of living tapestries will portray the joys and miseries of physicians throughout History. Colored *tableaux vivants,* romantic yet realistic, will revive great moments in medical history and the lives of great medical figures. Men, ideas, events, and places of memorable import in the story of Medicine will be resurrected. Like multicolored lamps, words and pictures will light up the still dark corners of the healing art and will conjure a great festival of the medical spirit in the multisplendored garden of History.

Pen, brush, and camera will take us on a safari across medical history's wonderland. They will show us the great medical shrines and landmarks that the centuries have failed to destroy: Hippocrates' plane tree on the sunny isle of Cos, the ancient walls of Byzantium, Avicenna's tomb in Persia, Boerhaave's house, the golden vineyards where Claude Bernard lived; and they will reconstruct for us in all their splendor those landmarks that have long been gone, thus uniting past and present and restoring flesh and soul to what, in our mind's eye, are only things of mist and smoke.

The Epic of Medicine will relate the first awakening of medical consciousness in the magic-governed shamans of the primitive world; the fight between sorcerer-physicians and the demons of disease in Mesopotamia and Egypt; the ceaseless spinning of subtle philosophies by philosopher-physicians amidst the harmonious geometry of white marbles in ancient Greece; the practice of medicine by slave-physicians in bureaucratic, militaristic Imperial Rome; the compilation of monumental medical works by physicians in walled-in Byzantium, who thus sought to escape their cloistered world, just as the Byzantine artist sought escape through the magic windows of multicolored miniatures and the stained glass windows of basilicas; the achievements in alchemy and hygiene of the Arabian *hakims* in the Baghdad-to-Cordova empire created at the point of scimitars by Islam; the birth in the so-called "Dark" Ages of the first hospitals and universities, plus the Gothic cathedrals and *The Divine Comedy,* which made this an era not of darkness but of blazing splendor; the exploration of the human body by artist-physicians in the Renaissance, which paralleled the exploration of the new world beyond the Atlantic waters; the discovery of the circulation of the blood and the beginning of scientific research in the Baroque, a period characterized by motion and emotion in art; the endeavors of the experimenters and visionaries of the Enlightenment and the Romantic periods, who heralded the transition to the nineteenth century's naturalist positivistic medicine; the transition from medicine based on qualitative impressions to present-day medicine, based on quantitative measurements, which has led to psychiatry, antibiotics, ataraxics, and space medicine, and is leading to a biochemical, physical, and—once again—philosophical medicine and to the submission of man and the universe to objective evaluation and subjective integration.

The Epic of Medicine will consist of twelve installments and will be followed by *The Physician's Saga,* a series depicting the story of the physician as an individual, exemplified by the lives of great physicians, and *The Patient's Progress,* which will be dedicated to the forgotten and yet the most important man in the History of Medicine: the patient.

The Epic of Medicine will endeavor to give substance and meaning to our daily work. For the History of Medicine *is* Medicine. Our medical activities—administering an antibiotic, making a psychoanalysis, performing a laparotomy—acquire meaning only when we interpret them in reverse, like a film shown backwards. Only thus can we find the historical meaning in everything we do in our profession. Our medical work—preparing a clinical history, making a diagnosis, applying treatment—would be far more efficient if we knew the *why* of what we are doing and if we could anticipate its future course. This is possible only by making, as we shall try to do in this series, *living* history of all medical work, and by doing this with love and imagination, so as to let fly once again the many-hued butterflies pinned between the pages of the huge book of History.

There are three ways of handling historical events: if they are minor, they can be *described;* if they have historical dimension, they can be *interpreted;* if they can be integrated with other events in life, they can be *narrated* like a true tale of wonder. This *MD* intends to do. There are many *histories* of Medicine, but there is only one *History* of Medicine that is related to the history of civilization. Through the magic of interpretative narration, to turn all the stories of physicians, patients, countries, and epochs into *one* narrative, at once living and practical, imaginative and realistic—this is the new thread we seek to weave into the fabric of our dream.

PRELUDE OF MIST
Prehistoric and Magic Medicine

*a*nd from the remote mists of Time there emerged some solitary humanoid creatures who started a hard wandering life over the face of the earth. Between these the first prehistoric men—polished links in a long biological chain—and the original amorphous amoeba there already existed a distance of millions of years.

There was little difference between the preceding anthropoids—our cousins, the apes—and the first prehistoric men, except that when the latter descended from the trees and learned to walk on two feet, they lost their powerful strength of jaw and abdominal muscles, and instead developed a larger cranium to accommodate a heavier cerebral mass. Of these creatures there remains only the testimony of fossils, weapons, tools, and the paintings they did by torchlight on the dripping walls of their caves.

Impelled by hunger, cold, and fear, these creatures roamed the vast natural tapestry of desolate land and steaming jungle, under the silent threat of the myriad eyes that flashed in the immense black velvet of the heavens.

Even before man appeared on the earth disease already existed among beasts. Fossils, bones, and teeth tell the tragic tale of prehistoric man succumbing to disease. A sickly man indeed he must have been, his body and mind wasted by sleeping on the cold, mud-tainted ground, which he shared with snake and toad, by lack of food, by traumas, fears, and stresses. A versatile hunter, he used animal teeth and horns as weapons, and he communicated with his fellow creatures through

From *MD*, the MEDICAL NEWSMAGAZINE, 3:13, May, 1959.

grunts, gestures, and blows. Two revolutionary discoveries—the flint axe, a stone fingernail that spared his own torn and bleeding nails, and the leather handle subsequently attached to the axe—changed his life, which was further facilitated by the scarlet mystery of fire.

The first physician was man himself; the first medicine, his own instinctive attempts at self-healing, by licking, sucking, and blowing on his lesions. When these individual reactions became stereotyped, the ritual became as important as the treatment. Accidental or battle wounds, cutting up animals, and cannibalism gave man an idea of the visceral content of the human body, as revealed by paleolithic paintings in which the heart is shown as the best spot to strike a mortal blow. And when man began to eat animals' organs, the principle of opotherapic similitude was born.

Tools formerly used as weapons began to be used to make incisions and trepanations. Licking and sucking were replaced by bloodletting, scarification, amputation, and surgery with stone tools. Covering fractures with mud, in imitation of monkeys, provided the first natural cast when the mud dried. And the discovery of fire brought with it burns, but also cautery. A powerful sociological agent, fire beckoned human creatures to gather together in its warm, golden chambers.

Disease developed according to mechanisms identical to those that prevail today: alterations in growth and metabolism, tumors, traumas, and infections. Fossils and carved stones imprisoned the message conveyed by this primigenial humanity, which roamed the earth before the beginning of history.

Millennia passed, and out of the prehistoric mists there emerged neolithic man who, upon learning to grind and shape stone and turn it into weapons and tools—the missile and the hammer—ushered in somewhere around 12,000 B.C. the history of civilization. These primitive men we know about through carved stones, myths and legends, and the primitive tribes of today, people isolated in an isle of Time.

Neolithic man—Caucasians, Mongolians, and Negroes—lived in Europe and Asia, in a world that was turning temperate and humid and where, there being no notion of distances, incredibly long trips were undertaken on foot. Respect for the laws of Nature was born as the only way to conquer it; biologically correct social habits were developed; and community life began. In the endless nights, primitive man (isolated man is perhaps a better term) created astrology and astronomy and came to know the heavens before he conquered the earth. He also devised a mathematical system based on counting his fingers and toes; he learned to use the wheel; lining a basket with mud, he discovered ceramics; he polished stone, horns, and bones, cultivated plants, domesticated animals, and invented textiles.

Diseases—respiratory, osteoarthritic, gastrointestinal, genitourinary, traumatic, arteriosclerotic, infectious, and mental—were treated if minor with domestic remedies (diet, herbs, plasters, massage), often in imitation of wild animals; if severe, like smallpox, serious fractures, psychoses, the patient was killed to relieve the community of his burden, or the healer was summoned.

Besides empirical healers, who employed physiotherapeutic methods, there was the medicine man or shaman, usually a psychopath or schizophrenic, who practiced exorcism, made prophecies, and combined the functions of physician, magician, priest, statesman, and troubadour. The shaman's technique was based on magic. Magic was the precursor of science, man's first attempt to understand Nature. Preventive magic considered disease as a *plus* (entry in the body of a foreign object or spirit) or a *minus* (subtraction of the soul by magic).

The main techniques of the shaman were homeopathic magic, based on similitudes; contagious magic, based on destruction of the enemy; and direct magic, which required special rituals to prevent disease. Defensive magic used *fetishes* (objects endowed with magical powers), *amulets* (protective objects against black magic), and *talismans* (good luck objects). The shaman based his diagnosis on the concept that there was only one disease, which he identified with the cause; the "clinical history" consisted in an interrogation on the existence of fetishes, evil dreams, or broken taboos; prognosis depended on auguries and oracles; treatment was based on the afore-mentioned concept of intrusion of a foreign object or spirit, or on subtraction of the soul. Once the direct cause was determined (magic, witchcraft, death dreams, or moral delinquency), intrusion by a foreign object was treated by magic, sucking, extraction rituals, massage, baths, or vegetable drugs; and possession by a spirit, by exorcism, bloodletting, and spells.

The herbalist and prophet, therefore, coexisted with the shaman, who emerged from the millenary mists as the first medicine man, priest, and artist, in whom were joined Medicine, Religion, and Art, knowledge, belief, and creation. His magic was an art of arts, which attempted to govern the demons. It was a pseudoscience, based not on rational observation, as science is, but on the shaman's own experience of emotional states. It sought to treat human-produced and supernatural causes through mechanistic and psychological magic rituals, based on analogies and not on experiment; and "natural" causes through empirical resources, such as setting fractures, giving medicinal herbs, isolating the "possessed" (infectious or mental), practicing cranial decompression to expel the demons in an epileptic, and variolation. To combat disease, the shaman used sucking, bloodletting, and cupping, accompanying his treatment with dramatic gestures and much drum-beating and rattle-shaking, until the "culprit" incarnating the disease, usually a pebble or tiny insect, was suddenly produced and the patient was declared cured. Other times the shaman used professional "soul catchers" to retrieve the wandering soul of the patient. And in all cases he practiced verbal psychoanalytical exorcism.

Magic medicine, which still prevails in present-day primitive communities, avoided harming the patient and accepted the existence of a psychic component in all diseases. Therapy was of a cathartic nature (bloodletting, purgatives, diuretics). Thus, magic medicine was based on the *who* (the personality of the shaman), the *where* (the sacred place for his rituals), and the *when* (the magic hour); just as scientific medicine today is based on the *what* (what is done), the *how* (the technique used), and the *why* (etiological motive of the therapy).

Seeing and *believing*—empirical experience and mystic faith, natural medicine and magic—these were the first two attitudes adopted by man when confronted with the mystery of disease. These two great channels—*empirical* and *magic*—through which flowed primitive medical thought, would later be widened by the current of *thinking* and *knowing:* the *rational* knowledge of disease and of its treatment.

A man of culture, power, and prestige, the shaman was the first statesman and leader and the most brilliant man in his community. With his attempts at healing he gave man, who ignorant and helpless was a victim of his physical frailties, the first chance to face and solve the riddle posed by the sphinx of disease in the prelude ot mist to the Epic of Medicine.

LANDS OF SUN, LANDS OF DEATH
Mesopotamian and Egyptian Medicine (6000 B.C.–600 B.C.)

On the sun-drenched shores of the sapphire Latin sea the first civilizations were born. Between the rivers Tigris and Euphrates the Sumerians erected their first cities, while Egypt passed from the neolithic world of the flint to the splendorous world of the pyramids. Mesopotamia, like Egypt, was a gift from the river, a sowing of cultures in the desert that cropped up as bacterial colonies crop up in a Petri dish when one strikes it with a platinum loop dipped in bacterial culture.

The Mesopotamian civilization was man's answer to the desert's challenge to try to survive in its sun-charred, sand-whipped vastness. The Bible has perpetuated the story of Mesopotamia, whose idyllic peace, accented by sheep and palms, was often disturbed by desert nomads and mountain people craving the comforts of the cities in the plainland. Located on the route of the caravans, Mesopotamia benefited from the news and ideas that were as much a part of the caravans' cargo as gold, spices, and incense. Sumerians and Semites dug irrigation canals and invented cuneiform writing, passing from mud villages to fabulous cities with soaring towers and hanging gardens. Their leaders blazed a trail of heroic legend: Sargon in Akkadia, Hammurabi in Babylon, Ashurbanipal in Assyria, Nebuchadnezzar in Chaldea. An atrocious deluge, followed by sandstorms that buried buildings and roads, obliterated the Mesopotamian civilization, leaving us only its cuneiform tablets.

The message inscribed on these dusty tablets tells of great cities, of the Tower of Babel and the ziggurats, those skyscrapers of the desert

From *MD,* the MEDICAL NEWSMAGAZINE, *3*:11, July, 1959.

where a table of gold, a soft bed, and a handsome wench waited for the god that ruled the city through his "business manager," the great priest. The tablets also tell about temples crowned with vast terraces, whence the priests tried to probe the mystery of the star-sparkled celestial velvet. Centers of the city were the marketplace and the temple, where virgin-priestesses waited for the stranger who, with caresses and a silver coin, would deliver them from their vows. And there were majestic avenues brilliantly illuminated (by that same petroleum that is still today coveted by nations), flanked by huge bronze lions, threaded with colorful bazaars, and redolent of myrrh.

Writing and metals added new dimensions to human life. The anthropomorphic religion demanded offerings of bread and wine to the Mesopotamians' god, and the slavery-based economy contrasted sharply with their theocratic democracy, which required everyone to labor at the canals in peacetime and to be a soldier in wartime.

Mesopotamian art was an art of duration, static, geometric, massive, agoraphobic. It glorified gods, demons, and the dead. It feared open spaces, the awesome flatland that stretched endlessly all around, and the unfathomable celestial immensity above. It sought to fight the amorphous universal chaos through a rigid geometry, opposing nature's curved lines with man-created straight lines.

Communication was limited by the lack of roads, which barred the use of the wheel except in war chariots. All travel was done on foot, donkeys, or river rafts. Kings were buried together with their court, their jewels of gold, silver, lapis lazuli, and malachite. Remarkable were their mechanical inventions: the wheel, the pulley, the screw, the level, the wedge, and the inclined plane.

To fight disease (dysentery, the scourge of the river; ophthalmic ailments, the curse of the sands; and arthritis, the bane of humidity), the Mesopotamians resorted to a medico-religious medicine, since they believed that disease was either punishment by the gods for their sins or possession by demons, and they considered the diseased person impure or taboo.

Mesopotamia therefore was the cradle of necromancy and magi. In Mesopotamian demonology, in their belief that demons and spirits "specialized" in causing certain diseases, lay the seed of the future doctrine of specific infectious germs. Infections and neuroses were treated through magic rituals. Medicine was a secret art taught only in temples, and all physicians were priests. Surgery progressed as wars increased and the surgeon became the physician par excellence. The Mesopotamians had knife doctors ("surgeons"), herb doctors ("internists"), and spell doctors ("psychiatrists").

Their Code of Hammurabi, inscribed on a pillar of black diorite and set up in the temple at Babylon, represents the first historical codification of medicine. It established both the fees payable to physicians for satisfactory services and the penalties should their ministrations prove harmful. Medical care was completed by laying the sick in the public square so that passers-by might offer advice had they ever had the disease themselves or known of any who had suffered from it. Prescriptions were discussed by the laity as freely as today we discuss dishes on a restaurant menu. The Mesopotamians created an astrology that was concerned not with nativities but with the study of the heavenly mechanics, and that was the precursor of astronomy. After the heavens they studied the earth in search of auguries, the most important of which, together with the flight of birds and the flickering of flames, was hepatoscopy. Examination of the liver of sacrificed animals was a costly practice. The liver was considered the seat of emotions and the most vital organ in the human body, since it appeared so large and full of blood during sacrifices. Its examination was performed in situ, in the "palace of the liver," its scarlet architecture of vessels and ligaments sharply etched beside the green moon of the gall bladder.

Diagnosis, which was based on hepatoscopy, astrology, dreams, and auguries, led to "etiological" therapy through repentance for sins committed, expiatory rituals, the expulsion of demons, sympathetic magic, and offerings of milk, honey, and beer. Symptoms were believed to be the disease itself. Also used in therapy were fruit, cereals, spices, flowers (garlic, roses, oats, laurel, and tamarind), mineral and animal substances, massage, plasters, and baths. Besides an extensive pharmacopoeia, the Mesopotamians had a sewage system, they established the notion of certain days for resting, they had a calendar, mathematics, archives, and libraries, and they realized the necessity for isolating the sick. The cradle, together with Egypt, of medical culture, Mesopotamia is an immense wall on which archeologists are still rapping their knuckles in search of the rich historical treasures hidden within its ancient stones.

Mesopotamia's rival, yesterday as today, was Egypt, a "socialist" theocracy in which the Pharaoh was a god, just as Mesopotamia was a "democratic" despotism and the king was a mortal. Egypt was an oasis in the desert, a corridor of fertile land watered by the sacred Nile. On the Nile's periodical inundations (attributed to the tears shed by Isis over her husband Osiris) depended the Egyptian economy. The Egyptians forced the people to erect dikes and dams, adopt a solar calendar, invent geometry in order to delimit private property whose boundaries were wiped off periodically by the inundations. They were also compelled to organize a complex social state to maintain the unity of the people, which was constantly threatened by the river, as well as the greatest bureaucracy in history, with the inevitable loss of human individuality.

For many centuries the land of Egypt, victim of numerous successive invasions, kept contracting and expanding in the same manner as an amoeba contracts and expands under the microscope. Originally an amalgamation of neolithic clans, unified by Menes, Egypt had a history of feudalism, anarchies, invasions, and vast military powers, which used horse-driven war chariots. Small in size, great in enterprises, a veritable stone coffer locked by rock, sand, and sea, for millennia its language and writing remained local and hieratic, until the Rosetta stone was deciphered.

From a neolithic culture, Egypt, under the Pharaohs, almost jumped to a civilization that knew hieroglyphic writing, metals, how to make papyri for writing purposes, alphabetic signs, colored glass, and metal alloys, and that had a caste of scribes from which would spring the first physicians. They built the pyramids by means of the level, the ramp, and the roller. They embalmed the human body so as to preserve the soul. Tombs, mummies, and steles reflected the Egyptians' obsession with death and with preservation of body and soul. The climate itself helped to preserve all things: papyri, silks, stones, and the dead. Outstanding among the Pharaohs was Akhenaton, who instituted a monotheistic cult to the sun and who had his wife, who was also his sister, immortalized in art. Thanks to him, she of the swan neck, the beauteous Nefertete, still gazes upon us, her single crystal eye sparkled by some inner dream.

The Egyptians' lack of individuality was reflected in their art—uniform, rigid, massive, and crowded with columns, as if with such optical crutches they sought to combat the visual agoraphobia that bedeviled them. Monumental, monolithic, sepulchral, and funereal, their art made of homes transient places and of tombs the eternal dwelling. Each tomb was a temple where the deceased substituted for the god. Not realizing that there was immortality in biological paternity, they sought it instead in death, around which they created a gigantic cult. Ruled by the law of frontality, their art never represented a lifted foot, rarely a woman, never a smile. Instead, it teemed with sphinxes, gods, lotuses, and papyri. An art for the illiterate, it reflected the technology of the times and was a hymn in stone to the immortality that comes only with death.

Stones and papyri describe the Egyptian way of life—their consanguineous marriages, simple garments, and meticulous pulchritude; their meals of bread, fish, dates, and beer; their houses made of adobe or mud and lit by castor oil-soaked salt; the cruel life of the slaves toiling at the mines or pyramids; and the women, their busts gilded, their eyes painted with lead sulfur, and their lips stained green and black.

Mummification was developed to a remarkable degree, for the

Egyptians believed that the *ka* or soul returned to the body after death. If the physician's duty was to prevent putrefaction of humors inside the living body, the embalmer's duty was to prevent putrefaction inside the dead body. Sodium bicarbonate, cedar oil, wine, and aromatic herbs were used in mummification; the viscera were removed, the body was swathed in gum-soaked linen, and the face was traced with cloth of gold and precious stones. The mummy was then laid to rest in the sepulchral chamber, together with canopied jars containing the viscera, to wait for the Final Judgment. Yet, though millions of embalmings were performed, not the slightest progress was recorded in anatomy, which was studied only in animals in the kitchen or in sacrifices at the temples.

Medical papyri, written twelve centuries before the *Corpus Hippocraticum,* give us an idea of Egyptian diseases, which were transmitted by water, flies, and food. The Edwin Smith Papyrus reveals the Egyptians' progress in traumatic surgery, though they feared to cut open the major organic cavities. It compares cerebral circumvolutions with "melted copper," cranial fractures with "a crack in a ceramic jug," and it lists surgical symptoms and their empirical and magical treatment. In describing cases and lesions, the author of this papyrus seems to have been moved by a spirit of inquiry. The Ebers Papyrus, of a later date, describes internal diseases and lists traditional therapies, just as household remedy books did in the seventeenth century. Besides amulets and talismans, Egyptians used at least one third of all the medical substances known today—from opium to gentian to castor oil and colchicum—though they ignored their specific indications and collected drugs merely as a child collects toys.

It is important to remember that the most ancient scientific documents are *medical* and *mathematical,* and the most ancient of all such documents is believed to be the *Corpus Hippocraticum* (compiled in the fifth, sixth, and seventh centuries B.C.). But prior to the *Corpus* there existed a scientific tradition that was already old when Greece was young. Pythagoras, Thales, and Hesiod, in the sixth, seventh, and eighth centuries B.C., respectively, linked their work on mathematics with the old Egyptian theories. The *Iliad,* which grants credit to Egypt as the place of origin of Greek drugs, already contains the beginning of a medico-rational system, which dates medicine as far back as the tenth century B.C. But if Greece left us an important literary selection of its writings, Egypt left us only what time itself preserved, chiefly religious breviaries and funeral texts and stones. Greek texts are a product of their Golden Age; Egyptian texts are merely copies of ancient texts made when Egypt's sun wás already setting. This explains the inferiority of Egyptian texts, though the Edwin Smith and Ebers papyri record several scientific observations that were repeated twelve centuries later in the *Corpus Hippocraticum*. (The Greek miracle, therefore, was a resurrection of the scientific tradition of Egypt and the Near East.)

Medical practice—which was shared by physicians, priests, and medicine men—reached such a degree of specialization and hierarchy that some physicians were exclusively "guardians of the anus" of the Pharaoh, and most of them were experts in one disease only. The physician was summoned for an ordinary ailment, the priest for a grave one, and their fees were paid in kind. The patient's clinical case history was studied first, after which he was given a general examination, in which the physician's sense of smell was as much a guide as palpation, percussion, and pulse taking. When the diagnosis was etiologico-magical, the demon or spirit that had to be expelled was specified. Empirico-rational diagnoses were symptomatic, and the symptoms—pain, fever, tumor—were believed to be the disease itself.

Therapy was based on diet, herbs gathered from the patient's own garden, enemas (in imitation of the sacred bird of the Nile, the ibis), and external application of animal fat, particularly oxen fat. Physicians themselves, assisted by their servants, prepared all medicaments. They also used lancets, cautery, psychotherapy, and, above all, an eliminative and humoral therapy that made of purgatives a daily cosmetic and of regular bowel movement an eternal blessing.

In Egypt, magico-religious medicine, which was popular because it was inexpensive, coexisted with empirico-rational medicine, which because of its high cost was limited to the wealthy. Only near the end did the latter veer toward magic. A basic etiological cause of disease was considered to be the *wḥdw,* a substance in the materia peccans in the fecal content of the bowel, responsible for putrefaction. The Egyptian concept of the nature of disease was based on an elemental physiology: alterations in the air, in ingested foods, and in the blood (of which there was so much and loss of which they knew could kill a man). The religion-influenced physiology believed that "conduits" carried the blood and the air through the body, which to the Egyptians was a mass of flesh and bones traversed throughout by canals, with a heart in the center. Since their land was a web of canals through which flowed the most vital element, water, the Egyptian mind conjured an anatomical image of numerous canals through which flowed blood, air, food, and sperm, and which, like their irrigation canals, were susceptible to obstructions, droughts, floods.

Egypt gave birth to Imhotep, "he who comes in peace," a man with pensive eyes and shaven skull, "the first figure of physician to emerge clearly from the mists of antiquity" (Osler). Vizier to King Zoser, physician, priest, astronomer, and architect, Imhotep built the great pyramid of Sakkara, the most ancient stone structure extant.

Upon his death, Imhotep was transported up the Nile in a funeral barge, his body swathed in perfumed linens, a necklace of talismans girding his neck, and his flower-lined coffin surrounded by moaning women with bare torsos. This was the beginning of his glorification as hero, semigod, and ultimately god of medicine, and his cult was eventually identified with that of Aesculapius in Greece. Imhotep and Egyptian medicine are the connecting links between the world of calcined deserts of archaic medicine and the sunlit polished cosmos of Greek rational medicine.

Meanwhile, India, a great nation, was rising in the Orient under the Emperor Asoka, who built hospitals and academies. During the Vedic and Brahmanic periods of its medicine, epidemics were studied, surgery progressed (particularly rhinoplasty, because there were so many punitive facial mutilations), a physicians' oath was introduced, and three classical medical texts were born: *Charaka, Susruta,* and *Baghbatha,* all based on the *Ayur-Veda,* the supreme mystic document of Hindu medicine.

In its turn, China, influenced by the Buddhist philosophies imported from India and by Confucianism in the North and Taoism in the South, would develop a civilization far more technologically advanced than any Western civilization would be up to the Middle Ages, having invented the compass, gunpowder, silks, porcelain, and printing. The Chinese even "invented" the pocket handkerchief centuries before it was used in Europe. Chinese medicine, based on Confucianist principles, after an initial period of magic became cosmological and botanical, developing a fantastic pathology system, a veritable ivory tower with a purely theoretical foundation. Diagnosis was based on examination of the tongue and the pulse, which was regarded as a musical instrument. The Chinese discovered numerous drugs, from ephedrine to camphor, and practiced acupuncture, moxibustion, and variolation. The first consisted in the insertion of fine needles into the "canals" through which flowed the blood and humors, a method inspired by the irrigation canals in their land, and the second required the subcutaneous application of ignited combustible cones.

The Hebrews from Judea originated three great religions—Judaism, Islam, and Christianity—to purify the soul, and a public health system to purify the body. The Bible—which meant even more to the Hebrews than the Homeric epics did to the Greeks—records cases of leprosy and epilepsy and the most ancient prophylactic-hygienic legislation.

The Amerindian cultures—Mayan, Aztec, Incan—followed the same magico-empiric lines of primitive medicine.

And while these cultures sparkled the horizon, there came to happen the Greek miracle, a brilliant epiphany in which man found his full historical dignity.

AT DAWN THE SUN SHINES
Greek Medicine (776 B.C.–285 B.C.)

*t*he golden sun of Attica for many years had already been sparkling the orange and olive groves of Greece when a small
band of courageous men, the first philosophers, dared for the
first time in History to formulate formidable questions: What is man,
and what is Nature?

These were the men who initiated the Greek miracle: the awakening of human conscience. The small rock-girded peninsula, washed
by the wine-colored waters of the Latin sea sung of by Homer, thus
contributed to the "time-axis," that momentous period in History
when philosophers from Greece, prophets from Israel, Confucius and
Lao-tse in China, and Buddha in India, six centuries before Christ,
created the first great religions and philosophies of mankind.

The first great task accomplished by Greece was the unification of
its peoples, dispersed throughout the isles surrounding the mainland.
Two things maintained this unity: First, the epic hexameters of the
Iliad and the *Odyssey,* compiled about one millennium before Christ
by a wandering blind bard called Homer. These poems reveal the
existence of an empirical, chiefly surgical, medicine. Before Homer,
the seat of life was placed at the liver; with Homer, it was transferred
to the heart; after Homer, it passed to the brain. Second, the Olympic
games, which, held every four years, served to measure time. Their
Marathon race commemorated the feat performed by an athlete who
ran without pausing from Marathon to Athens, whereupon he fell
dead, probably as a result of acute hypoglycemia.

From *MD,* the MEDICAL NEWSMAGAZINE, *3*:11, September, 1959.

Half a millennium later, the Greek philosophers opened the luminous path that would lead Greece to its Golden Age. Thales of Miletus, Heraclitus, Anaximenes, Democedes of Croton, Empedocles of Agrigentum, Pythagoras, and Alcmaeon of Croton—these men advanced the basis of the two great doctrines that for many centuries to come would rule medicine: the humoral and the pneumatic.

In this sunny landscape there blossomed two great systems of medical philosophy: the Aesculapian cult, or temple medicine, based on religious suggestion and psychotherapy; and empirical medicine, based on rational thought.

Just as today people go to spas, in classical Greece people made pilgrimages to the temples of Aesculapius. From Greek mythology we learn that the god Apollo, jealous of the nymph Coronis, had her slain with arrows. The lovely Coronis fell dead, her slim torso bejeweled with rubies of blood, whereupon her son Aesculapius was secreted to a mountain by the kind and gifted Chiron, the centaur, who taught Aesculapius the healing art. Aesculapius performed numerous miracles of healing, became a god, and was worshipped in Asclepieia throughout Greece.

To these temples, erected on scenic grounds with natural springs and provided with stadiums, theatres, and bathing pools, came flocks of miracle-hungry pilgrims, avid to read the temple tablets—their equivalent of our electronic newsboards—listing the miraculous cures performed, and to practice the healing ritual known as "incubation" or temple sleep. At the foot of the marble and gold statue of the god, they lay down to sleep, and during the night the god, incarnated in the Asclepiad or priest, appeared in their dreams, followed by his daughters Hygeia and Panacea, and prescribed healing herbs and even performed operations. In the morning the patients departed, often cured, after making a sacrificial offering of gold and sheep or songs and prayers, according to their means.

Side by side with this psychotherapeutic temple medicine there blossomed an empirical medicine that regarded disease as a disharmony in the *physis*. This medicine was practiced by *periodeutai,* or itinerant physicians, by court physicians, and by military surgeons. The *periodeutai* were wandering craftsmen who traveled ceaselessly. In the public square of the town they would exercise the art of oratory, sing, and recite poetry, in an effort to attract people to their *iatreias* or offices. They were also experts in the art of *pronoia,* and often bombarded the onlookers, before they had a chance to say a word, with a detailed description of their ailments. This empirical medicine, which used diet, herbs, and drugs in treatment, was represented by the old school of Cnidus, which was interested in diagnosis, and later by the school of Cos, which specialized in *pronoia.*

One man was responsible for this new attitude in medicine. We know little of his life—even less than we know of Christ's youth—yet Hippocrates of Cos has passed into History as the Father of Medicine. Like Homer, Christ, and Socrates, Hippocrates never wrote a word, yet the *Corpus Hippocraticum* consists of no less than seventy-two volumes and contains an exposition of the knowledge of this great physician, the first to treat *patients* instead of diseases and to prepare clinical case histories with a modern biographical approach.

In the center of the town of Cos, there still stands the plane tree in whose shade Hippocrates is reputed to have taught his pupils while examining his patients. He accepted the existence of *many* diseases instead of just one, and regarded them as natural processes that altered the humors of the body, of which he believed there were four, based perhaps on observation of the four layers formed by clotting blood. He believed in the curative powers of Nature. With the advent of Hippocrates, the sick ceased to be considered sinners, while sinners began to be considered sick people. Patients became human beings who went through a certain process in their life history that was called disease. This biographical approach prevails every day more in medicine. Like a wreath of laurel crowning his work, there remains the *Hippocratic Oath,* a great code based on the golden rule that to be a good physician one must first be a good and kind man.

Many schools sprang up in those times, the most outstanding being the dogmatic, the empirical, the methodist, the pneumatic, the eclectic, and the peripatetic. Eventually Hellenic knowledge leaped from Athens to the shores of the Nile when the Greek Ptolemy I Soter founded in Alexandria the *Museum* or home of the muses, which housed one of the most famous libraries in the world with more than half a million volumes. Here taught Archimedes, Euclid, the Hippocratist Herophilus of Chalcedon, father of anatomy, and the Galenist surgeon Erasistratus, who discovered the tricuspid valve. Here also was born the first great clinical school and university in the world, complete with laboratories, cafeterias, and publishing house. In this school anatomic dissection was first practiced, ushering in the concept that the seat of disease was the *organs,* not the humors.

Greek art reflected the Greeks' attitude on life. The Nike of Delos, the first effigy ever made of a woman not only running but *smiling* as well, is a symbol of the Greek spirit, which humanized the gods, while deifying man. Whereas Egyptian temples were fortresses, the Parthenon atop the sacred hill was more like a marble harp suspended from the radiant blue, an eternal symbol of the Greek miracle.

To the work of the Greek philosophers modern civilization owes an immense debt. Socrates taught man to think; Plato regarded the brain as man's most noble tool, established the unity of body and soul, founded the Academy, and in his "Symposium," through the lips of Eryximachus the physician, described medicine as "the art of understanding the love affairs of the organs of the body." His pupil Aristotle, whose mind was a vast empire of knowledge, restored medicine to the kingdom of biology. Whereas his master Plato accepted all knowledge as emanating from *within,* Aristotle contended that everything emanated from the *outside* and was absorbed through the senses and perception.

Greek medicine is not the beginning, but the *middle* of the history of medicine. More than two thousand years separate Hippocrates from Imhotep, and about as many years separate Hippocrates and Fleming. Only by being aware of this fact can one realize how ancient medicine is.

Great and noble is our Greek medical heritage: the objective observation of the patient; the concept of disease as a process of natural causes, cured spontaneously by Nature; and the creation of a new type of physician—a humanist and a humanitarian, conscious of his mission and his destiny, as the kind and good Hippocrates himself was.

A TORRENT OF LIONS
Medicine in Imperial Rome (285 B.C.–A.D. 476)

L ike a torrent of lions the Romans fell upon the historical scene, and their proud imperial eagles swept across the skies of the world.

Strong warriors the Romans were, as well as highly adept in law and administration. Originally a handful of Aryan merchants ruled by Etruscan kings, the Romans created an aristocratic republic, with a caste of patrician families lording it over the masses. Their history encompasses bloody triumvirates, mighty emperors—sadists and philosophers, schizophrenics and saints—who created a vast and powerful empire, only to succumb to a plague and inflation. Military curse of the world, Rome was redeemed by its genius in jurisprudence and organization, by its men of letters, its patricians, and, above all, its physicians.

Mining and agriculture for slaves and laborers, and war for all and at all moments, were the main occupations, which engendered an aristocracy of force. A world of athletes and adventurers, empire of the javelin and the lance, the sword and the bow, the Romans ascribed great importance to that *offensive* weapon par excellence —the shield, for no one who is innocent of the desire to attack his fellow men would trouble to provide himself in advance with a means for protection.

The Romans boasted of splendid brick, clay, and marble cities, with fine torch-lit streets and wide roads. They made exquisite painted ceramics and porcelains, wrote on parchment (nontanned

From *MD*, the MEDICAL NEWSMAGAZINE, *3*:11, November, 1959.

lamb hide), had arsenals and central heating, travel agencies, draining canals, food inspectors, and military hospitals. In their *prandium* and *convivium* they ate bean porridge and nonfermented bread dipped in honey, and drank diluted wine and oxymel. Their technology was based on slavery until they realized that horses, though they ate more than slaves, were stronger and therefore more economical. Their art reflected their megalomania for the colossal, just as Greek art reflected a craving for beauty. With its triumphal arches and colonnades, vast coliseums and arenas, Roman art epitomized the Roman cult of force.

Originally Roman medicine was magical. When the pendulum of world knowledge swung to Rome, side by side with the Aesculapian cult there flourished all sorts of quacks who dealt in wholesale healing, though often their only medication was goat fat or, as in the case of Cato the Censor, cabbage juice, which he prescribed for all ailments alike. He even ordered his patients to bathe in the urine of persons who had fed on cabbage and with his experiments finally succeeded in killing his own wife.

For a long time practiced only by priests, which therefore made it inferior to philosophy and poetry, medicine was left chiefly in the hands of slaves, until the first Greek physicians arrived in Rome, particularly Asclepiades of Bithynia, who with his golden tongue conquered Rome and created a solidistic philosophical system based on the notion of atoms. Thereafter several schools of thought flourished. There were Methodists—Themison of Laodicea and the great gynecologist Soranus of Ephesus—who considered disease an alteration in the organic pores and thus simplified the treatment of the great masses of slaves in the plantations; Pneumatists—Athenaeus of Attalia, Archigenes and Aretaeus of Cappadoccia—who recognized as vital force the *pneuma,* or soul of the world, any alterations wherein produced disease; and Eclectics, such as Pliny the Elder, Dioscorides, the naturalist and master of medicinal plants, Rufus of Ephesus, almost as great as Galen, and the elegant, sophisticated, erudite Celsus, of golden Ciceronian eloquence.

The first physicians in Rome were slaves. Later they became *medici liberti manumitidis,* when Julius Caesar granted freedom to all freeborn Greek physicians practicing in Roman territory. A kind emperor, Antoninus Pius, instituted state regulations protecting municipal physicians, enabling some of them, Antonius Musa, for instance, to amass great fortunes and, though they were only liberated slaves, to be honored with monuments. Physician-slaves, on the other hand, could be bought for some $340, less $60 if they had been castrated. Physicians of the invincible Roman legions and of military hospitals or *valetudinaria* coexisted with palatine or imperial physicians and with "specialists." After the establishment of medical licenses in A.D. 200, medical societies and civil hospitals were created, and imperial laws for medical students, such as the one prohibiting the visit to brothels, were passed, much to the grief of the students.

Even then therapeutics comprised magic. Next to the polished effigies of the new gods hung ancient Etruscan mirrors of polished bronze engraved with images of succubi. A barbaric polypharmacy (turtle blood, camel's brains, crocodile excrement) was used as much as new drugs and techniques in the treatment of epilepsy. Fear of touching the dead body paralyzed all progress in anatomy, which was studied only in animals and during vivisection of criminals. To study the great organic cavities, so feared by the ancients, they dared practice short and quick—to forestall putrefaction—dissections in Barbary monkeys.

The most important Roman contributions to public health were the marvelous aqueducts, which to this day make Rome the best irrigated city in Italy, public baths and swimming pools, sewers, fountains, and wells. At its zenith, Rome could boast of having more than 122 gallons of water per inhabitant. Yet, the poor had to bathe in the Tiber, the streets were filth ridden, and in small towns and villages excrement streamed down the streets. The Romans had public health inspectors but personal hygiene degenerated into an end instead of a means, into effeminacy and depravation. Sports evolved into athletics, and hygiene into weakness. Later, with Christianity, the body was neglected and the filthy body became the only possible dwelling for the pure soul, and the naked Greek statuary of fluid line was replaced by the rigid, austerely robed statuary of Christianity. Overindulgence in the pleasures of the body—succulent banquets of highly spiced food, torrents of wine and hydromel (the Roman Coca-Cola), torpid siestas in the shady atrium, massages by the sensuous hands of expert slave girls—set the Romans far on the road to degeneration and destruction. Little or nothing could the Roman physician do against all this, even if the physician was the great Claudius Galen.

To this day Galen excites a feeling of ambivalence among physicians. Since Roman medicine is linked to such unpleasant things as slavery and dogmatism, which is exactly the opposite to what medical progress requires, that is, a climate of absolute freedom, Galen's glory must be constantly revindicated. But Galen, whose word and work were articles of faith for fifteen hundred years, is really a *modern* author.

Born at Pergamum, Galen was baptized Galenos, meaning a tranquil sea, he who was so atrabilious! In his seventy years of life, he served as physician first to gladiators and later to the Roman emperors—Marcus Aurelius, the gentle philosopher, Commodus, Pertinax,

Didius Julianus, and Septimius Severus. Galen conquered the Imperial City with his gifted tongue and his great culture, and he left a pyramid of more than 500 works, which would be the basis of his dictatorship in Medicine for fifteen centuries. His anatomy, based exclusively on dissection of monkeys and only two human corpses, was nevertheless correct; his physiology and pathology were speculative; his therapy was empirical; and his endorsement of the Aristotelian notion that the body is the vehicle of the soul was the basis for the monotheism of Arabs and Christians.

Galen believed in the Hippocratic nosology and in humoral pathology to the effect that the blood *moved,* not circulated, through the arteries; he also accepted that the body was made of *parts,* not humors. Later, in the Renaissance, Paracelsus would destroy Galen's pathology; Vesalius, his anatomy; and Paré, his "first intention cures." Galen's theological viewpoint, which made him the spoiled child of Christian psalmists, did great damage to his physiological investigations.

While Hippocratic medicine was humoral and philosophical and therefore antiquated, Galenic medicine was anatomic and consequently modern. His concept of a *pneuma* breathed by man, which at his death returned to its source of origin, becoming a universal *pneuma,* accepted that such a spirit turned into *natural* spirits in the liver, was distributed through the veins and transformed into *vital* spirits upon reaching the left heart, was then distributed through the arteries and finally became *animal* spirits in the brain, and was then distributed through its "branches," the nerves.

Galen initiated the use of "Galenicals" or vegetable simples and turned practical hygiene into applied physiology—the Eclectic application of rest, diet, sleep, and exercise. In accepting the Aristotelian concept of the relation between body and soul, the responsibility of the individual, and the Christian interpretation of life, Galen once again reunited medicine and philosophy, which had been separated by Hippocrates.

After Galen, Christianity imposed a curative religion and disease became an act of purification and divine grace. Galen's disciples were excommunicated and priest-healers were glorified. Upon his death, Galen's writings disappeared and were not resuscitated until they were translated into Latin in the thirteenth century, which helped prolong the cultural coma that was to last one thousand years. In decreeing that every human organ was made perfect by the Creator, Christianity discouraged anatomical studies and experimental medical research.

The Roman contribution to the progress of mankind included improved collective hygiene and public health, irrigation, draining, aqueducts, thermal baths, gymnasia, inspection of markets and brothels, antimalarial measures, military hospitals, legalization of the medical class by such means as title-licenses and examinations, medical insurance, social and military medicine, systematization of medical instruction, and a higher social standing for the physician.

Until one day the boots of barbarians from the North invaded Rome and trampled the imperial purple and the blood-soaked togas strewn all over the floor of the Roman Capitol, which rang with the clang of bronze and steel, announcing the beginning of the Middle Ages.

THROUGH A STAINED GLASS WINDOW
Byzantine Medicine (476–1453)

O n entering a Gothic cathedral today one feels as if a weird fauna were rushing down from windows and capitals. Griffins, gargoyles, and dragons, long imprisoned in the Gothic cage, that "trap of fantasy," seem ready to set off in chase of that elusive quarry of the Infinite. Man must have felt much the same at the beginning of the Middle or so-called Dark Ages, when upon him descended the avalanche of beauty and squalor, romanticism and roguishness, chivalry and sadism that characterized the age of the Crusades, the Gothic cathedrals, the *Divine Comedy,* and the *chansons de geste.*

We should not call "Dark Ages" a period that gave birth not only to such men as St. Thomas Aquinas, Albertus Magnus, and Arnold of Villanova, but also to the three great bases of modern medicine: universities, hospitals, and public health. True, in the first four centuries of this period, man wallowed in magic, and the invisible threads binding him to stars and amulets ruled his life; but for the remainder of the Middle Ages he valiantly combated the ignorance and bigotry surrounding him. Rather than the "Middle Age," that is to say the maturity, of Europe, this was her childhood, when she began to awaken to a new view of man and of things.

In the fifth century the pendulum of history had swung from Rome to Byzantium, the city with a thousand gilded domes bathed by the waters of the Golden Horn and the Bosporus. Thereafter, for the next thousand years, until the fall of Constantinople to the Turks, or,

From *MD,* the MEDICAL NEWSMAGAZINE, *4*:11, January, 1960.

if a medical date is preferred, until the publication of Vesalius' *Fabrica,* Greco-Latin medical learning would flow through three channels—Byzantium, the Arabian empire, and the monastic universities—which would later converge into the resplendent broad stream of the Renaissance.

Byzantium, later called Constantinople, and now called Istanbul, kingdom of God on earth, was for ten centuries the unattainable dream of the barbarians, who coveted its rich treasures. A walled bastion in a hostile world, defended by the walls built by Theodosius and the azure waters of the Bosporus, Byzantium defied the pagan hordes for a thousand years after Rome herself had succumbed. Century after century, Mongols, Turks, and Tartars, attracted by the glittering domes and the legend of its treasures, vainly attacked the invincible city.

Life in Byzantium was cloistered. The people, deprived by the city walls from looking ahead, looked up and back: at heaven and at the past. Their emperor, the basileus, was regarded as Christ on earth; his political code was the Bible; his parliament, the holy apostles; his offices were the basilicas, vast and towering and ablaze with gilded mosaics in all the colors of the rainbow. He appeared in public "pale as death," robed in white and surrounded by his twelve apostles. His meals were replicas of the Last Supper; his garments and countenance, of those in sacred icons. His palace was yet another church where even the porter was a priest. The finest silks and porcelain, gilded mirrors, carved ivory chess sets, damask tapestries, jeweled enamels, coats of mail, diamonds and other gems, gold chalices, sandalwood and ebony caskets, jewelry and table services inlaid with precious stones, carpets and ceramics jammed the treasury of the city, which like a golden cloud gleamed above the Bosporus and the Golden Horn. Founded by Romans, Byzantium was inhabited by Greeks, Romans, and Asiatics. Its basilicas were the house of God; its palaces, the house of the church militant.

The lack of statuary was compensated for by the abundance of paintings—the "books" of the illiterate ancients—in which the Byzantines depicted what they *felt,* just as the Egyptians depicted in their art what they *knew,* and the Greeks what they *saw.* In Byzantium the dung-piled streets contrasted with the splendor of the palaces; the strange Christian democracy, with the stern ruling theocracy.

Under Byzantium's three great emperors—Constantine I, Julian the Apostate, and Theodosius—Byzantine culture developed in flight from the present to the past, its art turning from the classical portrayal of the human being to the introvert world of mosaics, bas-reliefs, and miniatures, and its medicine taking refuge in endless compilations of Greek learning.

The Crusades introduced Europeans to the cultured world of Byzantium, a world protected by its geographical position on the confines of two worlds, at the end of a landlocked sea, by the principle of unity known as "Hellenism"—a community of language, ideas, and culture—and by the intricate web of Byzantine diplomacy and their genius for weaving political intrigues.

In Byzantium—whose art was the art of Eastern Christendom, just as Roman art was the art of Western Christendom—the basilica was the house of God, an arrogant granite mass symbolizing the Church on a war footing and its everlasting might capable of resisting all sieges. The basilicas contained no statuary, for that was a symbol of paganism; in fact, they contained nothing that did not reek of religious asceticism. Religious imagery was prominent in mosaics, which were placed on walls and ceilings and not in the pavements as in Rome; for man, in his greater meekness, now looked toward heaven rather than to earth. The Oriental aversion to depicting the human form turned Byzantine art toward abstract and geometric motifs. The mosaics and multicolored paintings in the basilicas were an inspiration to visionaries, and its gems, to which were attributed magic properties, bore an obvious analogy to the mystical descriptions of heaven.

Typical of this art were the painted glass windows, ivory and metal filigrees, and illuminated initials sparkling with golden luster and precious stones. Stained glass windows in the Middle Ages were intended to inspire emotional ecstasy. Later, when the printing press was invented and, with the advent of the Reformation, the Bible was read inside the churches, church windows were made of transparent glass. Fraught with perfectionism and preciosity, Byzantine art was symbolic of the besieged capital, where man's only escape from his walled-in existence was to roam the limitless regions of time.

Renouncing travel in space, since fierce enemies were ravening on the other side of the walls, the Byzantines journeyed into time: the artists devoting themselves to time-consuming stained glass and filigree work; and the physicians turning to the past in search of knowledge, since learning makes man lose his sense of isolation. As a result, Byzantine medicine turned backward, and was based not on investigation but on compilation. To Oribasius of Pergamon, Aëtius of Amida, Paulus of Egina, Alexander of Tralles—to these men we owe the monumental tomes in which is preserved the medical lore of ancient Greece.

There being no one in Byzantium to garner the heritage of Galen and again raise the torch of experimental medicine, medicine became a matter of faith. The sick person was regarded as a potential saint; prayer was adopted as the best medicine, the priest as the best physician, the Church as the best hospital, and Christ as the the Supreme Healer.

In the Byzantine empire, medicine was in the hands of priests and magi. The guardian saints, Cosmas and Damian, shed their light over the city. Nevertheless, the Roman appetite for luxury and sensual pleasures endured. Paradoxically, philosophical mysticism and the Oriental influence of demonology, magic, and alchemy existed side by side with the influences of Christianity. A medicine of priests, Byzantine medicine bowed to ecclesiastical authority. Taking their example from Christ, their first physician, the fathers of the Church practiced medicine. They also erected hospitals, one of which with its annexes could accommodate 7000 patients. The sick were fed on fruit and wine, temple sleep was practiced, and physical and spiritual healing was promised to the faithful. Smallpox plagues, which scourged Constantinople often, were described by the priest-physicians.

The ancient pagan cults survived solely among the healthy. Christianity, with its appeal to the unclean, the diseased, and the sinners, became a powerful revolutionary force. The diseased person became a privileged being, and medicine was founded on faith and miracles, the Divine Word, and prayer. Faithful Christians renounced classical hygiene. The patients of the priests were mostly laborers and the needy, not the well-to-do classes, and the diseased body was extolled as the only possible dwelling for a healthy soul.

After surviving the ventures of the Crusaders, Constantinople finally fell in 1453, after a siege lasting several months, when the Ottoman Sultan Mohammed II, commanding half a million men, with the aid of greased log rollers hauled seventy-two galleys from the heights of Pera in twenty-four hours and in a single night placed them on the waters of the Golden Horn opposite the city, using his artillery to support his attack on the coveted prize.

One tragic day, through the *Kerkoporta,* at the shout of the warcry *Yagma!* (Plunder!), the enemy poured into the thousand-domed city. Constantinople fell before the fury of the invaders who, scimitars in hand, spared neither Byzantine man nor Byzantine art, but set the seal of Ottoman art and religion on them both. In Istanbul today one can still see traces of that fatal hour: the shattered walls of Theodosius, which for one thousand years guarded the colossal basilicas, that miracle of architecture, symbol of an unprecedentedly beautiful and mighty civilization. Concurrently, Byzantine medicine yielded to the Ottoman medicine of the invaders.

With the fall of Constantinople, Hellenic learning migrated to the West, driven by the force of *humanitas,* that is to say, culture and the heritage of "man as a measure" of Nature.

The Byzantine contribution to medicine was the creation of hospitals and the monumental compilations of medical knowledge by men who seem to have given no thought to the approaching storm, who, ignoring the fact that they stood on the brink of an everlasting night, toiled as if they were bathed in the light of dawn. Byzantium stands in history like a bridge across the ocean of Time, thanks to which the Renaissance was enriched by the Greek classical learning imprisoned in the Byzantine compilations, whose pages were as subtle and eternal as the moon's reflection on the waters of the Bosporus.

WHILE SCHEHERAZADE TELLS HER TALES
Arabian Medicine (732–1096)

*a*nd on the 436th night, Scheherazade began the tale of Abu
al-Husn and his slave girl, the fair Tawaddud.

A "rose of crystal and silver, scented with sandalwood
and nutmeg . . . with eyes like gazelles' eyne . . . cheeks like
anemones of blood-red shine . . . and hind parts heavier than two
hills of sand," Tawaddud prevailed upon her impoverished master to
sell her to the caliph Harun-al-Rashid. Once in the presence of the
caliph, Tawaddud offered to answer all questions on "syntax, poetry,
jurisprudence, exegesis, philosophy, the divine ordinances, arith-
metic, geodesy, geometry, ancient fables, the Koran, the exact sciences, medicine, logic, rhetoric and composition, the lute, dancing
and fashions." The answers of this fabulous creature to the questions
on medicine, anatomy, and physiology afford a revealing picture of
Arabian medicine in its golden age.

Arabian medicine was Persian and, indirectly, Hellenic in origin.
Long before the Arabian conquest there lived in Constantinople one
Nestorius, an eloquent Aramaic priest who was banished to the
Libyan Desert, because he dared maintain that the Virgin Mary was
the mother of Christ, not of God. In a distant oasis, in the green shades
of the towering palm trees, Nestorius and his followers, having paid
dearly for their aspirations to heal man's soul, turned to healing man's
body. Disillusioned with their own times, the Nestorians cast their
eyes back to classical Greece and drank avidly of the medicophilosophical waters of the Greco-Roman school. Later, generous with
their new knowledge, they poured the ancient Hellenic nectars into

From *MD*, the MEDICAL NEWSMAGAZINE, *4*:11, April, 1960.

Syrian vessels, translating Greek medical works into Syrian and establishing the famous medical school at Jundishapur and others in various Persian towns. Thus the Nestorians revived in Persia the lost luminous Hippocratic-Latin tradition. Later, when the Arabs conquered Persia, they suddenly found their shepherds' pouches filled with the medicophilosophical treasures of the Greeks recorded on old Nestorian parchments.

A young and ardent Semitic people, the Arabs, who for centuries had been content to roam the burning sands of Arabia, spurred on by the monotheistic preachings of Mohammed, set out in the seventh century on a fabulous historical cavalcade, in the course of which their scimitars carved out an empire that stretched from China to Spain, including northern Africa. Centering their power in the caliphates of Baghdad and Córdoba, they created the mighty Saracen civilization, which was to perish in the thirteenth century with the sack of Baghdad by the Tartars and the expulsion of the Arabs by the Turks in the East and by the Spaniards in the West.

The Arabs never forced their religion on the peoples they conquered; they only required that the Koran be recognized as the vehicle for the divine word, and since the sacred book was written in Arabic, the conquered peoples had to learn the tongue of the victorious invaders. Thus the vast Moslem empire came to be united by one single language. Before Arabic became the official language among learned men, Greek, and later Syriac in western Asia, had been the preferred language. But from the ninth century on, both the humble rug vendor in the public market and the haughty physician at the caliphs' courts spoke in Arabic.

The only other term imposed by the Arabs upon the conquered peoples was the surrender of old Greek manuscripts. What splendorous times, when even beneath the warrior's mail beat a heart avid for culture! When Michael III of Constantinople was defeated, the penalty imposed on him was that he send a caravan of camels loaded with ancient manuscripts to Baghdad. The pen was mightier than the sword.

The Abbasside caliphs wisely recognized the importance of translating into Arabic their vast Greek cultural war booty. Never in history have translators played as important a part as they did at the beginning of Islamic expansion. Heroes of this period were the famous Syrian and Coptic families of translators, the Bakhtîshû and the Messuas, and that prince of translators, Hunain, also called Joannitius. Thanks to these men, the Arabs, whose total knowledge at the end of the eighth century consisted of a translation of a Greek medical book and a handful of alchemy books, before the end of the ninth century had become acquainted with all the Greek sciences.

The glory of Greece vanished and the might of Rome destroyed, there remained only the work of these Arabian translators and that of the Byzantine copyists to span a bridge of light across the thousand dismal years that elapsed between the fall of the Roman Empire and the jubilant explosion of the Renaissance.

Schools of medicine flourished in Samarkand and Baghdad, Isfahan and Alexandria, Córdoba, Seville, Toledo, Granada, and Saragossa. Through almost the whole of the ninth century, medical practice in Baghdad was in the hands of foreign Christians, whose skill was considered superior to that of the Arabs.

The eastern caliphate, or caliphate of Baghdad, was illuminated by the presence of four Persian luminaries: Al-Tabari, Rhazes, Haly Abbas, and Avicenna.

Al-Tabari wrote *Paradise of Learning,* a paper chest scented with Arabian vegetable drugs—tamarind and sandalwood, nux vomica, Persian vetch, gum arabic. For more than by any other branch of medicine, the Arabs were fascinated by pharmacology.

Rhazes, "the Experimenter," who alternately cultivated the gusla and medicine, head of the great hospital of Baghdad, physician to caliphs, proponent of a meager therapeutic arsenal in contrast to the abundant pharmacological fare served at the banquets of Arabian chemistry, was also a great compiler. His *Liber Continens* gained him much fame. It also lost him his sight. It is said that a hierarch whom he had offended ordered that he be beaten on the head with his own book until one or the other broke. Rhazes' head broke first.

To Haly Abbas, a Zoroastrian magician, we owe a *System of Medicine,* perhaps the best and most lucid of all Arabian medical works and the first to be translated into Latin.

With even greater brilliance shone Avicenna, the Persian Aristotle, prince of Arabian physicians, devourer of libraries, unparalleled dialectician in Moorish, Arabic, and Latinity, statesman by day, ready at night to forsake deep philosophizing for light-hearted feasts, well versed in old wines, chaser of fresh maidens, now wielding the vizier's staff, now turning to the guitar, the gusla, and the pen. Avicenna wrote the *Canon Medicinae,* the most famous medical book in history, a medical Bible whose million words made its author world dictator of medicine until Vesalius, supplanting for six centuries the medical dictatorship of Galen. In the *Canon,* epitome and summary of Greco-Latin medicine, the thorns of dogma bristle on the roses of science. The backbone of Arabian medical thought, it recommended the cautery instead of the surgeon's knife, for the Arabs had a horror of dissecting the human body. Today, a thousand years later, the principles of Avicenna's *Canon* still continue to heal the sick of Persia.

In the western, or Córdoban, caliphate the arts and sciences flourished, but except in mathematics and literature, the Arabs were compilers and transmitters, rather than creators. Their architecture, rich in domes and ornate surfaces, derived from Byzantium; their cloistered patios, from Rome; their medicine, from Greece by way of Syria and Persia. Above all, the Arabs catered to the pleasures and comforts of the body, to which they subordinated even the soul. Their cities boasted glass windows and street lamps—reflections of their yearning for clarity and light—and abounded in enchanting gardens, redolent of exotic flowers and resonant with the murmuring of brightly tiled fountains.

The caliphs were generous patrons to scholars, and next to their deep-in-sensuous-shadows seraglios stood their libraries lined wall to wall with yellowing parchments. Córdoba alone had fifty hospitals, seventy public libraries, and the most renowned university in Europe in the tenth century. In the library of Alhaquen II alone there were nearly three hundred thousand volumes, bound in leather and gold, containing in the sinewy and virile Arabic language the whole of Arabian knowledge. The Arabs assiduously cultivated astrology and alchemy, the mother of Arabian polypharmacy. There were numerous families of physicians, such as that of Avenzoar, which followed the medical tradition for three centuries. Next to sandalwood-scented mansions, the Arabs built hospitals, which, in Andalusia as in Baghdad, were also refuges for the insane and the destitute. And everywhere water, so prized by them, spurted and spun into braids of crystal for the baths and ablutions that were as indispensable as prayers. They led an indolent life in their flower-laden gardens, sipping fruit- and rose-flavored drinks, watching the golden dance of the bees from flower to flower, while deep in myrtle and basil, rosebays and gillyflowers, the water gurgled in the tiled fountains.

Medicine was taught privately; a general education was acquired at the *medressen,* a cultural center attached to the mosques. Medical students learned first the art of mortar and pestle from an apothecary, then sought to enter the service of an experienced physician with an extensive library.

They considered the heart the sovereign of the body; the lungs, its fan; the liver, its guardian and the seat of the soul; the pit of the stomach, the seat of pleasure. They combined alchemy with ancient Chaldean magic, establishing "correspondences" between stars, spirits, metals, and the anima mundi. Seeking the elixir of life and eternal youth, they founded medicopharmaceutical chemistry; searching for potable gold, they discovered aqua regia. Led astray by Galenic polypharmacy and by Aristotelian dialectics, the Arabs also believed that it was sinful to open the human body and so halted progress in anatomy.

The giants of the Córdoban caliphate were four. The Córdoban Albucasis the surgeon, the Arabian Vesalius, wrote *al-Tasrif,* beacon light of European surgery until the time of Paré. Defying tradition and the Koran, he illustrated his texts himself. He adopted the iron cautery, tied arteries, described the position for lithotomy, practiced transverse tracheotomy, and differentiated between goiter and thyroid cancer. The Sevillian Avenzoar, an anti-Galenist, a ladies' man, physician to Almohad caliphs, was perhaps the greatest clinician of his period. He despised Avicenna's *Canon* and was the most Hippocratic among the Arabian physicians. The Córdoban Averroës, Aristotelian and pantheistic philosopher, perhaps the initiator of medieval scholasticism, physician to a caliph in Marrakech, influenced even his opponents with his subtle heterodox philosophies. The wandering Córdoban Maimonides, the greatest Jewish humanist and philosopher of the Middle Ages, whose services Richard Coeur de Lion tried in vain to secure, physician to the Sultan Saladin, practiced medicine in Egypt, whither the intolerance of the Almohades had forced him to flee. By basing theological principles on reason, he did for Judaism what Averroës had done for Islamism and St. Thomas would do for Christianity. Devoted to medicine as an art, he studied patients, not diseases, reconciling reason and faith, rejecting astrology, and left as heritage his wisdom-permeated *Guide for the Perplexed* and his priceless axiom: "Teach thy tongue to say I know not, and thou wilt progress."

The Arabian legacy to civilization was vast and varied, comprising fireworks, as colorful and explosive as the Arabian temperament, exquisite gardens and palaces that have endured to this day, geology and algebra, ceramics, textiles, botany, medical chemistry, and the first materia medica. The Arabs discovered various acids, nitrate of silver, benzoin, camphor, saffron, sublimate of laudanum, and anesthetics; developed the alchemical techniques of crystallization, distillation, and sublimation; and created the first pharmacies, which displayed their vast polypharmacy and their medical panacea: the mellitums, together with numerous vials containing all sorts of weird things, from fetuses to frogs and scorpions. These pharmacies served also as meeting centers where all sorts of information and news were exchanged and discussed. The Arabs enriched man's language with such words as "drug," "alkali," "alcohol," "sugar," and many others. Their search for the philosopher's stone led them to advance laboratory methods and to invent the art of compounding prescriptions, sirups, juleps, poultices, electuaries, pills, powders, and alcoholates, which they kept in majolica jars, magnificent examples of pottery, embellished with fruits and leaves because at first they were used for preserves.

Above all, the Arabs built splendid hospitals, such as Al Mansur in Cairo, equipped with wards for both sexes, murmuring fountains to cool feverish limbs or soothe restless minds, libraries, dispensaries, reciters of the Koran, music for the sleepless, singers, and storytellers. Discharged patients were provided with money so that they need not go to work immediately. Their high rate of blindness from trachoma led the Arabs to make a thorough study of the human eye, and to progress markedly in optics and the removal of cataracts, the latter operation being symbolic of their thirst for more light.

Arabian medicine, reflecting the Hellenic sun on the Arabian crescent, illuminated the medieval darkness until the dawn of the Renaissance.

THE CROSS AND THE EAGLE
Monastic and University Medicine (1096–1453)

*t*hrough the bloody dust stirred up by the medieval wars, over which still hovered the shadows of the Christian cross and the old pagan eagle-like symbols of conflicting civilizations, a new type of man was emerging—a man forever on the defensive, eternally tortured by the terrors of the beyond, by the fear of God in heaven and of devils and plagues on earth.

For a thousand years medieval man had lived in perpetual conflict with God, with the world, and with himself. Ravenous for knowledge, he crowded into the public squares to listen to the golden words of Albertus Magnus, Abelard, Duns Scotus, or St. Thomas Aquinas. Obsessed with saving his soul, he neglected his malodorous body, concealing it with voluminous garments, heavy perfumes, and architectonic wigs. Burning with sexual desire, brutal and gluttonous in his pleasures, mystical and romantic in his deeds, rebellious against the law and enslaved to classical dogma, believing, under the spell of astrology and alchemy, that invisible zodiacal-magical filaments connected men, stars, and matter, fear and faith were the opposite poles of his soul. He sought refuge in the love of God, in the collective security of medieval cities—where everything, including disease, was collective—and in the perpetual imperative of action, from tournaments and single combats to the gigantic collective adventure of the Crusades. He exchanged the celestial bodies of astronomy for the cabalistic signs and symbols of astrology, and the test tube of the chemist for the crucible of the alchemist. But he also created master-

From *MD*, the Medical Newsmagazine, *4*:13, July, 1960.

pieces. He built the Gothic cathedrals, soaring hymns in stone, sky-rockets of granite and glass, with rainbowed windows, illuminated missals, and statues and paintings that extolled, to literate and illiterate alike, his world of allegory and symbolism. He wrote the *Divina Commedia,* immortalizing through Dante's lips his own spirit and deeds. And—perhaps his greatest claim to glory—he was the first to create, on a vast scale, universities, a public health system, and hospitals. From such as he sprang the modern European man.

The medieval cathedrals were, so to speak, centers of entertainment and instruction, whither flocked the pilgrims to pass long days huddled around the still time-untouched dazzling white walls, gazing in wonder at the stained glass windows (their equivalent to our electronic newsboards, just as the religious processions with their pomp and pageantry were their cinema and television), whereon were recorded in jewel-toned colors the news, stories, biographies, and even technical advances of the period.

In an age that was collective, medicine was faced with the problem of "collective" diseases (plagues, leprosy, dancing mania), just as it was faced with "individual" diseases (syphilis) in the individualistic Renaissance. Symbolically, the Middle Ages began and ended with terrible pandemics: leprosy, which made of its victims, with their gray sackcloth, peaked hood, and sinister rattle, the most dreaded of phantoms; and the Black Death, which killed the majority of lepers but also a quarter of the population of Europe, causing some forty-three million deaths, spreading over the entire planet through maritime and caravan routes. Among its social consequences, it dealt the death-blow to feudalism, increased the value of labor by making laborers scarce, and caused loss of faith in the Church and priests by showing that they died like anyone else, which helped to spread the Reformation. Ironically enough, the Black Death inspired a cynical and irreverent Florentine to write the immortal *Decameron.*

The collectivistic characteristics of the Middle Ages partly determined the monastic nature of medieval medicine. Medieval man sought protection and safety in the anonymity of either huge armies, like the Crusades, or monasteries. Located on the main routes traversed either by foot or on horseback by all travelers, the monasteries were at once inn, refuge, hospital, news agency, and nerve center of medieval life. Here a handful of dedicated men toiled to learn the new universal language, Latin, which for a thousand years would replace Greek, already supplanted by Arabic in the Islamic world. In these monasteries study and calligraphy were made paths to heaven.

Knowledge became for the Church the means of consolidating its power and authority. Thus clerics came to study, among other things, medicine. Sickness became a divine punishment, and repentance a prerequisite for its cure, with the medical arsenal including relics, rituals, scapulars, and prayers. Medical aid was free until the High Middle Ages, when medicine for the first time became a profession commanding remuneration.

Monastic medicine coincided with Romanesque art, man being then subservient to the Church militant, even as, later, the medicine of Salerno coincided with Gothic art, and the birth of nationalities at this time, together with the rise of the universities, threatened the Church's medical monopoly. The state of mind of the peoples of both periods was reflected in their architecture: in the former, it comprised fortress-like—squat and square and windowless—granite carapaces that provided collective shelter against individual fears, while in the latter period it soared into spiraling towers, symbol of alertness and power.

The monk-physicians accepted the Hippocratic doctrine of the four humors and the correlation between the macro- and the microcosm. Therapy was based on the polypharmacy, bloodletting, cupping, baths, emetics, purgatives, and diuretics described in the antidotaries and herbals, basis of all monastic medical knowledge. To be a physician one first had to be ordained a priest, though monks practiced medicine only in the monasteries.

Theurgic therapy, based on saints' miracles and magic herbs, had its first center in the monastery of Monte Cassino, founded in 529 by St. Benedict of Nursia on the ruins of a temple of Apollo, and the model for future "cathedral-schools." The monks at Monte Cassino practiced religious psychotherapy and physiotherapy, and devoted much time to copying classical medical texts. There the monk Cassiodorus combined classical Greco-Latin and Christian thought, and Greek formularies and compilations were translated into Latin. More a vast medical library and general teaching center than a genuine medical school, Monte Cassino was the cradle of western *religious* medicine. A mass of stone atop a hill near Naples, often sacked during the centuries and finally destroyed in World War II, Monte Cassino had its golden age in the eleventh century. The moving spirit of its medicine was Constantine the African, a mysterious physician disguised as a Benedictine monk, who studied medicine and magic in Babylon. He translated into Latin the works of the Arabian, Jewish, and Greco-Roman physicians, especially Galen, and his translations initiated the lay emancipation of medicine and formed a bridge between Monte Cassino and Salerno.

Some one hundred twenty-five miles from Monte Cassino, on the azure Tyrrhenian Sea, was Salerno, an ancient Greek colony. The

School of Salerno, created as a *civitas Hippocratica,* three centuries after Monte Cassino, by a group of students organized in a *universitas,* and a group of physicians composing a faculty, was the oldest center of *lay* medical instruction and the first school to confer diplomas and the title of doctor.

Supported by neighboring Benedictine monasteries, Salerno combined Greek, Latin, Jewish, and Arabian cultures. In Salerno, though most of the teachers were clerics, medicine was taught freely, even by women physicians like Trotula, the "Dame Trot" of popular tales, and became emancipated from the clergy. There anatomy was taught, though only pigs were dissected; there the first medieval pharmacopoeia was compiled, and surgery, practiced often on the mangled bodies of returning Crusaders, made progress. In Salerno was written the most famous hexameter poem of popular medicine in history, the *Regimen sanitatis Salernitanum,* later attributed to Arnold of Villanova. Nearly a thousand editions were published of this work, which recommended diet, exercise, herbs, drugs, rest, and recreation. And in Salerno, disease was regarded as arising from natural causes and not as a result of divine punishment, astrology and magic were rejected, and the path was opened that would lead to the medieval universities.

The universities crystallized the passionate desire for knowledge that permeated medieval Europe. The center of knowledge shifted with political power, passing successively from Salerno to Bologna, Paris, Montpellier, Oxford, Cambridge, and Padua. Physicians were still "book doctors," more philosophers than clinicians, for their clinic was the library, although already in the fourteenth century genuine clinical histories were being written, such as the famous *concilia* of Padua and Bologna. Horror of blood made the Church abandon surgery to barbers, executioners, and quacks. The *universitates,* or free associations of students, attired either in full cloaks and tabards or clerical habit and tonsure, finally originated more than eighty universities in Europe. Students led a hard and difficult life, constantly threatened by hunger, cold, and other discomforts, but at the same time they were gay and given to wild pranks that often ended in bloodshed.

The University of Bologna was governed by lay students (whereas Paris University was governed by the masters), and the streets of Bologna often rang with festive graduation processions, with much beating of drums and waving of banners. Luminaries at Bologna were: the surgeon of the Crusades, Ugo de Lucca; his son Theodoric, who used a soporific sponge soaked in opium and mandragora; William of Saliceto, who substituted the cautery for the knife; Taddeo Alderotti, immortalized by Dante and creator of the *concilia;* and the astronomer Copernicus, whose thinking revolutionized the whole universe. Bologna witnessed perhaps the first autopsy in history (1281) and made great advances in anatomy under Mondino, the first man to dissect a human body in public, whose *Anathomia* was the basic anatomy textbook for three centuries.

A group of students from Bologna founded the school of Montpellier (1208), whose roster of students included such illustrious names as Arnold of Villanova, physician to popes and kings, the most extraordinary figure in medieval medicine, possibly the author of some of the first hundred medical books printed in Europe, advocate of wine in therapeutics, and defender of naturalistic observation against the magic and dogma of the Inquisition; the Franciscan Ramón Lull, who in the shade of the tortured olive trees of Majorca wove his immortal philosophies; Bernard de Gordon, whose work made perhaps the earliest mention of reading glasses; and the magnificent Guy de Chauliac, whose textbook on surgery was the most authoritative until the eighteenth century.

The school of Paris was founded by Peter Abelard. Its students had to remain unmarried on pain of losing their title of doctor. Paris was illumined by the greatest genius of the thirteenth century, Albertus Magnus, *doctor universalis,* the most learned man of the Middle Ages, master to St. Thomas Aquinas, to Roger Bacon, and to the only physician to become Pope, Petrus Hispanus. Such was the fame of Albertus Magnus that he had to teach in the open in order to accommodate the thousands of students who flocked to listen to him. His work marked the beginning of experimental medicine. Outstanding too were the surgeons Lanfranchi of Milan, Jan Yperman, father of Flemish surgery, and Henri de Mondeville, whose observations on the qualitative change in the humors added a new dimension to the humoral doctrine.

The school of Oxford sprang from that of Paris. A school of clerics governed by masters, mother of the liberal and naturalistic school of Cambridge, it sheltered the mysterious Michael Scot, physician and magician; the Franciscan Bartholomaeus Anglicus, author of the most poular encyclopedia of medieval medicine; the *doctor mirabilis,* Roger Bacon, the first modern scientist, defender of experimentation against dogma, who described the magnetic needle, gunpowder, and reading glasses, and predicted radiology, the discovery of America, the airplane, the steamship, and television; and John Gaddesden, author of the *Rosa Anglica,* a book divided into five parts, like the petals of a rose, and immortalized in Chaucer's *Canterbury Tales.*

Daughter of Bologna, the school of Padua, where the student was lord and master, was an isle of liberalism under the protection of the fair Venice. In Padua, the illustrious Pietro d'Abano, an Averröist philosopher, used the "dry" aseptic technique to treat wounds and reconciled Arabian medicine and speculative philosophy. Accused of practicing magic, d'Abano was burned at the stake.

All the universities, especially that of Montpellier, were fertilized by the cultural stream from Toledo's school of translators, where Christians and Jews happily fraternized and a new type of medieval scholastic physician was born, a doctor-cleric crammed with book knowledge and dialectic and highly versed in Latin, the *lingua franca* of educated men.

Set by their office above all manual labor, physicians eschewed surgery, which was practiced briefly by barber-surgeons, with scarcely any preliminary technical training, and by empirical barbers, bloodletters, and executioners. This occasioned countless conflicts between the "long-robed" surgeons (schoolmen and clerics) and the "short-robed" empirics. Surgery used tampons, cautery, sutures, and the soporific sponge.

Medieval art attained its highest form of expression in illuminated medical manuscripts and miniatures of daily life. Animals and flowers gradually replaced the earlier figures of kings and emperors. Herbals, luminous with colored pigments and gold, supplemented the popular botanical gardens of the friars, whose herbs Charlemagne called "friends of the physician and the cook."

Other healing practices coexisted with university medicine, such as the healing miracles of patron saints, like St. Sebastian and St. Roch, and the "Royal Touch," healing performed by a mere touch from the hand of a king. Medieval medical concepts were Galenic; the dominant pathology was humoral and pneumatic; diagnosis was based on the symptomatology and examination of the patient, especially of his pulse and urine. At the same time *pronoia,* the art of divining disease without questioning the patient, was practiced, and dreams were studied. Uroscopy, immortalized in medieval paintings, was the supreme diagnostic tool, for the golden liquid, believed to be filtered from the four organic humors, was revered; it was sent to the physician in flasks cradled in straw baskets like a noble old wine, and the physician, as portrayed in paintings, studied it with pensive eyes. Therapy employed phlebotomy, exutories, cathartic treatments by means of clysters, cupping, emetics and purgatives, symptomatic polypharmacy, and many fantastic remedies.

The medical man, who was first physicus and then doctor, became a professional when his services were at last remunerated, but hospitals continued to be little more than refuges for invalids.

Weird diseases prevailed, such as the epidemic of flagellants, who scourged themselves to the sound of bells; and the dancing mania, exorcised by the church and depicted on canvas by Brueghel, called in Italy tarantism, collective social phenomena revealing of the prevailing psychic contagion.

Belief in magic and demons flourished, and so did the use of amulets, gems, bezoars, and saints' relics, the doctrine of astrological signatures, and miraculous nostrums, the belief in incubi and succubi, fairies and gnomes, flying witches, demonic possession, and visions of the witches' sabbath, Ptolemaic astrology, and the signs of the zodiac. The addition of faith and prayers to these "curative" resources marked the change from natural to Christian magic.

Medieval medicine, via Arabian medicine and the European universities, preserved and passed down Greek medical thought. Worthy of admiration are the men who, though surrounded by a hostile and violent world, strove indefatigably to kindle the dawn in the medieval night. It was night, but night illuminated by Gothic cathedrals, musical with the verses of Dante and the discourses of Albertus Magnus, tempestuous with students at the universities, ablaze with the passionate adventure of the Crusades, and redeemed by medieval man's longing to set the barren desert of his soul abloom with the roses of his faith in the future.

IN A SUNLIT GARDEN
Medicine in the Renaissance (1453–1600)

a Belgian youth twenty-two years of age was the central figure in the brilliant procession that, one December morning in the year 1537, slowly advanced through the narrow gray streets of Padua toward the Bishop's palace. The masters of the University at the head of the procession wore sumptuous gowns; the soldiers' halberds glittered in the sun; poor students shivered with cold in their threadbare capes; plumes like cocks' combs fluttered atop the great hats of rich students; knights and clerics wore a sober mien; a band sounded the gold of its trumpets; nobles looked arrogant in beribboned uniforms; and at the tail of the procession the populace added a note of gaiety. At the Bishop's palace, the youth, named Andreas Vesalius, was to be granted the title of Doctor in Medicine.

Born in Brussels of a family of physicians, Vesalius had studied in Louvain and Paris, where, still under the Galenic tyranny, anatomy was taught by a master who read Galen while the *ostensor* and the *demonstrator,* usually barbers or executioners, dissected a corpse and exhibited its parts in time with the monotonous reading. The students were never allowed to approach the corpse. Rebel and visionary, Vesalius felt that anatomy could not be learned in such fashion. *Seeing* rather than listening was the only way. This visual nature of his mind, which made him oppose his masters, was the key to Vesalius' secret.

Determined to learn anatomy the right way, Vesalius even stole

From *MD,* the MEDICAL NEWSMAGAZINE, 4:11, October, 1960.

corpses from the Cemetery of the Innocents in Paris. In the dead of night, stealthily seeking his way through the dark tombs, he carried off under his cape the limbs and other members from the corpses of executed criminals. Back in his room, after soaking the parts in vinegar to disguise the terrible stench, he would by candlelight dissect them until all hours in the morning. Thus was anatomy learned by one who later became professor of surgery at Padua, wrote the greatest book in medicine, the *Fabrica,* and ushered physicians into the sunlit garden of Renaissance medicine.

Vesalius lived in a glorious period. The air was electrified by a new historical climate. Various historical forces had been set in motion. More than a revival of classic culture, this was a period of *rebirth,* which is more important than birth, for it involves the consciousness of being born. With the disappearance of empires, nationalities began to spring up in Europe. In Spain the Catholic kings had created the modern concept of the state as a *nation.* Everywhere new faiths replaced the uniform creed previously imposed at the point of swords. By preaching a return to primitive religious simplicity, the Reformation unleashed wars of religion. Gunpowder destroyed castles, and with them the feudal system, and created the new problem of firearm wounds. A new social condition confronted man. The static medieval societies and orders (clergy, nobility, corporations) were replaced by a dynamic society. The action of the bourgeois class, the use of money, the appearance of capitalism—these turned the spatial medieval economy into a *dynamic* one.

In vibrant response to the prevailing dissatisfaction with the present, Humanism arose, the longing to return to the classical past, to the clear springs of Greco-Latin wisdom. Learning Greek, the humanists launched a crusade against Arabianism. They sought to restore classical wisdom. This was the dawn of the artistic Renaissance. The rediscovery of the beauty of the naked human body aroused interest not only in its form but in its structure or internal machinery, stimulating progress in anatomy and medicine.

The discovery of the compass stimulated daring transoceanic explorations, which culminated in the discovery of America. The craving to know what lay beyond the ocean paralleled the craving to know man's inner anatomical space. The adventure of navigators and conquistadors had its parallel in that of anatomists and surgeons, who for the first time dared probe into the *terra incognita* of the human body.

The invention of printing and the manufacture of paper facilitated human intercommunication. The cosmography of earth, sea, and sky progressed. Academies and universities flourished, and Humanism advanced with Petrarch, Erasmus, and Boccaccio. Among the humanist luminaries of the Renaissance were physicians and botanists (intrigued by nature, almost all of the humanists were botanists): Konrad von Gesner; Thomas Linacre; Copernicus; Geronimo Cardano, physician, gambler and mathematician, who with his description of moral insanity introduced "modern" psychiatry; von Andernach; Andrés de Laguna; the Valencian Juan Luis Vives, father of modern psychology, voluntary exile in Brussels, where he wove philosophies as subtle as the lace his wife wove in their shop; Jean Fernel, humanist and physiologist, author of the *Universa medicina;* and the Spanish martyr Michael Servetus, discoverer of the pulmonary circulation of the blood, who for his heretical disputes with Calvin was in Geneva burned alive over green wood to prolong his death, a crown of sulfured thorns on his brow.

Solitary scholars began to flourish, Robinson Crusoes on the islands of their endeavor, contemners of the Arabs and devotees of classical Greek learning. New instruments, such as optical lenses and Galileo's telescope and microscope, exemplified the Renaissance thirst for novelties, as did new mercurial remedies and necropsy methods. But medical innovations came late in this period, following in the wake of discoveries in art, philosophy, and religion. Medical innovators were few, isolated, late to appear, and, except for Paracelsus, were all still to some extent Galenists. Nature was conceived as architecture by Vesalius; as an organism by Fracastoro and Paracelsus. The greatest triumphs of the Renaissance were Vesalius' new architectonic approach to anatomy; Paracelsus' and Fracastoro's new concept of medicine as dynamic pathology; and the new approach to surgery, as an empirical and conservative art, by Ambroise Paré.

Clinical histories progressed, developing from the medieval *consilia* to *observationes* of a biographical nature. In contrast to the "collective" medieval diseases typical of communal life under feudalism and in monasteries, new *individual* diseases appeared, such as exanthematous typhus and syphilis. Syphilis, which probably already existed in Europe, was aggravated by the new and more virulent American strains brought back in Columbus' ships and disseminated during the siege of Naples. Its nature and that of infectious diseases and their contagiousness were studied by Fracastoro, humanist, physician, and poet, who, a solitary figure amid the golden vineyards near Verona, created a dynamic epidemiology and established the fact that infection passes from one person to another either directly or indirectly. Fracastoro gave the "malady of love" the poetic name of syphilis after the shepherd hero of his beautiful poem *Syphilis sive morbus Gallicus*.

Four great Renaissance rebels started the revolution in medicine, surgery, anatomy, and psychiatry. Paracelsus was born near Zurich, among forests of pines and firs. Itinerant and adventurous physician, drunkard and wrangler, he studied the book of the world and nature and dramatized his iconoclastic scorn for classic dogmas by publicly making a huge bonfire with the works of Galen and Avicenna. He died prematurely, worn out by his bitter career of rebellion. Paracelsus bequeathed to medicine a dynamic pathology, establishing the fact that diseases often came "from without." He rejected the dominant polypharmacy in favor of simple medicaments, and introduced in therapy metals, tinctures, and essences, which made him the forerunner of medical chemistry. His concept of disease was a weakening of the vital principle or *archeus,* and his therapy was based on the curative power of nature, each malady having its specific remedy (*arcanum*) in the surrounding world. He left as legacy not a system but a rebellion like a flaming sword.

Beside the conquistador and the *condottiere* there stands out in the Renaissance the surgeon, whose great adventure was in exploring the human body. The importance of the barber in surgery had then increased, intensifying the conflict with the "long-robed" or licensed surgeons. At the same time there was an increase in the new problems created by firearm lesions. The ambition of Parisian Ambroise Paré, a good and humble man, was to be a "short-robed" barber-surgeon. He attained fame when, having exhausted his supply of boiling alder oil for treating "infected" gunpowder wounds, he improvised a compound of egg yolks, oil of roses, and turpentine, thus breaking the tradition that such wounds were infected and ending the terrible trauma produced by the brutal boiling oil treatment. Later, Paré completed his contribution to *conservative* surgery by using onion poultices (rich in bactericidal principles) on infected burns; by replacing cautery by arterial ligature; and by practicing both herniotomy without castration and podalic version. Paré summed up his creed in the modest and beautiful words: "I dressed him and God healed him."

Plastic surgery progressed with Gasparo di Tagliacozzi; the new respect for women inspired by Erasmus, Luis Vives, and Sir Thomas More helped obstetrics; and ophthalmology advanced through the new visual attitude, the respect for the *saper vedere* recommended by that great visual genius Leonardo da Vinci.

The revolution in anatomy was accomplished by Vesalius. But interest in the human body was spurred by other things as well. Violence, stirred by families like the Borgias and by the *condottieri,* required one to learn the art of killing in order to survive. The spring and power of the muscles, the strength and weakness of every part of the body, had to be known, for such knowledge was vital in fighting an enemy or safeguarding life. This inspired the new pictorial approach in art, best exemplified in Michelangelo's "Last Judgment" and particularly in his magnificent "Moses," which Sigmund Freud would later psychoanalyze.

Forerunner of Vesalius and the greatest genius in the history of mankind, Leonardo da Vinci, "physician," engineer, architect, poet, musician, and painter, performed numerous dissections, leaving 1500 anatomical sketches and 7000 pages of notes. He united science and art, an endeavor made glorious by the brilliant anatomical artists of the Renaissance: Verrocchio, Pollaiuolo, Cellini, Raphael, Donatello.

Before Vesalius interest was focused on the *origin* of the bodily organs; with him it became focused on their *design*. For Vesalius each part of the organism was, as the title of his *magnum opus* indicates, the *fabrica,* the structure and architecture of the human body. Not only did Vesalius know more anatomy than anyone else; he knew a different anatomy, correcting certain Galenic errors and introducing the concept of *living* anatomy, in opposition to the static anatomy of the past. With the help of Titian and his pupil Calcar, Vesalius sketched the corpses he dissected in "living" positions, using the lush Paduan landscape as background. The wood engravings completed, Vesalius sent the three hundred printing blocks on mule-back, across the Alps, to be printed at the famous Oporinus press in Basel. The violent criticism aroused by his colossal and incomparably beautiful book, *De humani corporis fabrica,* made him flee to Spain, where he became physician to Charles V. Returning from a pilgrimage to the Holy Land, he died on the island of Zante. With his new architectonic anatomy (his physiology was Galenic), Vesalius launched the concept of the body as the *fabrica* and statue of man, later developed by his followers Fallopius and Fabricius ab Aquapendente, who dissected the venous valves. Vesalius revolutionized medical teaching with his beautiful illustrations of dissected men, who, endowed in death with a strange beauty and a supreme dignity, appear to be pleadingly revealing their anatomical structure to an invisible deity.

The fourth revolution—after that of the concept of the human body as *fabrica* and architecture by Vesalius, that of the humane conservative approach to surgery by Paré, and that of internal medicine as dynamic pathology by Paracelsus—occurred in psychiatry, when the Swiss physician, Johann Weyer, regarded "witches" as unfortunate mental patients with hallucinations. Belief in witches was then universal. Almost a million were burned in Europe, especially after the inquisitors Sprenger and Krämer published their infamous *Malleus maleficarum,* a penal code regulating the unmasking and punishment of practitioners of witchcraft, a book that caused countless mental patients to be tortured and burned. The quixotic crusade against the hunting and burning of witches was started by Johann

Weyer in his book *De praestigiis daemonum et incantationibus ac veneficiis;* his thesis was later reinforced by Juan Luis Vives.

The smile of Vesalius, depicted in the frontispiece to the *Fabrica,* is that of the rebel who, in the Renaissance, defied a thousand years of medical tradition and dogma, tyranny and superstition. The other famous Renaissance smile is that of the Mona Lisa, who exemplifies the defiance in art of that other great rebel, Leonardo. Da Vinci symbolized in his "Gioconda" the attitude of men who, loving truth and beauty, fought dauntlessly to master them. They were men with sun in their hearts, who illuminated the flowerbed of beauty that is Art, and the flowerbed of truth that is Science, in the sunlit garden of the Renaissance.

WHIRLWIND IN THE SOUL
Medicine in the Baroque Age (1600–1700)

four candelabra and eight candles illuminated with their ballet of light and shadows the anatomical theatre of Padua, a small cylindrical structure of wood on whose tiers restless students from all Europe stood, packed closely together like matches in a box.

The door squeaked like a soul in torment, heralding the entrance of the teacher, Fabricius ab Aquapendente. The air suddenly became electrified. All eyes focused at once on the dissecting table, on which there lay a corpse. The flickering light from the candles, like the pale tongue of a compassionate dog, licked the naked flesh. The master's hands, bejeweled with the rubies of gout, promptly and deftly laid bare the intimate mysteries of man's anatomy. Among the youths watching the great master was a dark-haired, dark-eyed English student named William Harvey.

In the seventeenth century Galen's theories were still accepted, but the way was already being paved for momentous changes. The Spaniard Michael Servetus had already discovered the pulmonary circulation, and Realdo Colombo had clearly described it; Fabricius ab Aquapendente had dissected the venous valves; Cesalpino had shown that the blood flows and that the heart is the central organ of the circulatory system. But it was William Harvey who was to revolutionize medical science.

The mind of a scientist mirrors the atmosphere of his times. Perhaps the seed of Harvey's work was already beginning to grow as he

From *MD*, the MEDICAL NEWSMAGAZINE, 5:17, January, 1961.

watched, through Galileo's telescope, the motion of the heavenly bodies in the glittering sky of Padua; perhaps it was nourished further by the whirling motion that characterized the triumphant baroque art, and even further by the literature of the time, particularly Shakespeare's plays and John Donne's poems and sermons, which often rang with the mention of the words "blood" and "heart." In any case, Harvey dedicated his life to studying the two basic *motions* of the human body—pulse and respiration—and finally demonstrated that the blood flows and that it flows in a circle. With this animate anatomy, Harvey set in motion the static anatomy created by Vesalius, and with his concept of local motion in the human body, he ushered in modern physiology.

Other investigators completed Harvey's work. Leeuwenhoek, a Dutch lens grinder, with his homemade lenses materialized the invisible world of animalculae, infusoria, and living organisms contained in a drop of water. (It is noteworthy that while Leeuwenhoek was dedicated to investigating the world of minute living creatures, his neighbor, the painter Jan Vermeer, in a significant coincidence of interests, was himself dedicated to immortalizing in his paintings the minute details in the world around him.)

Marcello Malpighi, pioneer in microscopic anatomy, described the delicate network of the capillaries and their circulation, thus unraveling the riddle left unsolved by Harvey of how arteries and veins communicate; Jean Riolan and Jean Pecquet confirmed the white mystery of the lymphatic circulation, already foreseen by Gasparo Aselli; with the discovery of the circulation of the blood and the lymph—the two main fluids of the human body—and of the fact that the lymph does not travel to the liver, this organ was stripped of the supreme hierarchical rank conferred on it by Galen.

This work was supplemented in other fields by the search for the basic structure of the human body, which both the French humanist Jean Fernel and the Italian anatomist Gabriel Fallopius situated in a *solid* entity—the "fiber"—thus displacing Galen's humoral physiology. And Harvey, with his embryology, established *anatomia animata* in time, just as earlier, with his new physiology, he had established *anatomia animata* in space.

The atmosphere at that time was electrified by the prevailing thirst for motion and emotion, two characteristics that found expression particularly in art and gave the baroque age its name. For this was the period when, in rebellion against the pure, austere, classic Greek style, the dynamic curve was preferred to the rigid straight line in art. The world was rediscovered in its infinite mobility, and all this motion was celebrated with profound emotion. Greatest among the great exponents of this trend were fantastic El Greco, emotional Bernini, dramatic Caravaggio, photographic Velázquez, realistic Zurbarán, sentimental Murillo, joyful Rubens, and perceptive Rembrandt. They gave meaning and glory to the baroque age.

Medicine, too, strongly reflected the trend. The static Vesalian structures of the human body were set in motion and were even infused with emotion and embellished with decorations in the work of those miniaturists of the circulatory apparatus, "water-color painters," as it were, of the capillaries and the lymphatics.

In a parallel development, the baroque age saw the new religious movements flourishing at the same time that new horizons were opening across the seas and that printing and the stagecoach were shortening distances between minds and between cities. The compass had already dispelled the mystery of what lay beyond the ocean; gunpowder had put an end to the tyranny of the feudal system; the concept of state evolved; great scientific societies were born, and the first periodical of any kind, *La Gazette* (later *La Gazette de France*), made its appearance. Published at first as a weekly political and civic newspaper by Théophraste Renaudot—physician to Louis XIII and founder of the first pawnshop in France—and later changed into a medical journal, the motto of *La Gazette* is still of value today, 330 years after its creation: *"Le journal tient de la nature des torrents— qu'il se grossit par la résistance."* ("A journal is like a torrent—its power increases with resistance.")

Individual endeavor, the rise of a middle class, and increasing industrialization were changing the face of Europe, and while the power of Spain was undergoing its sunset of grandeur, that of England and Russia was ascending. The incredible voyage of the *Mayflower* planted the first seed of American democracy. The French philosopher, René Descartes, who died, coughing and shivering, at the Court of Christina of Sweden, and whose medical ideas followed the iatrophysical system, established the scientific value of doubt, the mechanistic concept of the "human machine," and the dichotomy between soma and psyche; and the philosophers Francis Bacon and John Locke emphasized the value of the experimental method in science.

The dynamic universe of Kepler, Galileo, and Newton replaced the somewhat static universe of Copernicus. The qualitative impression of nature was replaced by quantitative measurement. Science became mensural and rational. General motion in space was replaced by local physiological motion; the torch of learning passed from Padua in the sunlit south to Leyden in the misted north of Europe; illustrious physicians investigated the mysterious structure of the organs of the body—Francis Glisson, the lining of the liver; Johann Georg Wirsung, the pancreatic duct; Niels Stensen, the parotid gland.

Clinical medicine in the baroque was illuminated by the multi-colored lamps of three new medical systems: the iatrophysical, the iatrochemical, and the systematist. The iatrophysicists—philosophical heirs of Vesalius and Galileo in Italy, of Harvey in England—regarded the body as a machine and sought to explain all its workings accordingly. Outstanding exponents of the school were Redi, Borelli, Baglivi, and Sanctorius. The last named spent thirty years of his life seated in a huge scale weighing himself while in different emotional or physical states, such as sleep, anger, sexual excitement, sadness, thus initiating the way to the modern concept of metabolism. He considered pathology a matter of the "tensional state of the fibers" and of the density of the humors of the body.

The iatrochemists—philosophical heirs of Paracelsus—regarded the body as a laboratory where organic motion was the result of organic fermentation, a theory advanced by the Flemish mystic, Jan Baptista van Helmont. He regarded water as the substratum of the body and the archaeus as the life-giving principle. His mild medicinal plant tinctures were a healthy reaction against the barbaric horse-medicine therapies of the period. His work was supplemented by Francis de la Boë or Sylvius, who showed that fermentation was but one of the many changes that occurred in the body, and by Thomas Willis, whose delicate, exquisite dissections, precise as enamel miniatures, laid bare the vascular ring at the base of the brain, now known as the "circle of Willis."

Among the systematists there stands out the figure of Thomas Sydenham, a soldier in Cromwell's Roundhead army, just as Harvey was a Royalist, a scholarly and kindly physician and a spiritual descendant of Hippocrates. Sydenham shut his books and opened his eyes to look at the patient; he recommended naturalistic clinical observation, the study of the *whole* patient, and of a "species" of diseases instead of "disease" in general, as had been the previous practice; he introduced the biographical element into clinical case histories. He divided diseases into two classes: acute, biological, or animal (epidemiological); and chronic, biographical, or human (psychosomatic). Once when asked by Sir Richard Blackmore to recommend a textbook of medicine, he replied, "Read *Don Quixote,* it is a very good book, I read it still."

There was little interest in therapeutics in the Baroque age, though quinine and ipecacuanha had been brought from South America by the Spaniards. The forceps and blood transfusion were introduced. The enmity between physicians and surgeons persisted, until finally the latter were accepted by the medical class and were permitted to wear the "long robe." Always fighting barbers and charlatans, surgeons, with a few physicians, made this a period of "vampirism" in therapeutics. Their abuse of leeches and other forms of bleeding, it is said, drew more blood from the people than the French Revolution. Physicians prescribing such therapy became the target for Molière's satirical darts.

Across the Atlantic, the *Mayflower* pilgrims—nearly half of whom died within three months after landing on American soil—in their struggle against a hostile nature, the Indians, and disease, particularly smallpox and typhus, initiated American medicine, the first seed of which had been planted by the conquistadors, who in the sixteenth century conferred, in Peru, the first degree in the New World of Doctor of Medicine, founded in Mexico the first chair of medicine, and printed also in Mexico the first medical book in the Americas.

Colonial physicians fought disease with the assistance of surgeons, like Lambert Wilson and Thomas Wooton, and of clergymen doubling as physicians, like Samuel Fuller and Cotton Mather, who practiced the first vaccinations, and Thomas Thacher, who wrote the first American medical publication on smallpox. With this "angelic conjunction" of physician and pastor, America saw the beginning of what would eventually become the most advanced medicine in the world.

Everywhere on both sides of the Atlantic, man looked for new wonders. While the settlers struggled to conquer the rugged nature of America, in Europe a great physician and humanist, Sir Thomas Browne, wrote a beautiful and inspiring book, *Religio medici,* in which, in a prose as delicate and colorful as a Gobelin tapestry, he reconciled mystical faith and scientific skepticism. In the pages of this book he wrote his answer to man's eternal quest: "We carry within us all the wonders we seek without us. There is all Africa and her prodigies in us."

STARS AND GLOWWORMS
Medicine in the Enlightenment (1700–1800)

O n one side of the heaving quicksilver strip of channel that separated her from England, eighteenth-century France was, first, a turbulent stage for the epic drama of the Revolution and, later, the horizon over which the historic career of Napoleon rose like a blazing meteor only to fall in the end like a burnt-out rocket. While the lamps of the Enlightenment illumined the royal courts and later the people's courts in France, Cossack swords were carving out the growing might of Russia. The eighteenth century was, like the ninth century (the time of Charlemagne), a century eminently *European* and not merely a period in which isolated nationalities prevailed. The French monarchy tumbled, with the walls of the Bastille, in a blood bath in which a number of physicians played a part, among them Marat, the rabid revolutionary—"physician of the incurable" and director of *L'Ami du Peuple,* the newspaper of the Revolution—and Dr. Guillotin, who bequeathed to posterity the huge bloody scalpel of "mercy"—the *louisette* or guillotine—that he invented with his colleague Dr. Louis.

The eighteenth century was bathed in the light shed by the new ideas of the Enlightenment—the triumph of reason; philosophical optimism; the quest for complete happiness; the scientic spirit; philanthropy; satiric writing—formulated by the ruling classes and the courtiers in power. This ideology, herald of the French Revolution and Liberalism, slowly emerged during the critical years of the cen-

From *MD*, the Medical Newsmagazine, 5:11, April, 1961.

tury, from 1721, when Montesquieu published his *Lettres Persanes,* to 1780, when, after thirty years of labor, the *Encyclopédie* was completed. It is impossible to appreciate the spirit of medicine in the Enlightenment without at least a glance into the depths of this French encyclopedia, where is reflected the image of the ideas that piloted its preparation.

Revolutionary in this Encyclopedia was the alphabetic classification for the first time in a *printed* work of what eighteenth-century man knew. Until then all knowledge had been entrusted to memory, with the consequent chaos. A dictionary of scientific and technological subjects, between whose lines, however, flitted a political purpose, the *Encyclopédie* took its philosophical inspiration from Cartesianism, the empiricism of the physician-philosopher Locke, Newton's ideas on physics, Voltaire's rationalistic belief in knowledge, and Rousseau's enthusiasm for the sovereignty of the people. But its principal inspirational strength—which to a certain degree gives us the key to the philosophy of medical learning in this century—lay in Diderot's words: *"Hâtons-nous de rendre notre philosophie populaire"* ("Let us hasten to bring our philosophy to the people.")

Because of this spirit, the true Encyclopedist was not a genuine investigator, since he thought he already knew practically everything, and his concern was rather to spread swiftly his knowledge among the people. The real creators of the science of the Enlightenment were not the active Encyclopedists but a minority of fertile minds who were concerned more with ferreting out the secrets of nature than with compiling dictionaries of their knowledge. But the *Encyclopédie* exerted a transcendental influence. As the enlightened despotism of the courts was replaced by the historic rise of a cultured *bourgeoisie* and popular sovereignty, knowledge became democratized. Greater concern with public health caused a fall in mortality and a rise in population, and the cultural level also rose, thanks to two new foci for debate, polemics, and the exchange of ideas— namely, scientific meetings in the academies and popular gatherings in the cafés.

A typical example of the influence of the *Encyclopédie* on medicine was the advance of surgery, since the *Encyclopédie's* accent on the manual and mechanical arts enhanced the social status of the surgeon. Another example was the growth of scientific interest in botany, cultivated by many physicians, which paralleled Rousseau's call for man to return to nature, and the renaming, during the French Revolution, of the months of the year with natural names such as might have come out of one of Vergil's *Eclogues.*

Enlightenment art reached an early peak in that perfumed, garden-girt marble coffer that housed the court at Versailles, symbol of autocratic power. There, Madame de Pompadour, as expert on the royal couch as she was at the diplomatic table, sponsored an art that, through the brilliant brush of Boucher, glorified the feminine domination of the period. Ceramics, hangings, tapestries, and furniture already showed that the violence of Baroque art was being tamed, leaving but a mere caged beast behind the golden bars of the Rococo.

Like her predecessor, Madame du Barry stimulated the Arcadian and voluptuous art of Fragonard, who, with Watteau and his *fêtes champêtres,* left us a naïve, fairytale vision of the courtly world of the period, a sensual world beneath whose silks and satins throbbed the feline cruelty of professional seducers, exemplified in the novel by Pierre Choderlos de Laclos, *Les Liaisons dangereuses,* which enacted in literature the same erotic marathon that Casanova, in the same century, ran in real life. The whole of this art finally succumbed to the impact of Diderot's rhapsodies on feeling and Rousseau's return to nature, and was replaced by the naturalistic art of Chardin and the stoic and virtuous classic art of David, the art dictator of France, who restored the dignity of the man-in-the-street and social morality, becoming the artistic herald of the French Revolution.

This Europe, where fresh ideas were fermenting like new wine, exported its Encyclopedist tenets to North America, where the champion of the new ideology was the worthy and talented printer, Benjamin Franklin. The Encyclopedist school of thought was the great ideological trend behind the political forces that after the War of Independence gave birth to the United States.

Inspired by the concept of man as a rational animal endowed with the faculty to create and to attain, through intuition, reason, and experiment, a knowledge of the reality of nature, great systems of medical philosophy and speculative doctrines sprang up. Within this framework the physician developed his new concept of disease.

The faith of d'Alembert and Voltaire in reason, the faith of Rousseau and Diderot in feeling and sensation, and the faith of Buffon in the observation of nature, inspired fresh medical achievements. While in politics the two great characteristics of the age were enlightened despotism as a means of government for a nation and balance of power as a measure of international coexistence in Europe, in medicine, along with the philosophical "despotism" of a few great isolated physicians, there prevailed a conceptual balance between the various systems and doctrines of the age, which encouraged stabilization in medical thought. In this eighteenth-century world, the sky glittered with both dazzling stars and mere glowworms.

The natural sciences—biology with Linnaeus, astronomy with Laplace—advanced under the impulsion of the new ideas. Physics adopted the rational mechanics of Euler and Watt. A new wondrous physical force called electricity, which had one day convulsed the frogs' legs that Galvani was preparing for his wife Lucia, revolutionized the world as well as the literature and poetry of the age. Poets and writers spoke of "electrifying" ideas, of the "spark" and "current" of love. A group of talented chemists, including Priestley and Scheele, the discoverers of oxygen, and Lavoisier (Lavoisier, who discovered the similarity between combustion and hematosis yet whose head rolled at the foot of the guillotine because, as they said, "The Revolution has no need for savants!") initiated modern chemistry.

One of the most famous medical systems then current was *animism,* created by two friends who later became irreconcilable enemies: the brilliant, magnetic Friedrich Hoffmann, who revived the Methodism of Themison, distinguished himself in medical chemistry, and held that the force of the vital principle, or ether, was transmitted through the nerves to the organic "fibers," any disturbance in which caused "atony" or "hypertonia"; and the surly, taciturn George Stahl, an adherent of expectant therapy, whose animism, a Christian version of the Hippocratic system, made him the herald of vitalism.

The second system, *vitalism,* which maintained that life was a property of living matter, reached its peak with Théophile de Bordeu, pioneer in endocrinology, Barthez, and Philippe Pinel (who perhaps should be acclaimed more as a classifier of diseases than as a psychiatrist), and was resurrected later by Bichat and Laënnec. Its exponent in Scotland was William Cullen, whose "neuropathology" claimed that the nervous "tone" of the solid parts was the supreme property of life, disease being caused by changes of this into "spasm" or "atony." He formulated the concept of lesion of sensitivity and movement without inflammation of the organs (equivalent to our current concept of neurosis). This system was opposed by the Scotsman, John Brown, a roistering cleric, who held that life depended upon excitability, which mobilized organic energy, and disease was caused by excessive or deficient—sthenias and asthenias—excitability and should be treated by the drastic *contraria contrariis.* It has been said that the Brunonian system destroyed more lives than the French Revolution itself. The National Convention of the Revolution approved this Brunonian system, which was to be modified in Germany by Reid and by Goethe's physician, Hufeland.

Above all these speculative systems towered the great figure of Hermann Boerhaave, the "Batavian Hippocrates," who in a twelve-bed hospital taught medicine to half the physicians of Europe. Boerhaave originated bedside instruction and the comparative study of clinical case histories, diagnosis, and autopsy. He was so beloved by his fellow countrymen that on one occasion, when he recovered from a severe attack of gout, bells were rung and the whole city of Leiden was lit up with torches.

The utilitarian "mechanical" spirit of the age spurred progress in comparative, topographical, and surgical anatomy, which advanced from Fallopius' "texture" to Bichat's "tissue." Outstanding was the *anatomia animata* of Morgagni, who, in his five-volume magnum opus, published in his eighties and containing seventy letters to a young friend (medical knowledge in those days was diffused by letters in default of periodicals), left a veritable gallery of the dead, a collection of autopsies of princesses, prostitutes, bishops, and bandits. Morgagni showed that every disease had its seat in *a particular organ,* and his dynamic pathology contrasted sharply with the still prevalent static anatomy. Other leading lights in this field were the Monros, Gimbernat, Scarpa, and Winslow.

Physiology advanced with the Swiss titan Albrecht von Haller, poet and polyglot, who left 2000 articles, 14,000 letters (despite his Catholicism, he corresponded with atheists like Voltaire and libertines like Casanova), and a mountain of papers on medicine, religion, philosophy, and botany. He held that irritability was a property of the muscles; sensibility, a quality of the nerves; and life, a specific property of living matter.

Other shining lights in physiology were the Abbé Lazzaro Spallanzani, who, with cloth bags and perforated tubes filled with food that he made his patients swallow, proved that digestion was not simply putrefaction; and the Reverend Stephen Hales, who studied arterial pressure by introducing glass tubes into the arteries of horses. Embryology—physiology in time—advanced when its modern founder, Kaspar Friedrich Wolff, demonstrated that the organs are not preformed but *progressively* differentiated, which earned him scientific ostracism and led him to voluntary exile in Russia under the generous protection of Catherine the Great.

The heritage of Leiden passed to the Old Vienna school, founded by Gerard van Swieten and continued by Anton de Haen, to the Edinburgh and English schools. In music-loving Vienna, Leopold Auenbrugger, musician and physician, copying his father, a vintner whom he saw tap his wine casks to gauge their contents, tapped his patients' chest to listen to their sounds. This discovery, unrecognized in Auenbrugger's lifetime, was reintroduced and championed in France by Napoleon's physician, Corvisart, who—despite his rejection by the Necker Hospital for refusing to wear the wig *de rigueur*—eventually became director of La Charité. Auenbrugger's discovery, a "musicalization" of the sounds of human diseases, reflected the sensualism of some of the Encyclopedists and the musical atmosphere of Vienna.

Specialties made progress, particularly pediatrics, spurred by the interest in children aroused by the writings of Rousseau and Pestalozzi. Public health advanced with Johann Peter Frank, advisor to emperors, whose idea of a "health police" to protect the people's health (it even supervised the closing time of dance halls) made him the father of modern social hygiene. In psychiatry, Pinel freed mental patients at the Salpêtrière from their fetters, championed the rights of the mentally ill at the National Assembly, and made diagnosis an "exact" science based on a Linnaean type of classification of diseases.

The leading lights in England were Mead, Huxham, Pitcairn, and various other nosographers, while Scotland shone with the Monros, Bell, the Hunter brothers (world leaders in surgery), and Cullen. Heberden during this period wrote his classic account of angina pectoris, and Withering rifled an old wives' rustic folklore for the secret of the foxglove (digitalis) in treating dropsy.

Therapy was traditional, with a fashion for clysters administered beneath the skirt to the beautiful court favorites in the royal boxes during plays and concerts. Phlebotomy degenerated into blood-sucking vampirism, while surgery progressed with the separation of surgeons from barbers.

While the heavens of the Enlightenment Age glittered with the dazzling stars of medicine, on earth glowworms too gleamed. The Viennese Franz Anton Mesmer, inventor of mesmerism, clad in a purple robe and surrounded by foppish assistants (soon to be beheaded in the Revolution), mobilized the "magnetic fluid of the universe" onto his hysterical female clients with a magic wand and to the accompaniment of sweet music. The German Samuel Hahnemann held that diseases were of "natural classes" and treated them with drugs, in infinitesimally small doses, that caused mild forms of similar diseases, thus inventing homeopathy. Quacks and charlatans flourished, such as the fabulous Venetian Giovanni Jacopo Casanova, Cagliostro, the Comte de St. Germain, and the Scotsman James Graham, whose Temple of Health featured an electrified "celestial bed" for the connubial use of love-bitten couples.

The atrocious epidemics that scourged Europe—smallpox alone killed sixty million people—compelled fashionable ladies to insert in their powdered wigs sponges soaked in honey and vinegar to attract and confine lice. And then, on a memorable day for medicine, a country doctor, Edward Jenner, whose blue topcoat and silver spurs were well known to the local villagers, inoculated pus from a dairymaid with cowpox into a small boy, who later successfully withstood a smallpox inoculation. Thus Jenner's merciful vaccination replaced variolization.

The discovery of vaccination led to a glorious page in the history of medicine, when the Spaniard Francisco Xavier de Balmis journeyed around the world with twenty-two children, in whose arms he kept the vaccine alive by passing it from one to the other, and vaccinated hundreds of thousands of people around the globe. Balmis was assisted in South America by his heroic colleague and martyr to medicine, Francisco Salvany, who lost a hand and an eye and finally died of tuberculosis in Bolivia, a victim to this epic campaign. Facing terrible dangers, the antagonism of his fellow men, and a hostile nature, Balmis took the children carrying the vaccine to the Caribbean, Mexico, the Philippines, Canton, and Macao, thus making the first and only tour around the world accomplished by a physician on a heroic errand of mercy.

In the United States, life in the colonies was settling down. Physicians traveled to England and Holland to study. Great medical figures (Cadwalader, Shippen, Morgan, Benjamin Rush) shone brilliantly at the same time that Benjamin Franklin promoted the ideas of the French Encyclopedists, which, a quarter of a century after Rousseau had expounded them in his *Social Contract,* were finally incorporated into the United States Constitution. Then began the memorable westward trek across the vast, green prairies, where the Sioux and the buffalo reigned, opening up new horizons to American medicine, then still struggling with the problems imposed by its historical youth.

But even before the eighteenth century came to a close, the bells of history were already tolling the knell of Enlightenment Encyclopedism in Europe. The romantic seed scattered by Rousseau was germinating, while in another direction naturalism was flowering with renewed impetus. By the end of that century, Germany was already on the road to romanticism, whose philosophical idealism was to guide the first half of the nineteenth century, just as the second half was to be dominated by the positivism and naturalism of France and England. But in the first hour of the new dawn, there still lingered the light shed by the ideas of the sun-men of the Age of Enlightenment, a strong brilliant light that made the light of the glow-worms fade.

TAPESTRY WITH FIGURES
Medicine in the Nineteenth Century

*t*he beginning of the nineteenth century centered on the military exploits of Napoleon, until his dreams of world conquest were shattered on the snow-whipped steppes of Russia and on the sun-baked plains of Spain by those valiant Spanish *guerrilleros* whose heroism was immortalized by Goya. In his ill-fated Russian campaign, typhus and typhoid decimated Napoleon's forces, and there, probably, the curative power of artificial hibernation was for the first time envisaged, when it was observed that many of the soldiers half frozen by the glacial cold of the steppes survived their wounds.

After the defeat of the Napoleonic eagle, whose wings for a decade had arrogantly battered the skies of Europe, the Old World, exhausted by so much warfare, lapsed into a period of political apathy. With the gradual rebirth of imperialism, Napoleon III made of Paris a city of enchantment and wonder, of broad vistas embellished with leaf-shaded avenues and a tapestry of green parks and white sculptures under blue sky.

To the east, Nicholas I and his Russians gazed enviously toward Constantinople, that gorgeous gem of gold-domed mosques that for centuries had been coveted by many invaders.

When the long cherished French dream of setting up a universal empire was finally shattered, the nations of Europe strove to consolidate a system of equal and opposite forces in equilibrium, the so-called balance of power developed by Metternich and other diplo-

From *MD*, the MEDICAL NEWSMAGAZINE, 5:13, July, 1961.

mats at the Congress of Vienna. This "dancing congress" was attended by a great array of monarchs and princes from all Europe. Since then no other single assembly has commanded so many heads of states, except perhaps the great 1960 session of the United Nations in New York, at which there was no dancing but there were far more verbal fireworks.

As one of the diplomats of the time remarked, the monarchs who congregated in Vienna, no longer troubled by Napoleon, watched one another grow fatter and fatter. This balance of power lasted, with some modifications, until the outbreak of the first world war.

During the course of the nineteenth century, Great Britain and France aided Turkey against Russia, Italy was consolidated into a single kingdom, the Franco-Prussian war ended in the defeat of France, and Germany became a unified empire. The last quarter of the century was a period of relative calm and stability in Europe. On the American continent, the victorious march of the Latin American countries toward independence paralleled the technological progress of the United States after the horrors of the Civil War, and the march to its destiny as a mighty democratic nation.

Political influence in Napoleonic France stimulated a sober realism that crystallized into positivism and encyclopedism. In contrast, Germany sought refuge in idealism and gave birth to the antiencyclopedist idealist Natural Philosophy, the daughter of romanticism, whose standard-bearer, after Fichte and Hegel, was Schelling, a philosopher and honorary physician whose Brunonian therapy killed his own ailing daughter. Nature and mind were essentially identical in this philosophy, nature being reason in a dormant state, one degree before intelligence. Natural Philosophy and Kant's enormous influence aroused interest in pathology and anthropology. Natural Philosophy postulated three basic energies in nature: electric, magnetic, and chemical, and three parallel energies in the body: irritability, sensibility, and reproducibility.

While in Germany the gala celebrated on January 1, 1800, at the court of Weimar (where the incomparable Goethe played the part of Olympian Jupiter in the presence of many courtiers, including Schiller) symbolized the rebirth of a classico-romantic art and the birth of the nineteenth century, a mounting wave of technological progress was sweeping the world. Watt's steam engine, Fulton's steamboat, Stephenson's locomotive, Karl Benz' internal combustion automobile engine, Bell's telephone, and Marconi's wireless—these were some of the inventions that determined the climate in which modern medicine was to flourish.

This was the century when history, by paradoxical contrast, became national in the various countries and universal in its expansion throughout the world. This universalization was fostered by the opening of the Panama and Suez canals, the westernization of Japanese medicine, the first appearance of the modern nurse in the person of Florence Nightingale, the "Lady of the Lamp," and the creation of the International Red Cross by Jean Henry Dunant. At that time there began simultaneously the struggles of peoples for the sovereignty of their rights and for constitutional regimes, labor movements, and democratic ideas. Constitutional monarchies and the balance of power replaced the old absolutisms, and a renewed religionism took its stand against the positive philosophy of Auguste Comte in France, although he demanded merely the scientific analysis of data obtained through the senses. In turn, John Stuart Mill's logic, Herbert Spencer's social evolution, and Darwinism, in England, opened new paths of historic adventure.

Nineteenth-century art began under the dictatorial tutelage of David, the paramount painter during the French Revolution, to whose brush we owe the cruel portrait of Marie Antoinette on her way to the guillotine, and the picture of Marat, the physician, drained of blood by the knife of Charlotte Corday as he sat in the medicinal bath he took for his eczema. It was David who guided the neoclassicism of the Napoleonic empire, embodied in the Greek purity of the Madeleine, in the Roman arrogance of the Arc de Triomphe, and in the classic charm of his own portrait of Madame Récamier.

Cold neoclassicism, however, could hardly satisfy the spiritual needs of a Europe convalescing from bloody crises. This dissatisfaction inspired the artistic romanticism of Gros, Girodet, Géricault, and Delacroix, and the prose of Chateaubriand. Meanwhile Ingres' classicism was battling the romanticism of Delacroix and his "drunken brush," while the great English painters—Constable with his landscapes, Reynolds with his portraits, Blake with his visions, Turner with his nature studies—and the Pre-Raphaelites were making art history on the other side of the Channel.

The second half of the nineteenth century witnessed the advent of the painters of light, color, and gaiety, all of whom, with the exception of Holland's van Gogh, were French. The break with the academic tradition came in 1863 when the painters who had been rejected by the official Salon exhibited their work in the *Salon des Rejetés*. The public came to laugh at Manet's *Le déjeuner sur l'herbe* (today a priceless masterpiece) and were horrified by his nude *Olympia*. Alongside Courbet's realism flourished the cruel antimedical satires of Daumier, the golden poetry of Renoir, the sheer magic—air, light, and water—of Monet, the pure impressionism of Pissarro, the pointillism of Seurat, the geometry of Cézanne, the decorative displays of Gauguin, the violet world of van Gogh, the enchanted ballets of Degas, and the strange sorcery, almost Japanese in its expressive economy of line and color, of Toulouse-Lautrec. In this period medicine took a definitive step forward.

People were at that time experiencing the *maladie du siècle,* a nostalgic yearning for the Middle Ages. The Napoleonic period in the history of romanticism was followed by the reactionary and the progressive-liberal periods. People doted on "romantic" diseases, such as chlorosis, tuberculosis, fever, and "mortal pallor," but venereal diseases were considered a stigma. The towns were like pigsties and the mortality from infection was enormous. Medical practice was empirical, rational, or mystico-suggestive. But in the end, the romantic speculations of Natural Philosophy were replaced by the mensurative and practical examination of nature.

Modern histology and topographical anatomy were founded in Paris by Xavier Bichat, who in a single winter dissected 600 cadavers. Bichat localized disease in a *specific* organ and, in accordance with his concept *"La vie est l'ensemble des fonctions qui résistent à la mort,"* regarded life as a complex of functions resisting death. Bichat's "membranes," or tissues, became the basic unit of the living creature.

Progress with the microscope led to the development of the cell theory, thanks to Schleiden and Schwann, whose work was completed by Henle and Remak. At the same time, physiology made progress with the support of Bichat's vitalism and the work of Magendie and Johannes Müller. Müller, the great encyclopedist of sensory physiology, inspired by Goethe (who gave medicine his theory of light and colors), studied the nervous system, the physiology of secretions, and embryology, using the microscope for that purpose, as Bichat had used his eyes to create macroscopic anatomy.

In Vienna, the new school of medicine dug roots into the foundations provided by Rokitansky's 100,000 autopsies and his clinical case histories, supported by Skoda, the founder of modern physical diagnosis, by von Hebra, and by Schönlein, a man prodigal in action but sparse with words, who used hardly twenty lines to report his discovery of the fungal agent in tinea favosa. Another member of the Vienna School was the great Billroth, as expert at resecting an intestine as he was at playing the violin.

Pediatrics flourished, warmed by the love for children kindled through Dickens' sentimental novels; so did psychiatry. Surgery advanced with the work done by the surgeons of the Napoleonic armies, Percy and Larrey (the latter created the "flying ambulances" and took part in the holocaust of Waterloo), and in the United States with the work of Philip Syng Physick, James Marion Sims, architect of the vagina, and Ephraim McDowell. Surgery became more an intellectual than a manual task, but the pleuroperitoneal cavities remained sanctuaries uninvaded by the scalpel.

A notable achievement in the United States was the discovery of anesthesia, in whose romantic history the names of Crawford Williamson Long and the dentist Horace Wells, who used ether and nitrous oxide, still figure controversially. Surgical anesthesia began in Boston when the dentist William Thomas Morton, trained by Horace Wells and Charles Thomas Jackson, anesthetized a patient who was operated on by John Collins Warren, Jr.; chloroform fumes were used in surgery in Edinburgh by James Young Simpson.

Clinical medicine made headway with the discovery of the stethoscope by a French physician, the monarchist Catholic pupil of Corvisart, René Théophile Hyacinthe Laënnec. At the Necker hospital in Paris, finding it difficult to auscultate with the naked ear a plump young woman, and remembering some children on the street making noises at one end of a hollow tree while their playmates listened at the other end, Laënnec rolled a sheet of paper into a tube and applied it to his patient's chest. Thus the stethoscope was born, and pathology, which hitherto had been visual only, became auditory. The physician could now listen to the noises of disease, the language of pathology that nobody had heard before.

France in that period produced an abundance of clinicians, outstanding among whom were Broussais, who inspired an era of "vampirism" in therapy, increasing France's annual consumption of leeches to more than 41 million; Louis, a master of medical statistics; and Corvisart, the wizard of cardiology. In England there flourished Graves, Stokes, Corrigan, Bright, Addison, and Hodgkin. Germany also had its share of outstanding men. Specialization forged ahead, but therapy, based on vegetable substances, electrotherapy, and hydrotherapy, was either empirical or nihilistic.

In the latter half of the century, medicine ceased to be European and became national, positivist, and vernacular, perhaps because the nineteenth century was not a European century like the eighteenth, but particularist and nationalist as the seventeenth had been. Progress in diagnosis reflected man's curiosity about himself and the universe, and medical progress began to be made in the hospital instead of in the library.

In his turn, the physician, who had been an artisan in ancient Greece, a priest in the Middle Ages, and a "doctor" since the Renaissance, now became a hospital physician and public health servant, with the increasing development of health welfare services.

Anesthetics made more delicate surgery possible. Other developments were the cell concept of disease; the study of metabolism, of the role of the nervous system as an organic regulator, and of the unity between psyche and soma; the concept of the microbial origin of infections; immunization, and new instruments. The human body was studied in space (morphology and anthropology) and in time (genetics and embryology).

Hippocrates' humoral pathology was placed on the intimate level of the cell by the German Rudolf Virchow, who, with his cell concept of disease, displaced the concept that disease was seated in an organ, as asserted by Morgagni, or in a tissue, as Bichat maintained. Virchow also replaced the ancient "absolutist empire" of the organic humors with his "cellular democracy" or "republic of the cells," in which the cells were social classes, the organs and systems were their territory, and disease was a civil war between germs and the police of the cell state, the leukocytes. Then was born a new science with the work of the romantic revolutionary Jacob Henle, the Vesalius of histology and father of modern embryology.

Claude Bernard, born in the sun-radiant vineyards of the valley of the Rhône, was more than a physiologist—he was physiology itself. A failure as a playwright, in his married life, in his candidature for professorship, and in his early experiments, he succeeded as an experimenter and eventually became a teacher at the Collège de France and at the Sorbonne. He taught the medical world to "think physiologically," discovered the glycogenic function of the liver, and established the concepts of the *milieu intérieur,* functional correlation, and the principles of physiological experimentation: observation, hypothesis, experiment. Claude Bernard consolidated the philosophical positivism of his time, inspired Émile Zola's literary realism with his concepts, and affirmed his credo with the words *"L'Art c'est moi, la Science c'est nous."*

Other landmarks of progress in this period were the discovery of enzymes, clinical thermometry, thermodynamics, physiological recording apparatus, and the growth of public health, dramatized by Max von Pettenkofer's gesture in quaffing a culture of cholera bacillus. The laws of heredity were evolved by the Augustinian friar Gregor Mendel while counting his rosary of peas, and Wilhelm Roentgen discovered x-rays.

Britain ousted France from clinical leadership. But bacteriology originated with the remarkable work of a fine and noble French chemist: Louis Pasteur, investigator of wine diseases and ferments, microbe-hunter and maker of vaccines, who identified microbes with the ancient (and still mysterious) *contagium animatum,* and, seventy years before Fleming, studied the effect of *Penicillium* on ferments. Linked with him are the names of Koch, who established the microbial specificity of infections and isolated the tuberculosis germ; Von Behring, master of toxins and antitoxins; Klebs and Löffler, fishers of bacilli; Jaime Ferrán and his vaccines. The wave of discoveries that started the new biological therapy, with its serums, vaccines, antibodies, and phagocytes, the forerunner of the bacteriostatic and bactericidal drugs, was symbolized in the fight against tropical diseases and in the achievement of the Cuban Carlos Finlay, whose discovery of the transmissibility of yellow fever by mosquitoes made possible, with the support of Walter Reed, its elimination in Cuba and the opening of the Panama Canal.

The arsenal of therapeutics was enriched by new drugs, particularly by chemotherapeutic agents, introduced in his Frankfurt institute by Paul Ehrlich, who proceeded from his chromotherapy, or therapy through colors, to his anti-treponema arsenical "magic bullets," the forerunners of which were Paracelsus' non-Galenic heavy metals, just as Galenic phytotherapy was the forerunner of antibiotics.

Medicine became more physiopathological and physiochemical in its substrate, and clinical case histories became more dynamic and historico-biographical.

Outstanding in neurology—which was started as a specialty by Duchenne in Paris—were Charcot, the neurosurgeon, Paul Broca, and Pierre Marie, and in England John Hughlings Jackson, who explored the levels of the nervous system. Psychiatry took a step forward when Philippe Pinel liberated the mental patient from his chains and codified 2700 diseases in an endeavor to make medicine a natural science. Noteworthy was the psychiatric nosology of Emil Kraepelin, who reduced the chaos of mental syndromes to a cosmos of classifications.

Mental diseases remained dramatically *visual* until Charcot, but were made auditory by the Viennese psychiatrist Sigmund Freud, who "listened to" neuroses instead of looking at them. Freud, a poet in medicine, created a new medical anthropology with his therapeutic evaluation of the human instincts and his original concepts of the unconscious, and by integrating the patient's disease into his life history and using dialogue with the patient as a curative instrument.

The greatest advance in surgery of this century was antisepsis—*physical* disinfection of instruments and wounds with carbolic acid—initiated by the Scotsman Joseph Lister, the Lincoln of surgery, who liberated humanity from the chains of infection. Antisepsis later became asepsis—*chemical* and *preventive* disinfection of the air and wounds—which made surgery more physiological and less heroic.

Maternal mortality from puerperal infection was drastically reduced by Ignaz Philipp Semmelweis in Austria, who intuitively instructed his colleagues and students to disinfect their hands with a calcium chloride solution, and by the impassioned campaign of the

Bostonian Oliver Wendell Holmes, who independently discovered the infectious origin of puerperal fever. Antisepsis and anesthesia overcame the two age-old enemies of surgery—infection and pain.

In America there proceeded the westward expansion across the prairies, traversed successively by pioneers and trappers, traders, preachers, and physicians, with a transition from the empirical apprenticeship of physicians to schools of medicine, the regulation of instruction, and the founding of the great medical associations and medical magazines.

There arose the memorable figures of the statesman and pioneer psychiatrist Benjamin Rush, one of the signers of the Declaration of Independence; Ephraim McDowell, who performed the first resection of an ovarian cyst; the country surgeon Daniel Drake, who compiled a masterly medical geography; William Beaumont, who studied gastric function in vivo in a halfbreed's stomach laid open by gunshot; Guthrie who discovered chloroform or "sweet whisky"; Sims who performed the first vesicovaginal fistula operation; Oliver Wendell Holmes, physician and poet; Silas Weir Mitchell, neurologist and novelist; John Shaw Billings, the superb medical bibliographer and cofounder of the Surgeon General's Library; and Canada's Sir William Osler, professor at the universities of McGill in Montreal, Pennsylvania, Johns Hopkins, and Oxford, the modern ideal of the humanist-physician, good, kind, and courageous, whose wise and gentle voice still inspires today's physicians.

THE VAST THRESHOLD
Medicine in the Twentieth Century

*t*he twentieth century dawned on such trivialities as the still heated debate among Parisians as to whether the Eiffel Tower enhanced or impaired the beauty of Paris. Parisian wits retorted that the best view of Paris was from the Eiffel Tower, since that was the only place in the city from which one could *not* see the Eiffel Tower! But behind this mask of frivolity, the new century already loomed as a vast threshold to the most important era in the history of mankind.

It is impossible for twentieth-century man to write the history of this century, since he is actually living it. The history of contemporary medicine is not to be found in books; it is being made now, in magazine and newspaper articles, in the daily bustle of hospitals, in current clinical case histories, in medical schools and public health centers, in the world-wide endeavors of the great international medical organizations; it is being made, above all, by general practitioners, that glorious infantry of medicine, and by investigators, clinicians, teachers, and administrators, who with their dedicated and often anonymous toil are writing today the history of the medicine of tomorrow.

In this world of teamwork, trends and ideas appear more important than men, even though without the latter the former could not exist. The medical panorama of today is a faceless one. Only now and then a face, a name, leaps out from the crowd of dedicated men. Here therefore only ideas and discoveries will be mentioned. The few names

From *MD,* the MEDICAL NEWSMAGAZINE, 5:11, October, 1961.

evoked by them are very well known, and the reader may enjoy filling them in himself.

What I am going to show here will be like a richly embroidered Chinese robe turned inside out. The resplendent dragons on the outside appear then as a golden labyrinth of threads glittering against the black silk, threads that are the key to the sumptuous design on the other side.

At the beginning of the century, balance of power seemed to be the answer to all international problems. In art, Pablo Picasso's *Les Demoiselles d'Avignon* initiated cubism, which together with the rest of modern art—neoimpressionism, dadaism, futurism, surrealism, abstract art—was to disintegrate the human body, just as physics was to disintegrate the atomic universe.

Soon afterward the world plunged into the scarlet nightmare of the First World War. Then came the Russian Revolution, followed, after the failure of the League of Nations, by that great crusade for freedom, the Spanish Civil War, and then the Second World War and the Korean and other local conflicts. Our time also includes the atomic age, which began in 1945, and the aerocosmic age, which began in 1957 with the Sputnik, man's first attempt to conquer outer space.

The twentieth century has witnessed such spectacular inventions and discoveries as the airplane, radio, the splitting of the atom, radar, television, and space satellites. The natural sciences advanced with Planck's quantum theory, which revolutionized concepts of matter and energy, just as Einstein's theory of relativity revolutionized concepts of space and time, both theories combining to form a finite, curved, four-dimensional universe and a space-time continuum.

Physics, with its electron microscope and its new techniques for visualizing and measuring substances hitherto invisible and immeasurable, has technicalized medical research. New medical instruments and methods include electrophoresis and microspectrophotometry, pyelography, intracardiac catheterization, ventriculography, and tomography. Chemistry has become integrated with physics. Biology has been investigating the link, represented by viruses and genes, between the inorganic and the living. Anatomy, guided by the concept that form is function, has developed new methods of vascular injection, anatomical cinematography, and sectioning frozen human tissues. Physiology has become biochemical, studying hormonal and neurovegetative correlations, enzymes, and the adrenal-pituitary-hypothalamic axis. Anthropology has progressed with the study of anthropoid fossils and of blood groups and the Rh factor in the different human races. Psychology has advanced with the systems of Freud, Adler, and Jung and the new schools of physiodynamic psychiatry, psycho-

176

biology, psychosomatic medicine, medical anthropology, and psycho-analysis.

Medicine, which today is made in laboratories, just as in the nine-teenth century it was made in hospitals and in the Middle Ages in libraries, has become more and more a technology.

Clinical practice also has changed. The family doctor is being replaced by the physician-counselor and the physician-statesman. The physician now is not only the man who heals; he is also the man who plans, organizes, and promotes health in public health centers. This means that medicine is increasingly becoming a *social* science that uses the methods of a natural science.

In scientific research, the lucky accident of olden times is being supplanted by meticulous planning and design. The lone investigator of yesterday, like Jenner, is now being replaced by organized research teams, often in huge centers like the Rockefeller Institute, the Mayo Clinic, Johns Hopkins University, the Pasteur Institute, and the Oswaldo Cruz Institute.

Medical education, which became more *auditory* and *verbal* when dialogue with the patient (the method used by the Assyrian priests and Hippocrates) as a tool for diagnosis and cure was revived, has also become more *visual,* with the use of the cinema and television and of new techniques that have laid bare the hitherto inaccessible recesses of the human body.

Contemporary medicine is more technical in instruments and meth-ods but more human in its approach, more social and preventive, more specialized in its practice, more encyclopedic in its horizon. The principal task of medicine today is to fight diseases arising not, as of yore, from without (traumas, toxicoses, infections), but from within (psychoses, degenerative diseases, cancer, hypertension). In this re-spect, Karl Jaspers, the philosopher-psychiatrist, established a philo-sophical distinction between the three main groups of diseases by labeling them somatoses (organic), bioses (functional), and neuroses (psychogenic). Nonetheless, of the more than two thousand known human diseases we know the etiology of only about half the *biological* diseases common to man and mammal, while we know almost noth-ing of the etiology of the *biographical* diseases strictly inherent in human life.

Spectacular changes have occurred in the great branches of medi-cine. Remarkable advances have taken place in biochemistry and genetics, possibly the key to the still unrevealed secret of cancer, though the probability of recovery from some of its forms is now one in three, due to the multiple techniques used in its treatment.

Surgery, inspired by the new principle that form *is* function, is being integrated with medicine as it becomes more physiological and conservative. Asepsis and antibiotics have freed surgery from the shackles of infection, making it less heroic. Instead of a mad race between the clock on the wall of the operating theatre and the surgeon, bending with his scalpel over his patient like an archangel with his shining sword, surgery is now an adaptation to the patient's "biological clock." Today the surgeon works as much with his brain as with his fingers. Moreover, pain has been eliminated by the new anesthetics and analgesics, a more stable metabolism can now be maintained, early ambulation is practiced, and blood and organ banks are in use.

Artificial hibernation, a revolutionary method (foreshadowed when those soldiers who were half-frozen in Napoleon's Grande Armée in Russia survived their wounds) introduced in 1905 and later revived by an inspired French investigator to control the often excessive organic reactions to disease, sends—as he himself said—the adrenal-pituitary "couple" off on a "chemical vacation" by means of a "lytic cocktail" that puts the body in a state of suspended animation, thus preventing the organic defenses from becoming excited to an extent that might be mortal in its violence.

Besides the steel scalpel, the invisible ultrasound scalpel and the chemical scalpel of the enzymes are now used in surgery. The surgeon's ideal is to readapt his patient to society as quickly as possible. With this in mind, the physician and the surgeon, divorced from each other during the Middle Ages, have come together once more.

Enriched with biologicals, vaccines, and sera at the end of the nineteenth century, therapeutics in the present age (in which, perhaps because of atomic threats, the urge to find speedy and effective cures for all its ills is greater than ever before) relies on the magic alphabet of the "vital amines," or vitamins, and on new nutrition principles.

The flourishing field of immunobiology also relies on vaccines, such as the new antipoliomyelitis vaccine, to conquer many dreaded infections. The treatment of infections down the ages has changed from the archaic concept of exorcising demons to fighting miasmas by physical means to attacking germs, at first with the magic bullets of chemotherapy, later with "bacterial hypnotics" that produce microbial lethargy, like the sulfonamides, and finally with antibiotics. First came the golden magic of penicillin, accidentally discovered by a kindly Scottish investigator when a spore fell from the gray, smoky skies of London into a *Staphylococcus* culture in his laboratory; then streptomycin, discovered by a keen-minded Russian-American scientist in a lump of earth lodged in the throat of a chicken; and later the broad-spectrum antibiotics. The antimicrobial spectrum is now widening ceaselessly as new antibiotics are isolated or synthesized. A new approach in the battle against pathogenic germs is based on throwing metabolic "monkey wrenches" into the biological machinery of bacteria to disintegrate their biochemical structures. But perhaps the future lies in peaceful coexistence between man and bacteria.

The new therapies contrast sharply with the rather nihilistic therapies of the past century. This is illustrated in the humorous remarks of Oliver Wendell Holmes and William Osler, two of the greatest physicians to witness the transition from the nineteenth to the twentieth century. Wendell Holmes said, "If the whole *materia medica,* as now used, could be sunk to the bottom of the sea it would be all the better for mankind—and all the worse for the fishes." And Osler said, "The young physician starts off in life with twenty drugs for each disease, and the old physician ends up by having a single drug for each twenty diseases!"

In endocrinology new hormones have been isolated from the pituitary gland and numerous derivatives have been produced from adrenal cortisone. Revolutionary concepts—stress, for instance, an outstanding contribution by a Viennese-Canadian—have changed whole fields of medicine. Full of promise is the exploration of the role of the hypothalamus, the terra incognita of psychiatry, and of the adrenal-pituitary hypothalamus neuroendocrine axis, whose pathophysiology is a treasure chest full of fascinating surprises.

The symbolical search for mental peace in our age of anxiety—not unlike the search for the philosophers' stone in the forever simmering crucibles of the alchemists during the Middle Ages—has led to the development of the ataraxics (some of which can be traced back to the ancient folk medicine of India), which give the mind a chemical holiday, opening the door to mental peace. Hallucinogenic agents have also been introduced, creators of "pocket psychoses," which may some day prove that a simple organic mistake in the production of a hormone may be the determining factor of artistic genius in one man and of schizophrenia in another, depending on the quantitative magnitude of the error. It may yet be shown that many mental diseases are neither diseases nor mental, but alterations in the neuronal biochemistry sometimes unleashed and sometimes followed by an emotional and psychic change.

Other valuable conceptual contributions to modern psychiatry are the studies on the neuron and the "neuron jungle" by a Spaniard and on conditioned reflexes by a Russian; psychobiology by a Swiss-American; the integration of the nervous system by an Englishman; the neuroendocrine and physiodynamic mechanisms of psychosis by a team of young New York psychiatrists; shock- or seismo-therapies, introduced by a Viennese (insulin), a Hungarian (Metrazol), and an Italian (electroshock); psychosurgery, introduced by a Portuguese (leukotomy); and the biographical approach in psychoanalysis, conceived by a genius from Vienna and rounded off by two eminent followers, a German (inferiority complexes) and a Swiss (analytic deep psychology of the unconscious).

Important advances have been made also in classic specialties—for instance, the discovery by a Spanish oculist of the value of chymotrypsin in facilitating cataract removal—and new specialties are being born all the time. Of great and growing importance in present-day society, where heads turned silver by the years are more abundant than ever, are gerontology and geriatrics. The classic specialties have spread all over the world with the World Health Organization and the World Medical Association, creations of the modern political Aesculapius. Social welfare and industrial, forensic, geographical, and military medicine are flourishing on national and international scales.

Of quite recent date are atomic medicine which employs radioactivity to destroy necrosed tissues; travel medicine which studies the ecological changes of man in motion; and aerocosmic or space medicine which studies means of protecting man in interplanetary flights and is providing the key not only to the conquest of outer space but also to the physiological conquest of man's inner space.

Medical communication has followed pace with all this progress in medicine. Thousands of medical magazines, records, radio, films, television, and other means of communication are spreading medical knowledge on a vast scale.

Another outcome of present trends in medicine is the growth of a new humanism in medicine, characterized by the public's interest in medical problems and the physician's desire to know man better in all aspects. This desire is exemplified in the rising interest of physicians individually and of universities in the history of medicine, in the epic and romance of the physician of the past, as a means of fitting their present knowledge into the frame of history and acquiring a better perspective of the future.

We stand on the vast threshold of the medicine of the future, a medicine that will be dedicated—to quote the World Health Organization—to promoting health, preventing disease, healing and rehabilitating the patient, and lengthening life, just as of old it concentrated solely on healing disease. The present medical panorama is so vast that a historian, looking from the skyscraper height of his subject, can recognize but a few faces in the large crowd of men who, with their toil, ideas, and ideals, are shaping the medicine of today, cradle of the medicine of tomorrow.

If medieval medicine—"Gothic medicine" I would call it—soared vertically, even as the spires in Gothic cathedrals did, in search of God and the soul, and if Renaissance medicine spread horizontally to explore the nature of man, even as the navigators of the time explored the seas of the earth, contemporary "neo-Gothic" medicine combines the horizontal and spatial exploration of man's body with the vertical and historical exploration of his biological biography and his mind.

But medicine's greatest conquest in the future will not be that of cosmic outer space, nor even that of man's physical and mental inner space, but the reconquest of service and love for man as enjoined, more than 2000 years ago, by a venerable Greek physician in his oath of ethics and morals, an oath that still guides the physician of our space age, who is becoming ever more the best ambassador of good will among men and of health and peace on earth.

Thus, the Epic of Medicine will continue forever its search for new horizons to conquer, as the most noble expression of man's quasi-divine urge to be of service to man.

V. journeys/ ports/ peoples

THE FAMILY OF MAN

In a recent trip around the world, I had the opportunity of meeting, under the distant stars of remote skies, the family of man.

There is no better way of gaining a panoramic view of the family of man than a swift flight around the world, carried by the angels of the winds and the hands of the pilots. The earth and its inhabitants then become a whirling kaleidoscope of races and places, as diverse in appearance as they are alike in essence, as distant from one another in the horizontal dimension of geographical space as they are close to each other in the vertical dimension of historical time.

Perhaps nothing reveals the essential unity that exists in the family of man throughout the world as well as the dinner hour does, when men and women, joined by blood or spirit, gather to break bread and share salt under the same roof. This moment I have shared with diverse peoples of many nations.

I have dined with a Japanese family in Kamakura in the shade of the colossal *Daibutsu,* the ancient bronze statue of Buddha, its huge melancholy head wreathed in shimmering starlight. Squatting on *tatamis* around doll-size tables, I marveled at the swift ballet of my hosts' chopsticks, gracefully picking rice from small snow-white porcelain bowls or a green tendril from the miniature vegetable garden at the bottom of golden broth in red lacquered bowls. I watched their chopsticks selecting savory morsels of *unagi no kabayaki,* which is broiled eel bedded on rice, served in tiny black japanned boxes reminiscent of those used to hold water-color paints. But then, what is a

From *MD,* the MEDICAL NEWSMAGAZINE, 4:13, December, 1960.

Japanese dinner but a delightful water color, often served in graceful, serene private rooms opening onto those Japanese gardens—rocks, sand, dwarf trees, miniature waterfalls singing in the magic silence—that more than gardens are a shorthand of nature.

I have dined on the shore of Hong Kong's Aberdeen Bay, its waters carpeted with junks and sampans, whose huge mainsails look like the membranous wings of a bat. In this floating village, thousands of Chinese fishermen day after day eat their fare of noodles, abalone, and garrupa in their junks—where they are born, live, and die—by the light of a candle that shines softly, as in heaven a child's soul must shine.

With the Portuguese of Macao I have shared *pomba rostida* and white rice in the dingy taverns of the Rua de Felicidade, amid the clamor of fan-tan players, facing the tiny shops selling gold jewelry, which are dark and dismal cubbyholes in the daytime but become gold-refulgent grottoes like Aladdin's cave at night. Not far from here is Red China's frontier at Portas da Cerco, on the other side of which Chinese soldiers, gun on shoulder and eyes alert, stand waiting.

I have dined with the Siamese in their *klungs,* or canals, the floating markets of Bangkok, a Venice with sampans, where in huts mounted on stilts dwell the forever-smiling native families, who come down in the morning to pyramid their sampans with golden, amethyst, and coral-toned tropical fruits, meat, and fish. With dainty porcelain spoons we ate tongue-searing hot curries, hotter than the contortions of a Latin rhumba dancer, while nearby, in dazzling ceramic and marble temples, emerald- and gold-leafed Buddhas smiled down with millenary wisdom on the Buddhist monks who were clad in bright saffron-yellow robes.

In the steaming jungle of Cambodia, beneath palm trees throbbing with leaping monkeys, facing what long ago was the center of the fabulous Khmer culture of Angkor Vat, but which today lies almost razed to the ground by the ruthless green invasion of the jungle, I ate with a native family the produce of their swampy rice fields, where little naked boys like tropical fauns, their torsos polished by sweat, piped away on bamboo flutes.

In Beirut, close to the legendary cedars of Lebanon, whose timbers were fashioned into the Queen of Sheba's jewel caskets and with which Solomon's temple was built, I had a meal of *kebbeh* with an Arab family in the shade of the ruins of a medieval castle, overlooking the azure *mare nostrum,* where a thousand years ago out of the horizon came forth the vessels of the Crusaders, their swords gleaming in the sun like restless silver needles.

After seeing the peoples of the world in their native surroundings —Indians, impassive as centuries-old statues; Japanese, diminutive and efficient as a shorthand symbol, whose women are more bird or flower than women; Chinese, with their timeless dignity; Siamese, with their wheatstalk slimness and their eternal smile; Arabs, with their champagne effervescence—after seeing them all, I had the impression that the family of man is one and the same the world over, not only in its biological structure but also in its rituals and customs. The difference between the Parisian drinking his Pernod, the Spaniard his *manzanilla,* the American his cocktail, the Japanese his *sake,* the Lebanese his *arrack,* or the Quechua his *pisco* is purely a matter of form. For the main thing is not what people eat and drink; the main thing is their desire to dignify this purely biological ritual and raise it above the mere instinctive feeding of beasts. Eating is culture, and culture is eating. Animals *feed;* human beings *eat.* Man tries, with his family or his friends, to provide with his meals not only nourishment for the body but also recreation for the soul.

Whatever happens in any home, whether it be a neat little unpainted wooden domino-box of a house with straw mats and rice-paper windows in Kyoto, a solemn British mansion on Victoria Peak, a bungalow on stilts in Bangkok, or a mud hut on the banks of the Nile, whatever happens—being born, loving, eating, working, resting, dying —is the same the whole world over and reflects the basic unity of mankind. This unity is so well understood by men as individuals, but too often forgotten by nations and their rulers.

It is significant that in times of individual or collective crisis, man turns to his family, seeking there that moral and spiritual support that in normal circumstances is unwittingly taken for granted. At such moments of drama in life, the family suddenly acquires singular worth and prestige, power and dignity. It seems as though on such occasions the family reverts to the original mission it had in its historical beginning. I refer not to the biological mission of the family, but to its social purpose and function. For the family originated as a human and social unit that dwelled among many other such units but was completely autonomous and existed independently of the whole.

This family unit did not, by the simple addition of other similar units, give rise to the great complex national unit that is the state. Indeed, the state originally was born as an organism inimical to the family unit, a sort of private club of warriors and hunters who set themselves apart from their families to muster their daring and armed strength for hunting wild beasts, waging war, or abducting women. In such a sense, the original state was the enemy of any family that tried to resist it, and vice versa. For the family, in its biological essence, is an isolated conservative unit, dedicated to surviving, just as the state is an organism created for aggression and offense. In every nation in history, the state eventually has ruled over the family, though luckily nowadays in some nations, like the Swiss cantons, the family, through family-type political organizations, rules the government.

The states of the world today still preserve the unconscious memory of their historical origin as a club for sporting, military, or amatory adventures. That is why totalitarian states, aware that the family is their social and spiritual enemy, seek before everything else to destroy it. To this end, the totalitarian state begins by eradicating the three great spiritual forces that preserve the stability of the family: religion, the home considered as a miniature motherland, and the family regard for the father-image, replacing them respectively with the cult of the omnipotent state, acceptance of the nationalistic motherland as man's true home, and the creation of a mythical figure combining the images of God, ruler, and patriarch, usually incarnated in the person of the leader, dictator, or demagogue, who thus replaces the father-image in the home. Nowadays, moreover, the symbolic flame in the hearth that kept the family spirit warm has been displaced by the television screen, through which the aggressive eyes and voice of the political leader penetrate the home and become engraved on the mind of the family.

It is a pleasant surprise to observe the stability of the family in Oriental countries like Japan. In that venerable patriarchy, it is a joy to be a child or an old man, for both enjoy all the privileges and have few duties. To childhood and old age they grant the right to the chrysanthemum of family love; to maturity is entrusted the duty to wield the sword, the pen, the hammer, or the plow. What a contrast this is to the disrupted family life that exists in so many Western countries, as reflected in that serious psychological crisis through which many of our adolescents are passing. The introversion and emotional estrangement that are usually part of this crisis—manifested by the way the adolescent isolates himself with his books, records, and television in his own room, by his slovenliness in dress, and by his rebuffs to family affection—denote a phase of antifamily "schizophrenia," from which fortunately the majority recover.

It is of vast importance nowadays that we physicians do all we can as home counselors to strengthen the family of man, so vital in these critical times. In every human family—from the Holy Family, depicted by Murillo as an industrious carpenter, a loving mother, and a healthy golden-fleshed Child, to any other family in the world—there are powerful spiritual forces that are stronger and more enduring than all the atomic energy that man is now harnessing for his own destruction. To strengthen the family is to strengthen the spirit of nations and to make them still stronger by exercising not the sword but the soul.

In Byblos (with Damascus, the oldest town in the world to have been continually inhabited), near the time-darkened ruins of a medieval castle that was conquered during the Crusades by Raymond de Saint-Gilles, Count of Toulouse, I saw a Lebanese family pass by, their humble Arab robes dripping sunshine. The mother, with a child in her arms, rode a plum-colored mule that placidly chewed sunburnished straws. The father carried a basket of figs and dates and a jug of milk. This living Biblical scene reminded me that down the ages, even mightier than the sword of the Crusaders, whose only remains are the ruins of their castles, has been the example of love left by that other family who, nearly two thousand years ago, at the slow pace of a mule, like the family I was then watching, passed through honey-colored Biblical lands.

VAST AND WIDE IS THE WORLD

Should you go to Venice, that Byzantine *grande dame* who languorously reclines on the green mirror of the Adriatic amusing herself watching the black, swanlike gondolas glide by, visit the Ca'Polo. Stop a moment before this mansion, which is now but a pale remembrance of History, and let your thoughts wander to the daring Venetian lad who in the thirteenth century crossed Trebizond, Mosul, Baghdad, Persia, the salt deserts of Kerman, the frozen "Roof of the World" at The Pamirs, the jade-encrusted lands of Kashgar, the mysterious Gobi Desert, forever lashed by the demons of the wind, the Mongolian steppes, fabulous Cathay, and finally reached the vast empires of the Great Khan. Sixteen years later, Marco Polo returned to his native land. But not for long. He set out once again and roamed Tibet, Afghanistan, Burma, Siam, Sumatra, Ceylon, and India. His twenty-seven years of travel, captured like many-hued butterflies in his book *Il Miglione,* joined in one great, fabulous adventure the sophisticated Venice of Dante with the exotic lands of Asia.

Marco Polo not only became a prince of merchants, papal envoy, governor of a Chinese city, favorite of Kublai Khan, master of exotic languages, war correspondent, and the first traveler-writer, but his book, the most romantic travel epic in history, established the first bond between East and West. In his great cavalcade, Marco Polo integrated geography and history. His footprints across the vast Asiatic sands still endure on the sands of Time.

Jet planes today make Marco Polo's trip appear slow and erratic. Yet, few books convey as powerful a sensation as Marco Polo's does

From *MD,* the MEDICAL NEWSMAGAZINE, 3:11, April, 1959.

of the immensity of the world, of the importance of geography in the creation of history, and of the vital role of space in the march of events through Time. In our profession, which requires most of us to travel often, if only to call on patients, it is vitally important to remember that geography can greatly increase our knowledge of medicine.

Geography is neither the nacreous cloud puffs that float beyond the windows of the zooming stratocruiser nor the telegraph poles that rush to meet us on both sides of our speeding car. That is merely *space,* across which we speed in an attempt to overcome the tyranny of Time. Geography is the land, its climate, its wealth and poverty— it is all that contributes to the creation of the landscape, where man works, loves, fights, dreams, and dies. It is also the environment where man enjoys health or suffers disease, which is *always* influenced by environment. For, let us never forget the words of the Renaissance humanist, Jean Fernel: "Geography is to history what anatomy is to medicine." Geography, in other words, is the anatomy of history, just as anatomy is the geography of medicine.

Classical physicians, from kind Hippocrates to restless Paracelsus, searched for the secret of disease in the air, waters, and earth. But the invention in our time of "portable" pocket climates has resulted in the relegation of the study of environment to the medical geographer, whereas in reality everyone should be something of an ecologist to be able to understand better our own mental texture as well as the changes in the organic fabric of our patients.

Geography often determines the character of peoples. Coastal, plain, and mountain peoples all have different characteristics traceable to their environment. One can better understand Paracelsus' mystic thought and misty language if one remembers that his youth was spent amid the shivering pines and the fog shrouds of Switzerland, and one can better comprehend Avicenna's mental jumps from objective science to sheer fantasy if one recalls the sharp changes from cold to hot in the desert where he lived.

Having a wide vision of the world has given many a humanist— from Luis Vives to Henry Sigerist—the universality of his thought. But when life denies a man who craves universality the opportunity of fulfilling his craving "horizontally," by traveling through space, he then seeks fulfillment "vertically," withdrawing into his own spiritual self and drinking from his own inner fountain.

All physicians should travel as much as possible, and always with curious, loving, wonder-filled eyes. For to know the environments and geographies of the world we live in is the best way not only to understand health and sickness in man, but also to explore the mysterious geography of our own soul.

THE RESTLESS EMERALD

I am a lover of the sea. My first literary attempt was dedicated to the sea. Born on the shores of the Mediterranean, as a child I was lulled to sleep by the emerald song of the *mare nostrum*. Later, it molded the decisive years of my youth. In the incessant flux of the sea I learned the incessant flux of the spirit, the never-ceasing restlessness, the ever-mounting disquiet, that pushes one in life from preoccupation to preoccupation, even as the water is pushed from wave to wave. To this very day it still fills me with quiet joy to let my eyes roam from the bronzed sands of the beach, necklaced like a suntanned maiden with white frothy foam, to the sparkling azure sea, whence they ride back to the shore atop the snow-crested waves. Or perhaps they are held in the distance by a tiny sail or two, spread like paper fans on a carpet of blue, checkered in gold by the sun, which, high on the turquoise abyss above, bursts forth into a streaming palm of shimmering rays.

To contemplate the sea is sheer delight, for the eye is more carefree than when exploring the land. It neither crashes against rocks, nor soars up to or plummets down from cliffs. It only sways, gently, lazily, on the back of the placid blue beast, while the mind serenely wanders off across the wide open space above.

Musing about the sea makes me recall the passage from Pío Baroja's *The Restlessness of Shanti Andía:* "Those meek green waves, those whitish billows of foam upon which our eye peacefully sways, seem to brush against our personality until they make it purely con-

From *MD*, the MEDICAL NEWSMAGAZINE, *4*:13, September, 1960.

templative and at one with Nature." The Basque writer masterly described the, paradoxically, contemplative character of the sea, a dynamic panorama (in contrast to the static nature of landscapes) whose
chromatic range, the green-and-azure-toned symphony of sea and sky,
exerts a soothing effect on the spirit, distressed by the gray-black
monochrome of the city.

Lighthouse keepers, who spend their lives scanning the azure wastes
in search of the smoke plume heralding a ship, solitary seafarers,
islanders, and fishermen, all develop a contemplative temperament,
meager in words but rich in dreams. When Commander Joshua Slo-
cum, in 1898, alone in his small vessel, reached the enchanted waters
of the South Seas, he merely wrote in his log: "I again came to the
Pacific, and found it less tempestuous than the time before." And in
the accounts of Vasco Núñez de Balboa's expedition in 1513, when
the Pacific was discovered, we read: "Crossing the strait, we caught
sight of a new sea, as turbulent as those we had previously seen."

This lack of lyrical rapture in the accounts of seafaring men is the
penalty imposed by the sea on its worshippers, who are incapable of
expressing what they feel, only what they see. The writings of professional sailors about the sea are mere logbooks, as if the authors
feared that translating their feelings into words would destroy the
spell. Hence the reason why the seaman on land is like a detached
being, whose soul remains behind in the frothing foam, in the crystalline blue depths, in the rumorous silences of the sea. On land, he is
dépaysé, out of his element, out of orbit. Ashore, the seadog, who
might be expected to rhapsodize about the sea, keeps silent, his lips
sealed by the endless hours of wordless communion alone with the sea.

It should prove most interesting to ask people, in imitation of a
Rorschach test, what they see in the sea. We could thus study how
each person "feels" the sea, from Ulysses, with his voyage around the
Mediterranean teeming with delectable goddesses and cyclopean
Titans, to modern nautical writers. We could then appreciate whether
they see the sea as a means of communication that either separates
men or brings them together, as an ever-changing emerald wherein
blonde sirens dwell and gulls are a flock of arrows shot by an invisible
archer, as a residual evidence of the possibly liquid origin of our
planet, or as a place for a pleasure trip. The response might lay bare
many an unfeeling heart beneath the poet's mask.

The true rhapsodists of the sea were actually strangers to the sea,
untrammeled by the pledge of silence imposed by the sea. This is
why, except for a handful of sentimental essays, nautical yarns, pirate
tales, or technical studies, there is no such thing as a real marine
literature. Authors who with a few masterly strokes of their pen could
describe any landscape (Cervantes, for instance) seem to have flinched

The Restless Emerald   193 from the contact when they faced the sea. The sea is not once mentioned in Don Quixote's visit to the galleys. Chateaubriand in his *Itinéraire de Paris à Jérusalem,* which included a voyage from Constantinople to Syria aboard the polacre "St. John," speaks not a word about the sea. Only when the boat is sailing near Cyprus, one moonlit night, does he convey a feeling of the sea. "The moon seemed to swing suspended between the masts and rigging of the vessel." Fray Luis de Granada compared the sea to a "great fair and market place, crowded with buyers and sellers."

The sea, like a pure-hearted woman, surrenders itself only to him who approaches it with love and the craving to learn its secrets. Marine literature, from Cooper to Dana, from Marryat to Conrad, is dry and austere. The true spirit of the sea dwells only in salt-water yarns, told by sailors among themselves in harbor cafes or forecastles, through tobacco-stained teeth clenched on the stem of a meerschaum. In such tales floats the vision of fearful storms, moonlit nights, dusks in which the last rays of the sun fringe the pale horizon like golden curls on the ivory brow of a woman.

These popular marine yarns betray a mystic element in those whose love for the sea amounts almost to intoxication. For the sea is an intoxicating scene to the romantic, just as the Alps are on land, or, indeed, as is any scene not wholly grasped by our senses, which then respond with a mystic exaltation.

Nowadays we constantly scoff at romanticism. Thus, football is a satire on war, rock 'n' roll on the waltz, the "blues" on chamber music. In our subconscious eagerness to ridicule sentimentality, we have made fun of the sea, that idol of the romantic ancients, by confining its romantic immensity inside a box—the swimming pool, a parody of the sea in which the sea's multiplicity of shades and ever-feminine curves are replaced by a static, masculine straightness of line.

Among the allurements of the sea are its ever-changing iridescence and the evanescence of its waves, which constantly simulate feminine torsos. The sea is elusive, fleeting, slippery, evanescent, now advancing, now retreating, never doing more than promise, like a bow strung with the arrows of decisions that are never released. Most of its spell lies precisely in such elusiveness, even as the spell of love often lies in the possibility of its vanishing, or that of the green-shaded oasis in the knowledge that the blazing desert stretches interminably before and beyond this transient shelter. This incarnate transience of the sea makes me think of a poet. Perched atop a rock, he gazes dreamily at a distant lighthouse. Its light, glowing intermittently amidst pale clouds, makes him think that the sea is smoking a pipe. Descrying the distant sail of a fishing smack, the poet tears up his poem and scatters the pieces in the air, as though wishing to transmute them into companion sails to the lonely tiny sail on the horizon. Thus he expresses his nostalgia at not being out there himself.

Biology may explain the fascination exerted by the sea. In the dawn of our earth, next to its waters the first forms of life, microscopic and gelatinous, made their appearance. As a reminder of his aquatic origin, man carries inside him a sea amounting to 85 per cent of his weight. Both man and woman—even the most beautiful woman—are but four bucketfuls of water and one of salts, a souvenir left in our tissular intimacy by our sea-sprung ancestors. When we left our original environment, water, we simply carried it inside us. The attraction so many of us feel toward the sea may be the prodigal's attraction to his paternal home, the sea, the mere sight of which awakens a deep-rooted *saudade,* a longing to return, which is perhaps a manifestation of the instinct of death, of restitution to the sea whence we came.

In such a sense, sea-bathing is an unconscious way of fusing with the sea, of being swallowed up by it and finding rest in its bosom. The increasing brevity in swimming suits may be a further manifestation of that yearning to return to nature, to the sea, to the source from which we sprang.

Many have written of the incessant and purposeless activity of the sea, now quiet and peaceful, now surging and tossing and roaring, comparable to human life swaying along without any predetermined objective. But then, the sea, like life, is a resultant of the inner and external forces that govern it.

To approach the secret of the sea, we must first define "how we see the sea." I do not mean those green and blue splashes on the atlases, which are the sea's coffins. It is difficult to "see" the sea. We cannot parcel it out as we do land, for there are no points of reference in the sea. To see the sea, we first let our glance leisurely roam the whole blue immensity, until its deep indigo floods our retina; then we observe the little episodes of the sea: the fishing smack sailing along, its trembling shadow trailing close behind; the wisp of smoke curling high on the horizon; the nacreous clouds gently gliding by; the lighthouse, lone and silent, towering in the distance; the sea gull, now plummeting into the white-peaked waters, now soaring into the sky; and finally we gather all the episodes into one great scenario, and form our picture on the foundation of the immense blue-green stage with its tiny actors: the lighthouse, the sail, the wisp of smoke, the sea gull.

The sea enchants us not for what it is, but for what it it not. The evanescence of each wave or reflection makes the real unreal, turns what *is* into a forever-changing *non esse*. We love the sea for the mysterious things it evokes: the abysmal depths swarming with strange creatures and contorted coral, the distant verdant island, the moss-lined hulk of a lost vessel—all the things we cannot see but can imagine and pine for, the missing things that because they are missing are embellished in our imagination, the invisible landscape that we project against the backdrop of the visible scene. Far more than with its present reality, the sea beckons with its alluring possibilities, nucleus of all sea legends. The sea has the romantic beauty of our ideals, and therefore satisfies our longing for delusion, keeping open for us the magic postern of hope. The sea is the shell around the magic bell in which our daydreams dwell.

But the sea is no longer what it used to be. The old salts in Mediterranean ports will tell you this, while their dull eyes sadly rove over crowded wharves cloaked in smoke and riddled by the strident squeak of derricks and cranes, over oil flicks that stain the sea an ugly brown, over the mammoth liners that seem to hang from the sky on chains of black smoke, over tugs chugging their way through the crowded lanes of these mercantile Venices. Perhaps for a short instant their eyes may gleam as they alight on a peg-legged, piratical-looking sailor, a ghost surviving from the past, who, followed closely by his ugly sentimental dog, drags out crates of fish that shimmer like treasure chests of pieces of silver and broken mirrors. But the ornate, figure-head-embellished, tall-masted sailing vessels, with pennants gaily greeting the wind, have given way to drab, steel-armored freighters that cloud the air with their belching smoke. The wind, implacable god, magical and fickle Ariel, alternately protector and tormentor of sailors, guardian angel over spread sails, has given way to cavernous oil- or coal-devouring furnaces and to unfriendly, unfeeling, precise machinery. Now that modern navigational instruments function with absolute independence and magnificent accuracy, gone are the hours on deck scanning the horizon, filled with uncertainty and even anxiety, but also with intimate understanding and profound respect for the vast forces around. The old-time, weather-beaten, wind-swept, legend-filled, adventurer-type sea captain has been replaced by the modern streamlined officer, who combines the specialist with the bureaucrat.

But the sea's enchantment still endures, both in the sea itself and in those of us who so love it. It also endures in those who love the beach, particularly women, who approach the sea as if they were entering Paradise. Perhaps that is why women, seeking to be more in tune with this Garden of Eden, increasingly adopt the costume of Eve when on the beach.

The vertiginous tempo of modern life is drawing dangerously close to the immutable rhythm of the Cosmos. For this we are already being punished. For, our torrential speed through life allows us no time to enjoy the beauties of this earth. And therefore, just as every now and then we adjust our wristwatch by the tower clock, so also should we now and then leave the city and adjust our soul to the pulse of nature. For this purpose there is nothing like the sea. For, though man has mined the sea, and bound her (to landlubbers the sea is masculine; to seamen, who have wed "her," it is feminine) with submarine cables, and furrowed her with seaways, and restricted her with maritime laws, and stirred up her depths, and analyzed her waters, yet the sea continues to offer those who approach her with love a standard of greatness and a pathway to eternity.

THE CHASE OF THE BUTTERFLY

I am consumed by an insatiable yearning for liberty and for new emotions. My ideal is America, especially tropical America, that land of marvels."

The man who thus expressed the craving for travel and adventure, which he had nursed since childhood, when *Don Quixote* and *Robinson Crusoe* were his inseparable companions, was a young, newly graduated Spanish physician named Santiago Ramón y Cajal. Time and again Ramón y Cajal expressed this craving "to explore a virgin land." In his solitary ramblings along the steep banks of the Ebro River, the young country doctor fed his fancy with "the romantic desire to discover idyllic gardens and forests untrodden by human foot." How he fulfilled his dreams of adventure and conquest at a more advanced age is well known to all of us, and I shall return to this later. But, as in Ramón y Cajal, in many a physician there is a secret recess wherein smolders, ever since childhood, the desire to visit distant lands, to meet exotic peoples, and possibly, on turning some corner of the world, suddenly to come face to face with the marvelous.

Why did physicians so often become immortal figures in the history of exploration?

The gallery of explorer-physicians is crowded with men who, not content with exploring the physical space of man's body and the historical space of man's mind—that is, with exploring their patients in time and space: their biography and their organism—plunged into

From *MD*, the MEDICAL NEWSMAGAZINE, 5:11, August, 1961.

virgin lands and wide unknown seas, to scour the world, all mystery and adventure, that beckoned from over the horizon. Such physicians preferred to learn geography, the anatomy of the earth, to anatomy, the geography of the human body. To them exploration of the elusive mystery that lay beyond the blue horizon became as much an obsession as the chase of the elusive butterfly of truth is to the investigator.

Not only in the individual sense but in the historical sense also was this zeal for adventure of both explorers and physicians reflected in their endeavors and achievements, for while the former were exploring the earth and its oceans, the latter were exploring the human body. The best example of this historical parallel is to be found in the Renaissance, when, shortly after the Spanish and Portuguese explorers and conquistadors had begun their transatlantic and transpacific voyages of discovery, anatomists and surgeons in Italy, France, and Spain initiated the daring adventure of rediscovering and exploring the innermost recesses of the human body. With burning enthusiasm the sailors of those days set out in their ships, their sails driven as much by their dreams as by the winds, to discover the "promised lands" across the dark, stormy seas, which until then were as much a mystery to them as was the human body to the anatomist's scalpel.

This issue of *MD* presents the fascinating story of what medicine has contributed to exploration and vice versa. We physicians, whether we are quiet and sedentary or restless and adventurous, cannot read tales of explorer-physicians without feeling stirring within us once more the same yearning we felt at medical school while watching our teachers unfold before our eyes the intricate fabric of the human body —the yearning to race around the globe in pursuit of the elusive butterfly of adventure.

There is a sublime lesson of gallantry and abnegation in the life of the men who, with their science and their conscience, their heart and their heroism, helped to lift the green curtain that concealed the secrets of virgin lands. Fine examples of such men are four great Scottish physicians: Mungo Park, who upon finally seeing, after many hardships and privations, ". . . the long sought-for majestic Niger, glittering in the morning sun . . .," fell on his knees and drank as if from a sacred chalice the waters of the river, which he was to follow for more than a thousand miles without ever reaching the sea, meeting his death at the hands of savages; David Livingstone, who journeyed 29,000 miles, crossed the Kalahari Desert, traced the course of the Zambesi, discovered Victoria Falls, and died of dysentery, leaving his own heart buried in the soil of Africa like the symbolic offering of human viscera in a sacrificial rite; James Bruce, who studied medicine so as to be better prepared for the exploration that led him to the fabulous confluence of the White and Blue Niles;

and William Balfour Baikie, who sailed up the Niger farther than any other white man had done and died in Sierra Leone.

Many more names could be added to those four dauntless Scottish physician-explorers, fine examples of the magnificent endeavor of their admirable nation, which has given to adventure so many explorer-physicians, just as it has produced so many peerless writers of adventure, such as Robert Louis Stevenson, Arthur Conan Doyle, and John Buchan. But of these we speak in another part of this issue, including the great classic troubadours of the Arabian deserts—Burton, Palgrave, Doughty—who disguised themselves as physicians so that they might penetrate the mysterious sand wilderness that they later immortalized with their pens.

It is safe to say that since the medical journeys of Democedes of Crotona, two thousand five hundred years ago, few other professional groups have felt as strongly as physicians have that magic call to adventure, a call that is like a flame, kindling and warming the explorer's soul.

It is interesting to recall, by way of exception and contrast, that in the most important expedition in history the medical profession was, with one exception, represented only by second-rate physicians. I refer to Columbus' expedition to the Americas in search of the Great Khan. In Columbus' first voyage, his log mentions only one physician, Master Alonso, on the flagship, and one barber-surgeon, Master Juan, on the *Pinta,* no medical man being listed for the third caravel. Luckily, on the memorable sea passage that bore them from the roseate dawn of Palos to the golden haze of Guanahani, healthy conditions prevailed on all three ships. Thus Columbus could note: "Of all my men, not one had a headache or was confined to his bunk by sickness."

With the fifteen hundred men under Columbus' command on his second voyage came the famous Sevillian physician, attendant to Princess Joanna, Dr. Diego Alvarez de Chanca, to whom Their Catholic Majesties gave written instructions "to serve us, and tenderly preserve the health of those who go thither at our behest." Besides Chanca, who, Columbus says, "labored with great diligence and goodwill," there were also "chirurgeons of the fleet," who later became "healers of injuries" and tended fractures and wounds with knife, scissors, needle, and cautery. These, and Chanca, were the first to witness, on their own sailors, in Hispaniola, the curarization caused by the poison-tipped arrows of the natives, just as they also were the first to face the problem of the buboes of syphilis, which Columbus' sailors were later to spread throughout Europe.

Columbus' third voyage carried only one physician, one surgeon, an apothecary, and a herbalist, and the fourth and disastrous last

200

voyage had only a "Master Bernal." After this last catastrophic expedition, in which, according to Columbus' log, they underwent a terrific gale on the Coast of Adversities (Nicaragua, Costa Rica, Panama), "in that sea turned into blood, boiling like a mighty cauldron," Columbus, a victim of malaria, typhoid, gout, and starvation ("I used to eat," he tells us, "a pound of maggoty hardtack and a glass of wine,"), never sailed again and later died from an incurable cardiorenal affection. Perhaps the lack of physicians of high professional standing in Columbus' ships was due to the vilification heaped on the voyages once the initial enthusiasm about them had died down. But the physicians who accompanied later expeditions not only helped in the conquest and colonization of the new continents, but brought back to Europe a great treasure in foods, medicinal plants, and traditional aboriginal remedies that opened new frontiers to the medical world of their time.

This tradition of the explorer who though he was not a physician claimed to be one, like the traveler-authors in Arabia previously mentioned, has often been repeated in the course of history, thus showing that the explorer found a protective shield in this profession, which commands the greatest respect in all lands. A case in point was Alvar Núñez Cabeza de Vaca, who in 1527 joined Pánfilo de Narváez's Florida expedition, which landed at Tampa the following year. Of the four hundred Spaniards included in that expedition, only four survived, with Cabeza de Vaca as their leader. Posing as witch doctors and practicing empiric medicine and "Christian magic," these four men, in a gigantic hike that took eight years and covered practically the whole continent from coast to coast, crossed *on foot* Florida, Texas, Sonora, and Mexico, more than two thousand leagues in all, until they reached Hernando Cortes' headquarters at Sinaloa. The protective cloak of their medical ministry enabled these daring explorers to complete the most fabulous trek in the history of the Americas.

The finest example of what medicine combined with exploration has done for mankind is found in Francisco Xavier de Balmis' expedition to the American hemisphere and the Pacific for the purpose of introducing vaccination.

Balmis, born in Alicante, Spain, passed the examination of the royal surgeons-in-ordinary, bloodletters, and protobarbers, who granted him the right to practice the art of bloodletting with leeches and cups and to extract teeth, after which he graduated in pure mathematics and surgery and was appointed army surgeon. Later Balmis studied botanical materia medica in Mexico and translated into Spanish the *Vaccinators' Canon*.

Opinions in Spain on the subject of vaccination were still divided.

The family of Charles III suffered terribly from defective inoculations: the heir to the throne reacted with high fevers; the young princess María Luisa was disfigured for life; Maria Amalia, wife of the Infante Antonio Pascal, developed ophthalmia; and the physician-in-ordinary himself, Dr. Martínez Sobral, died some weeks later from anguish and chagrin at these tragic results. When an epidemic of smallpox broke out in Lima and Bogotá during the reign of Charles IV, the king, on the advice of his physicians, including the famous anatomist Antonio Gimbernat, organized a national expedition to vaccinate the peoples of the Americas. Years later, the royal favorite, Manuel de Godoy, "Prince of the Peace" and official lover to Queen Maria Luisa, was to eulogize this expedition in his *Memoirs,* and so did Jenner.

Not finding any cowpox-infected cattle to carry the precious lymph, Balmis decided to take instead twenty-two children who had never had smallpox, accompanied by their nurses, and to inoculate the children with cowpox three times in succession, keeping the fluid active by arm-to-arm transmission in two children each week and preserving the precious lymph and its virus (obtained from the pustules of children newly vaccinated the previous week) "enclosed between two glass slides," of which two thousand were used during the voyage; 210 children in all were employed, being discharged and replaced when they became immune.

The expedition left La Coruña, Spain, in 1803, on the 200-ton corvette *Maria de Pita,* calling at Puerto Rico, Puerto Cabello, and La Guaira, where it split into two groups. One group continued from Cartagena, Colombia, to La Paz, Bolivia, under the leadership of heroic Don José Salvany y Lleopart, on whom the great Peruvian physician Hipólito Unánue conferred the title of doctor at the University of San Marcos in Lima, and who, armless, blind in one eye, crippled, exhausted by mosquito bites, soroche, and pulmonary tuberculosis, died later from his labors. An idea of Salvany's epic toil can be gained from the fact that in Peru alone he vaccinated more than 200,000 people.

The second group, piloted by Balmis, went on to Havana, Yucatán, Veracruz, and Acapulco. From Acapulco, for two months and six days, on the *Magallanes,* Balmis sailed the turbulent waters of the inappropriately named Pacific Ocean, the violence of which most of the time kept him and the children in the hold among rats and refuse. Balmis took 26 children and their vaccines to the Philippines, the Visayan Islands, and thence to the coast of Asia, to Macao, at that time still subject to piratical attacks, and Canton, and back to Saint Helena. The landing in Macao was epic, with three vaccinated children in an open dugout, after their ship had been battered by a typhoon for six days, with the loss of twenty of the crew. From Asia, Balmis returned triumphantly to Spain with an illustrated atlas of exotic Chinese plants drawn on rice paper by Chinese artists.

What this humanitarian expedition did for the inhabitants of all the lands visited was expressed in a recent address by the Philippine physician, Dr. José P. Bantug. Commenting on the 6000 vaccinations performed by Balmis in Manila and Cavite, Dr. Bantug said: "The noble action of Dr. Francisco de Carriedo [the philanthropist who organized Manila's water supply] together with the introduction of vaccination in the Islands . . . made it possible for the half million inhabitants who formed our population at the time of the conquest to grow into the more than twenty million Christians we are today." The Balmis vaccine expedition is a perfect example of what medicine, allied with the impulse for adventure, has done for humanity in the course of history.

There is much of the psychology of the true explorer in the physician, especially in the scientific investigator. There are men whose moves in life are ruled only by lust for power, attainable through wealth, politics, or war; but there are others whose impelling desire is the conquest of truth through beauty, like the artist, or through belief, like the mystic, or through pure fact, like the scientific investigator.

Such is the key to the exploratory zeal of Santiago Ramón y Cajal, whom I mentioned at the beginning. Ramón y Cajal, apart from his journey as a soldier to Cuba, never fulfilled his dreams of adventure in strange lands; instead he transmuted these dreams into his work on the nervous system and even employed a botanical terminology, such as "gardens," "lianas," "branches," "jungles of the cerebral cortex," and "virgin forest," in describing the nervous and embryologic structures.

The finest symbol of the physician-explorer, therefore, might very well be Ramón y Cajal, who, in the virgin forest of the neuron, knew how to pursue, "into the floral garden of the gray matter, delicate and elegantly shaped cells, the mysterious butterflies of the soul, the beating of whose wings may some day, for all we know, reveal the secret of the mind."

DEPORTS ET SOLATZ

ω hen I was a boy my favorite sports were football, handball, and, above all, running and swimming, a significant choice, particularly since I remember that I always ran and swam with the fury of one who must get somewhere quickly. Now I swim only occasionally, and I run only to catch a bus or against time in my editorial labors.

This change in my sports is an instance of how man's worship of the body is a matter of youthful inspiration, since the human form is beautiful only in youth. On the other hand, worship of the spirit is the will of older years and reaches its peak when the body starts on its inevitable decline. Physical culture feeds on the enthusiasm of youth; spiritual culture attains its natural bloom only with age. Hence the quondam athlete, whose full mental development is often arrested, retains a childlike quality, just as the young philosopher is a herald of premature maturity. Youth craves to be looked at and admired, for the best in it is its outward appearance; maturity prefers to be listened to, since the best it has to offer is its intimacy.

Today the body takes precedence over the mind, the Olympic games outshine poetry contests, a symptom of the juvenile, even puerile, spirit of our age. This predominant love of sports merits a few moments of reflection to determine what symbolic meaning hides behind kicking a ball, racing over startled country roads, or punching the taut body of the boxer in the ring.

The distinguishing fact about sports is their antiquity and impor-

From *MD*, the MEDICAL NEWSMAGAZINE, *4*:11, August, 1960.

tance in history. The Greeks, to whom are due most of the great ideas that still inspire civilized man, maintained their solidarity through the centuries by means of two unifying forces: the Homeric epics and the Delphic and Olympic games. One of these games, the marathon race, commemorated the exploit of a warrior-athlete who ran without pause to bring his countrymen the glad tidings of victory over the Persians at Marathon and then, exhausted by the titanic effort, dropped dead, no doubt a victim of what now, more than two thousand years later, we would diagnose as acute hypoglycemia.

Why does man, a naturally lazy creature, practice sports that bring him no material reward but only sweat, palpitations, and fatigue? There are exhausting efforts, manual or mental, whose very purpose dignifies the exertion and results involved. Sports, however, are a spontaneous effort, an unrewarded luxury, distinguished indeed by the remarkable fact that they are thought of highly more for their own sake than for the ends they achieve. For the truly happy occupation is not pleasure but effort, and effort is real sport. Sports are free effort, whose enjoyment is inherent in themselves, just as labor is required effort, whose enjoyment resides in its outcome. Hence sports stand higher in the scale of life than labor, because they are a voluntary, unrequired effort, just as poetry is superior to bookkeeping and dreaming up fantasies is greater than remembering multiplication tables.

The etymology of the word "sport" is in itself highly revealing. Its roots go back to the old French *de portre,* what the Mediterranean sailors of yore were during their days of leisure and play in port while waiting for the next sailing. The culture of the medieval troubadours of Provence contains the phrase *deports et solatz. Deports* signified conversation and poesy; *solatz* stood for physical exercise, such as hunting, jousting, or dancing. A chronicle of the reign of Henry IV already contains the Provençal term *deportar,* meaning "hunting."

Nowadays there are two main forms of sports: the solitary sports, which remain solitary even when done in company, since each person is by himself when playing his part, as in hunting and fishing; and the more popular competitive athletic sports, which require strength, skill, and endurance, like football or tennis or jumping.

Hunting sometimes requires a solitude worthy of a monastic order or a military garrison. I am not speaking of the purely utilitarian hunting of the Bantus, for instance, who must kill the antelope so as not to die of hunger; I speak of hunting as a sport whose sole reward is the joy of the chase. Similarly, fishing—except for deep-sea fishing—has ritually acquired a meditative and philosophical character, belittled by some people ("Fishing tackle," as one jaundiced observer put it, "is a rod with a hook and bait on one end and an imbecile on the other.") but praised by the majority. Izaak Walton, for instance, spoke of "anglers, or very honest men." (One reader commented: "I prize that comma.")

Competitive sports have been a tremendous force in history. The State sprang from sports, not from the family, as a kind of club where young men came together to plan their sporting activities, whether these were of a warlike character (raids on enemy territory, elephant-hunting) or erotic adventures (ravishment of women from another tribe). Individual efforts, uncoordinated at the start, were eventually unified into organized collective effort, thanks to a historical superstructure that began as a sporting club and ended up as the State.

Modern sports represent the transition from worship of the human form, practiced by classic civilizations, to body culture, as practiced today. (Agriculture, similarly, developed from a religious ritual into a practical occupation.) All sports are founded on developing the anatomy and expanding the physiology of human endurance and endeavor; they therefore carry within themselves the seed of their own limitations. The human body in sports presents a simple and limited drama of forces and forms, in contrast to the complex drama of human thought. In sports, as in love, the human body finally becomes a rather boring thing, with meager limitations and a monotonous repertory. The sight of tons of naked female flesh, whether on the banks of the Ganges or on the beaches of St. Tropez, arouses in reaction a longing for asceticism and a taste for skeletons.

All said and done, modern audiences at boxing matches, like the peoples of old at their circuses, go mad watching two men punching each other into a bloody pulp for twelve rounds, but they could never bear ten minutes watching a crack mathematician extracting square roots. This indicates that the hyperarchaic tastes of prehistoric man are just as active in his modern descendant as are his "political" attitudes and docile submission to the blows and cudgelings of the strongest, which, in the past as in modern times, have too often wrought the downfall of democracies.

The triumph of sports in the modern world represents a victory of the values of youth—agile body, firm ankles, compact muscles— over those of older people. That has always been a danger. Greece when governed by mature men was the torch that blazed the way to civilization; Rome, misgoverned by young men like Nero, eventually ended in decay.

I prefer to look at the constructive aspect of sports, though without discounting their perils. The modern ubiquity of sports, their spread over the face of the globe, the world-wide conformity in conduct, uniforms, and rules in boxing, swimming, basketball, and tennis, whether in Los Angeles, Madrid, Tokyo, or Stockholm—all this is an expression of the solidarity of youth in our modern world, as exemplified in the Olympic games. The countries of the world today may differ in practically everything else, but they do agree on how football and tennis should be played. In that harmony of understanding in sports, in that desire to honor and obey the same rules in boxing or jumping, swimming or racing, we greet the possible birth of universal understanding and clean competition among nations.

THOSE GLITTERING TOWERS

O n arriving in a city for the first time, our attention is at once drawn to its roofs. The tarnished-silver roofs of Paris, the pink geranium-colored roofs of Lima, the golden domes of Istanbul. If we arrive by night, the city lights bewitch us. The jeweled tiaras on Rio de Janeiro's tawny brow, the mauve and emerald splendors of Venice, the glittering chessboard of the tall towers of New York's "ziggurats." Both these things, the roofs and the lights, are symbols of a community of people assembled for the purpose of performing, side by side, the difficult task of living.

To physicians the city is of vital importance, because it exposes patients to hazards—traumas, contagions, intoxications—that are less common to the country. An additional hazard springs not from the city but from us physicians who dwell in it, for the pressures of city life may create the habit of regarding patients not as human beings but as professional subjects. Thus we mechanize the human personality and hamper our understanding of the persona, without which it is difficult to heal, even with the aid of scalpel or antibiotic.

We should remember that, when man turned from his nomadic ways to life in organized society, his abode was at first confined to four walls. Later he created cities, thereby expanding the boundaries of his residence. The first manifestation of this transcendental advance was possibly the cities that sprang up on the blazing plains of Mesopotamia, when man erected a circular wall (a geometrical defense against the amorphous surrounding world) within which the city

From *MD*, the MEDICAL NEWSMAGAZINE, 4:11, February, 1960.

grew with the temple as its center, both sheltered and confined by its shell of stone.

The great innovation of the Greeks and Romans was to base their society on the city, which symbolized the agreement between friends and enemies to live peacefully together. Athenians and Romans first created the public square, then they built their homes and public buildings around it. Thus their cities sprang up, as in the joke that says a gun is made just by lining a hole with steel.

The *polis* or city grew up around a "hole," the agora or forum, the public square, a space wrested from nature and marked out for public assemblies, in contrast to the places intended for the private functions of shelter, sleeping, and procreation. The Greco-Roman city was a space carved out of the countryside, a human and civic zone limited and finite by reason of the houses that walled it in. The city was the house carried to its highest degree and peopled by citizens (just as the house was peopled by men and women dwelling in an "inner" space), who eventually created a State out of it—as occurred in Rome and Carthage. Some of these city-states lasted for many centuries.

To found a city in those days meant to defeat nature by creating a public square and to help in the triumph of the jurist over the peasant. If the country was for working and the house for living, the city (born of an impulse *opposite* from that which created the home) was created to enable people to leave their houses and go out to meet and converse with other people. The at-home *hospitality* of the ancient Mesopotamians and Egyptians was replaced by the outdoor, the in-the-street *urbanity* of the Greeks and Romans. Even today there are many people who know how to be hospitable yet who are not urbane, and vice versa.

When the barbarians laid waste Greek civilization, destroying its cities, the people were compelled to return to the country. The castle and the rustic fief eventually replaced the city. Feudalism, in its turn, succumbed when the monarchs supported the peasants, and the discovery of gunpowder facilitated the assault of castles, leaving many a feudal lord swinging from the highest battlement like a sinister scrawl against the sky. In the ceaseless course of the centuries, the city, as we now know it, came into being, and the original spirit that motivated its creation still throbs within it, as the heart throbs inside the breast.

Physicians can do much to restore the magnificent original impulse that created the city, the impulse to gather people together to converse and live in harmony. Recollection of this noble meaning of the city, which brought people together in ancient Babylon and Thebes as in modern Los Angeles and Oslo, will help us to take better care of our patients, because we shall regard them not as mere professional denizens of the city but as human beings.

Remembrance of the very human impulse that brought people together in the magic hour when the great cities were created will enable us physicians—the only men who can penetrate the living "short story" that unfolds behind each lighted window in the city— by word and action, to remind city dwellers in their tall glittering towers of their duty to restore the kingdom of the spirit over the empire of dust, smoke, steel, and cement.

For a city is not just a conglomeration of buildings constructed with the help of machine and muscle; it is also the expression of man's urge to build, and possibly the greatest expression of his creative impulse. As André Malraux recently said: the art forms that endure most in man's memory are the *invented* forms. Of all of these, the architecture not of buildings but of cities best embodies the nobility and dignity of the creative urge of our time.

The important thing is, however, to remember that a city endures if its people are counted not as millions of persons but as individual souls. The physician, in his capacity as architect of people, can help better than anyone to restore the most important and most beautiful thing in any city—not the contour of its buildings, but the contour of its souls.

THAT GREAT PHYSICIAN AND
GREAT FRIEND FROM KYUSHU *

a Spanish poet once remarked how alone the dead are left, but I believe it is *we,* the living, who are left alone when a great man—and there is nothing greater than truly being a man—such as Dr. Katsumi Kaida departs from our midst.

It was on the enchanting afternoon of April 7th a year ago that I first met Katsumi Kaida. The airplane carrying me from Tokyo settled like a giant metallic gull at the Fukuoka airport. Still shimmering before my eyes was the splendrous image of Fujiyama, more a silver chalice than a mountain. Now, stepping out of the plane, I saw the airport stretching out like a golden carpet under the bright sun. The sky above was a delicate blue, as palely tinted as the shell of a sparrow's egg. A dark-headed man dressed in blue approached me. Lips smiling, eyes twinkling, his was an open face, with the forehead high and wide, as though it wanted to provide the birds of ideas with ample space to nest. As an old proverb has it, you do not make friends, you *meet* them; and so it was, on the eve of the anniversary of the birth of Buddha, when I first met Katsumi Kaida.

Our friendship had sprouted through letters, thanks to a written introduction from a great mutual friend, an outstanding physician, Dr. Seymour Farber of San Francisco, California. It was the kind intercession of this ambassador of culture and goodwill—a task to which

* The author is most grateful to Dr. Masuo Mori, Director of Kyuden Hospital, Kashii, Fukuoka, Japan, for his invitation to write this tribute, which appeared in the Japanese medical journal *Kyudai-Ihō,* a memorial issue devoted to Dr. Katsumi Kaida.

From *International Record of Medicine, 174:*264, April, 1961.

he constantly applies himself, generously and skillfully—that first awakened Dr. Katsumi Kaida's interest in my professional endeavors. Later, on behalf of the Japanese Society for Tuberculosis, Dr. Kaida invited me to address as guest of honor the National Congress of Tuberculosis at Fukuoka.

From the very first, in Katsumi Kaida's letters, all in a warm, eloquent English, and in a hand as delicate and graceful as the contours of a cherry blossom, there shone through his kindness, generosity, tolerance, and friendliness, the sparkle of his clear intelligence, the fire of his all-embracing curiosity concerning men and world events, past and present. In our correspondence we discovered we had many things in common: we both liked the same cities in Europe; Vesalius was our most admired figure in the history of medicine; we both regarded our profession as medical anthropology, as the all-inclusive study of man, in sickness and in health, and his illnesses as "biographic episodes." Thus, through our thoughts committed to those fragile paper coffers that airmail envelopes are, across the vast American prairies and the towering Rockies, the blue and gray immensity of the Pacific, the cities and rice paddies of Japan, we forged a friendship that partook equally of spiritual affinity and professional kinship.

It was through this warm association, nurtured by no more than letters, mere slips of paper scribbled in ink, that I first came to know Dr. Katsumi Kaida, for they were the kind of letters into which sincere men pour the best of their mind and their being, and I recognized at once that I had come to know not just a friend, but a spiritual brother.

At the sessions of the 35th Japanese Society for Tuberculosis at Fukuoka, I had the opportunity to appreciate that Katsumi Kaida was one of those unique scientists who combine a great scientific intellect with a boundless humaneness. To his assembled colleagues from all parts of Japan he spoke brilliantly on scientific matters, yet out on the street I saw him tenderly pat a child's head as though it were one of those delicate little dolls from Hakata.

For Katsumi Kaida, the hallmark of the physician—indeed, of any man!—was humility, a quality he always carried about as a traveler carries his passport. He appreciated the fact that medicine, so noble as a profession, remains humble as a science.

Nothing concerning a physician is more revealing than the trajectory of his scientific thinking. In 1938 Dr. Kaida published an experimental study on the tuberculosis bacillus. In electing as basic theme for his work a disease that still heads the Japanese mortality figures, he was linking his scientific bent to his patriotic feelings. In 1941 he published his study on the early diagnosis and prognosis of pulmonary tuberculosis; in 1943 appeared his study on BCG vaccine; in 1949, his study on the problems of relapses in the adult tuberculous patient; in 1954, an evaluation of chemotherapy in tuberculosis and its prospects; in 1958 he published his study of the human constitution and its relation to tuberculosis, plus studies on the development and manifestations of tuberculosis and industry-linked tuberculosis. In these same 23 years there were produced more than 100 other works by him besides these.

If we look into the psychological meaning of these works, we can see that Dr. Kaida's scientific and humanitarian concern began with a study of the etiological agent involved in tuberculosis, then moved on to study early diagnosis, prophylaxis, then relapses and their prevention; he then studied and evaluated the future of the disease, ending up with the study of the "total" patient and the problems of statistics and public health. In other words, his restless mind, moving on from the specificity of laboratory microscopic views, soared like an eagle in flight to take in the entire panorama of public health in its efforts against the frightful white plague. Such is, in synthesis, the splendid development of the scientific thinking of a man, of his yearning to place his science and his conscience at the service of his country and of the health of his compatriots.

It is because of this, that on the day the heart of Katsumi Kaida stopped, countless lips began moving in prayer. He saved many lives and, when all is said and done, is this not the physician's greatest goal and glory? Are not the thanks of those still alive and who mourn for him still, those saved by his Samaritan endeavors, a far greater crown of glory than all the scientific honors paid him in his lifetime?

But more than this, Dr. Katsumi Kaida was a teacher who, with his profound words and wisdom and, above all, with his warm, sincere personality, gathered about him, both in Japan and abroad—as at the International Conference on Medical Aspects of Air Pollution held in Vienna last year—the affection and admiration of all his colleagues.

Enchanting above all else were his humility—always an inseparable attribute of greatness—and his sense of humor, which would burst forth with the spontaneous, candid laughter of a child, joyously ringing through the air.

Added to these qualities was his dynamism. Katsumi Kaida lived in a hurry, as though life itself were a journey and every journey a lifetime. That is the way great men live—men who know that there is much in life to be done and that they must do it fast, so that they may do still more—for life is so short! Perhaps he himself had an unhappy foreboding of his untimely death.

But can one call short the life of a great, creative man, who saved many lives and eased many sufferings, who leaves many friends and pupils and an admirable family, who leaves his stamp on the world of medicine? I think not. It is rather that these meteor-like men pass through more quickly than the rest of us, simply because they do so much more and consequently do not require as much time in life.

Virgil says in the *Aeneid: "Manibus date lilia plenis."* Give the lilies in handfuls. So we should bestow the lilies of remembrance, of love, and of gratitude upon Dr. Katsumi Kaida. His memory will live forever with those of us who had the honor of speaking, laughing, and living with him.

May his soul know the same peace and serenity that his presence afforded us, a serenity that can only be compared with the calm, peace, beauty, and inspiration of the marvelous sand and rock garden of Ryoanji in Kyoto.

VI. love, lust, and letters

ARS AMANDI

*W*hen not so very long ago marriage was an indissoluble institution, the cynical retaliated by ridiculing it. There is but one antidote for love, they mocked, and that is marriage, the only "eternal" happiness that lasts but a few months. Thus Daumier himself saw it and ironically depicted the situation in his famous drawing of a married couple yawning without restraint. In love, he thereby proved, the fatal thing is not the quarrels but the yawns. In those days people attended *both* weddings and funerals attired in black—"And a good reason there must have been!" the witty ones remarked, adding further that some men contracted matrimony only to have someone take care of them, which was the same as chopping off one's hands in order to dispense with wearing gloves, or else, with the idea that only those who have been "joined together" can be "put asunder," they married in order to get *out* of a woman's grasp.

Today marriage is the object of much concern by physicians. This is no mere professional curiosity, but the result of the conviction that medical advice can greatly help to restore confidence in marriage, certainly much more than by granting marriage the freedom of a bird, with the ultimate possibility of winging smack against a lighthouse in the dead of night.

One fact, however, is clear: next to the amorous communism of some animals, marriage between human beings symbolizes a step toward extreme specificity of the instinct. The capacity to love is

From *MD*, the MEDICAL NEWSMAGAZINE, 3:11, June, 1959.

practically the same in all men. The real difference lies in the *selection* of the beloved, which depends on the state of development of the instinct of the species, ranging from an absolute lack of capacity to differentiate in selecting the object of love to the maximum capacity characteristic of a perfect monogamy.

The state of development of the sexual instinct is revealed by the differentiation exercised in choosing the object of love. In such cases, when the ideal object of love is found, it sometimes coincides with the ideal marriage partner chosen at an earlier age. But if it fails to coincide, then either there is an adaptation, instinct becoming conditioned by the force of habit, or there is that seemingly inexplicable rupture (biologically explicable) of a marriage that seemed "perfect."

Before reaching the marriage stage, man goes through various stages: the stage of the unspecific love object, during which he blindly seeks a partner; the stage of group impulse, during which the opposite sex in general is attractive; the stage of attraction toward a specific group of the opposite sex endowed with certain specific qualities; and the "ideal" stage—the monogamous, in which attraction is felt toward *one* person only, as happens to men, like Don Quixote, endowed with a superlative sexual differentiation. Modern life, which has promoted a closer and more honest contact between the sexes, has facilitated the search for the ideal partner, for the Beatrice waiting for every Dante in his quest for love.

Man's love, therefore, is a monogamous emotional rebellion against the "polygamy" of sexual instinct. But love is *not* marriage. Man contracts matrimony, but he is bewitched by love, impelled by the yearning to be close to the beloved, to embark on a spiritual pilgrimage into the loved one, to merge into one with her. Such fusion impulse is corroborated by the peculiarly cannibalistic language of love: "I could eat you up."

Modern social conditions are doing away with some of the economic factors that in former times made marriage a burden to the poor. Among the half million inhabitants of Athens in 300 B.C., only a few thousand were sufficiently well off to get married. In feudal times, the upper classes and the *bourgeoisie* were monogamous for financial reasons and in order to protect private estates. Today, greater leveling of economic values has remedied this state of affairs.

In marriage, man seeks immortality through woman by having children, while woman seeks her own individual fulfillment through the reflected glory of man. Also in matrimony man seeks and loves woman, and woman seeks and loves children. The sad conclusion appears to be that no one seeks or loves poor man!

Love is often a mutual victory, which, if the erotic reserves in marriage are not renewed, ends in sexual boredom and polygamy. This is why it is advisable to cultivate once again Ovid's *ars amandi,* the erotization of marriage and the spiritualization of sex; to prefer the dangers of passion, which are those of life, to the dangers of conformity, which are those of death. For if man and wife learn to play the game with fairness and delicacy, they can together, without soiling their hands, prepare for themselves a magnificent feast at the table of life.

CASANOVA, THEN AND NOW

*t*he current issue of *MD* is devoted to the study of sex, next to hunger the driving force in life. It is proper therefore to recall that unique incarnation of *homo eroticus,* Giovanni Jacopo Casanova.

The fame of Casanova, one of the most interesting specimens of humanity, derives from his having purposely led a purposeless life, while remaining constantly true to his chosen destiny as a professional lover. A Venetian of Spanish origin, Casanova in the space of thirty years, from the age of 15 to 45, "knew" more than one hundred women in the Biblical sense of the word, which makes him a marathon winner in the Olympic games of love-making. In his old age, when "no longer capable of acting the god in the garden and the satyr in the shrubbery, he had become a wolf at the dining table," Casanova spent seven years in the chateau of Count Waldstein narrating his bedroom exploits in his *Memoirs,* whose words still ring with song and dance, like a baroque Venetian carnival. Later, he had to be content with only one meal a day and no women, which drove him to make a melancholy reappraisal of dishes—like *olla-podrida*—he could no longer eat, and of women—like Bettina, his first love—he could no longer love.

One hundred sixty years after his death, Casanova still fascinates us, perhaps because all men fall into three groups: those who think they could be Casanovas; those who think they have been Casanovas; and those who think they could have been had they only taken the

From *MD,* the MEDICAL NEWSMAGAZINE, 4:11, June, 1960.

trouble. The myth of Don Juan, the man who spends his life seducing women, is eminently Spanish, but, like the Don Quixote myth, it has become universal and eternal, and its roots can be found in Ovid, Machiavelli, Tirso de Molina, Molière, Mozart, Dumas, and Shaw.

In Spain—cradle of the myth of Don Juan, and of its antithesis, the pure and romantic Don Quixote—Don Juan was an antisocial rebel and polygamist, perpetually in conflict with God and the state, an epitome of the cherished Spanish dream of everyone doing whatever he well pleased.

Casanova had neither Aladdin's lamp nor the houris of paradise, but his indestructible energy won him the treasure cave and an ever-changing harem of odalisques. He lived to love, and he loved to live. Pushkin, Byron, Alfred de Musset, Benjamin Constant, all were Don Juans in real life; but of all philanderers-extraordinary the most outstanding example was Casanova. And yet he cannot be considered a typical Don Juan, for he lacked the sentimental and spiritual components, the religious piety and scruples, that ultimately drove Don Juan to repent and won him a pious burial beneath a crimson rose-bush in lovely Seville.

As physicians, we should find Casanova's physique interesting. He was ugly but interesting in appearance, with olive complexion and with piercing eyes. Thus he is portrayed in the painting by his brother, extant at the Daschoff Collection in Leningrad. He had a large nose, often a sign of great sexual capacity; but he was also extremely tall and had a receding mandibula. Paradoxically, gigantism and maxillary hypoplasia are characteristics of a eunuchoid morphology, just as the opposite—short height and a prognathous mandibula—is characteristic of the hypergenital type, symbolized by the satyrs in mythology.

The portraits of Don Juan by Murillo and Elías Salaverría reveal also a slightly effeminate figure. Casanova had a tenor voice, which, whether in Don Juans or crooners, has always attracted women, particularly intersexuals, because of its enigmatic ambiguity, just as Carmen's deep contralto voice attracted men with a weak personality. Casanova's hand gestures were elegant and vain, and always endeavored to suggest his sexual assets. He loved to dress in rich velvets and flashing jewels and was always impeccably groomed, an important detail, since the more undifferentiated a man's personality is, the more overfastidious is his apparel. He suffered countless venereal complaints, which he "cured" as best he could; but his energy was imperishable, as evidenced by his amatory exploits, his escape from *Il Piombi* in Venice, his writing for fourteen hours a day, and his playing cards for forty-two hours at a stretch.

Casanova always took extreme pains to enter a town with great pomp and ceremony. The townspeople had to be impressed and the ground paved for his amatory conquests. He always protected himself against the dangers of a single love (to love only once, for some men, is always too long) by seducing several women at the same time. He found it easier to be the mediocre lover of many women than the perfect lover of only one.

Casanova was not the kind of Don Juan who when young is forever lovesick or skirt-crazy, and when old is pleasure hungry or a glutton. Nor was he a sentimental Don Juan, like Goethe. As he himself admits in his *Memoirs,* love to him was a profession and a way of life. He was also a professional gambler. Gambling and Donjuanism nearly always go together. A Don Juan's erotic victories are as irrational and capricious as a gambler's victories at the gaming table. Besides, gambling to Casanova was imperative, for without money the road is hard for the professional lover. Casanova was also a medical quack, making up with verbosity for his lack of basic knowledge. But what he most excelled in was the art of love, graduating *honoris causa* in his self-created university of love.

What was Casanova's secret? His technique, which can be studied in the four-thousand pages of his *Memoirs,* was an almost scientific application of various psychological principles to the chasing of women. A born psychologist, Casanova exploited the ambivalent feeling of admiration-hate in the men whose women he stole. For this they hated him, but they also admired him for being what they themselves secretly wished to be: the man who by conquering and abandoning women takes revenge for the slights inflicted by women on all other men. Casanova also exploited feminine resentment against men. In allowing themselves to be seduced by the Venetian adventurer, women, even those who apparently despised him, unconsciously took revenge on the other men who had subdued, spurned, or forsaken them.

Casanova mobilized all these favorable psychological forces by availing himself of various resources to create the myth of his amorous prowess. His erotic prestige with women was due above all to the impression he strove to make among men. In every town he visited, the first thing he did was to compel male admiration, knowing full well the repercussion this would have on the women. He assiduously cultivated the great men of his time, including Voltaire and Haller. Gold, power, mystery, these were the main weapons of Casanova.

Another clue to his successes is the type of women he attracted. No woman of sterling feminine qualities did the Venetian ever clasp in his arms in the thousand and one nights of love in his life, but only epicene types, lacking in distinct personality, pretty women with bored souls, women generally avoided or neglected by normal men, who, even if they are less-attractive and even ugly, prefer more interesting and complex women.

Casanova pandered to the female ego by simulating a great respect for it, while in fact he had no interest whatsoever in it. We men, more so than women, nurture a secret "ideal woman," within which we usually frame the beloved, while completely ignoring her own ideal. We want to possess her soul by locking it in the framework of our life, by imprisoning it in our dreams, while her own dreams mean nothing to us. Amazingly, women do not fight against this pattern. Casanova never fell in love; he therefore never interfered with a woman's inner self or dreams, which he was incapable of understanding. Hence the reason women found Casanova "different." They failed to realize that this was positive proof that he was not in love with them.

To his technique of first arousing the admiration of the men— family, husband, fiancé, male friends—surrounding the woman he had marked down for conquest, Casanova added two other weapons that even today would assure any man of success were they not precluded by our way of life. First, he dressed his promises in burning emotion. Not only did he swear eternal love and everlasting marriage to all his women, but he did so on bended knees, with tears streaming down his face, which he wiped off in the folds of the skirt of the overwhelmed victim. Few could resist such blandishments, just as a century and a half later few could resist the Italian poet Gabriele D'Annunzio. When they resisted, he displayed his colossal audacity (always a characteristic of the professional seducer), rushing them into his embrace with passionate advances.

His other weapon was time. Neither clock nor calendar meant anything to Casanova when he laid siege to a new damsel. Time and space do not exist in his *Memoirs*. The clock was only a reminder of the hour of assignation; and space, that is, scenery or background, had no significance. An erotic adventure occupied his pen throughout multiple pages, but not a single line did he ever devote to the landscape, witness of his escapades, though, like all Don Juans, he traveled extensively. In fact, his cosmopolitanism, which ensured an endless change of women and environment, was another of his weapons. With his astonishing contempt for time and space, concentrating solely, whether for a day or a year, on his current quarry, few women among the sheltered ladies of Venice, the dressmakers of Turin, the nymphs of Chaillot and of the *grands boulevards* of Paris, the *Fräuleins* of Vienna, the courtesans of England could resist the man who made them feel desired above all things, who showed them that nothing existed or mattered besides his love for them.

After all these years Casanova has not yet been subjected to the clinical autopsy he deserves, which I hope some day to make. His morphology does in fact reveal a great deal. His dark complexion, his great height, his receding lower mandibula and eunuchoid features, indicative of low sexual potency and sterility (only a few and unconfirmed cases of paternity are mentioned in his *Memoirs*), are as revealing in the biological sense as his narcissism, irreligiosity, anti-social tendencies, indifference to his mistresses, sexual cynicism, exhibitionism, and typically schizo-manic, sexual-psychopathic aggressiveness are in the psychological sense.

Casanova's psychobiological autopsy would probably reveal, paradoxically, a man of limited sexual potency, who made of his mistresses friends, just as Don Juan turned his friends into mistresses; who did not choose love, but was chosen by love; who loved with the same urgency of an autumnal woman nabbing one last love affair or of a commuter catching the last train. He was a man who chose especially not very intelligent, unfeminine, young girls; who made love in public, deliberately making an exhibition of himself, in contrast to normal love-making, which is more modest and discreet; who accepted the love of protective often elderly women; who instead of working and struggling for a living, as most men do, preferred not to toil and made love to women instead. Was not victory in this pursuit so much easier? This giant with maxillary hypoplasia, with a penchant for mendacity (a sign of sexual weakness), was sexually immature and as unspecific to the women who accepted his love as they were to him.

Why is Casanova's figure so fascinating? Perhaps because his *Memoirs* is the most picturesque book of the eighteenth century; because he was not tragic, like Don Juan, but gave pleasure to every woman who knew him, a pleasure that sprang not from his amatory powers but from his supreme skill in satisfying woman's peripheral amorous proclivities and vanity; because to a certain extent he was as faithful to the destiny of professional lover he designed for himself as a mystic is to his chosen faith.

Unlike a normal lover, Casanova was incapable of jealousy or gloom. He created his own erotic propaganda. He made not of work but of sex, not of competing in work with other men but of seducing women, his profession. His treasure chest was crammed with women, women without quality. His sexual promiscuity betrayed his low masculinity, for the man who has known many women, or the woman who has known many men, like some film stars or playboys of today, merely proves that he exerts an attraction on many but can hold none. Nowadays, when the telephone has taken the place of the love letter and telegrams and flowers have replaced the love ballad, when we live fighting the clock and the calendar and fear to display our emotions, Casanova could not exist.

To us physicians Casanova is as worthy of study as is an exceptional clinical case, for his life is a review of the foibles, vices, and deceits of the eighteenth century. He is also of interest to us because, by contrast, he makes us realize the joy there is in loving only one woman, which he himself could never do. And yet. . . .

Voltaire once told Casanova that they should both respect Albrecht von Haller as the greatest medical figure of the eighteenth century. Casanova replied that though Voltaire had a high opinion of Haller, the latter had a very poor one of Voltaire. To which Voltaire replied: "Perhaps we are both wrong." Perhaps *we* are wrong in thinking of Casanova as merely an erotic rascal and in underestimating all the forms of love.

A LETTER FROM MADAME

a "personal form of literature" was Ortega y Gasset's definition of the letter, and once more his conceptual arrow hit a bull's-eye. "Letters," Goethe said, "are the most beautiful, the most immediate breath of life." This literary form, unfortunately, has been swept away in our vertiginous way of life, which precludes letter writing as it should be done: like a horse carriage gently jogging along in the countryside instead of like a jet plane speeding thunderously across the sky.

In this issue of *MD* dedicated to woman, I want to write, as Robert Louis Stevenson said, "a footnote to history"—to the history of the most typically feminine literature, letter writing. Dr. Gregorio Marañón once remarked that among the many things that have suffered from the feverish pace of contemporary life are two arts that seem commonplace because anyone may practice them without an academic training, though perfection in them is reserved to very few: the art of letter writing and the art of conversation.

Haste, the jinni that has transformed modern life, has made more difficult every day those two facets of a single art, which, through direct communication between two minds, can create mutual understanding among men. Indeed, many people may ask why spend hours in conversation or writing when a few minutes on the telephone or a few lines in a telegram will do just as well? But when we write to another person, we are creating with another distant soul an oasis of intimacy in the desert of space. Greater than the miracle

From *MD,* the MEDICAL NEWSMAGAZINE, 5:11, June, 1961.

of the telegram's speed through space is that of the letter's eternity in time, because of the everlasting bonds it creates. Today the letters of George Sand to Alfred de Musset, of Vincent van Gogh to his brother, evoke a profound emotion in us. The same thing happens when two people talk for the sheer joy of exchanging ideas. Modern substitutes for conversation and letter writing being within everyone's reach, only a chosen few can still write a good letter or sustain a good conversation, and of the letter writers the best are women.

Unfortunately people nowadays rather than write prefer to send a telegram, a medium formerly reserved for very bad or very good news. Not so long ago there even were post cards, half joke, half tragedy, on which the lazy husband when traveling could check off printed phrases posting his darling wife on the progress of his trip: his trip was going fine; it was raining; he missed her; he had played poker; he lost his eyeglasses—everything, absolutely everything except the truth: that he could not be bothered to write letters to her. Had the truth been printed on the card, it would never have sold.

Still, the letter has been not only one of the supporting pillars of literature in history but also one of the formative elements of the conscience of our ancestors. The Spanish philosopher Miguel de Unamuno related how his epistolary style was born from the fact that during his engagement he and his fiancée lived far apart, in different Basque villages, and since they could not see each other often, they wrote daily. This they did so faithfully for fifteen years, never missing a day, that when they were finally married, in order not to break the habit they went on writing to each other.

Men are very poor letter writers. We do not visualize at the other end of our pen or typewriter the real person to whom we are writing but see instead an imaginary audience that will cheer or hiss when they read what we have written. That is why our love letters often read like sermons. Women, on the other hand, do not turn their pen into a loud-speaker; instead they pour on paper the thousand and one marvels of the magic night, athrob with promise and fantasy, that is their soul. Woman individualizes herself most in her letters; man in his letters usually dramatizes and collectivizes his spiritual intimacy because of his unconscious feeling that some day his written word may become a public manifesto of his thoughts.

Jessamyn West has said: "A woman feels that it is ludicrous to begin any writing on the subject of love except such writing as is headed: My dear love. Men may write about women; they do so all the time; a woman prefers to write *to* a man. A man writing about love analyzes emotions and searches for phrases. A woman's instinct is to put an end to all that nonsense with a kiss."

In a world where the art of letter writing is vanishing, we might think that we could look to lovers for help in preserving the art. One South American government some time ago offered to cut in half the postage on love letters, provided these were sent in a special bright crimson envelope for identification purposes. But lovers ignored the offer. Rather than waste time and money, lovers prefer to get married and spare themselves both the trouble and the expense of letter writing. After marriage, when parted by a journey or other reasons, they write to each other, but the lack of romance in their letters is shattering. They speak of forgotten undergarments, of household expenses, of the little spaniel left behind, of the weather and the food, and poor Cupid, filled with shame, blushes a red deeper than that of the lover's envelope mentioned above.

Years ago, a charming book by Helen Scheu-Riesz was published containing a compilation of love letters of famous men and women, from Isabella of Angoulême down to Abraham Lincoln. Reading this volume, one realizes that even the style of love letters is influenced by the architectural style of an epoch, which is one proof of the correlation between art and life in the history of nations.

For instance, the mystic multiarched Gothic architecture was reflected in the "Gothic" letters written by Arthur, Prince of Wales, to Catherine of Aragon; the stability and vigor of the Renaissance pillar, in the lusty letters of Henry VIII to Anne Boleyn; the emotionally conceived, overornamented architecture of the Baroque, in the ornate and emotive letters of John Russel to his future wife, Lady Frances Rich, daughter of Oliver Cromwell; the absurd florid elegance of the Rococo, in the highly embellished letters of Jonathan Swift to Miss Mary Scurlock; the cold, sober, metallic ornamentation in the Directoire and Empire styles, in the laconic, straightforward letters of Laurence Sterne to Elizabeth Draper; the simple, austere, economical Colonial American style, in the direct letters of the parson-physician, Cotton Mather, to the "immaculate gentlewoman" who lived two doors away from him.

(Sending letters is not the exclusive privilege of the human being. The polar explorer Sir George Wilkins once related how penguins declare their love: when the male finds the female he wants to mate with, he picks up a pebble and deposits it at her feet. She inspects him from top to toe and, if she likes his looks, accepts the pebble and carries it to the place hidden in the rocks where she wants to set up housekeeping. There the two penguins in love build their nest and start a family life. One polar expedition included a painter who sat down every day to sketch the penguins as they wandered about the rocks. One morning a male penguin slowly approached and dropped a pebble at the artist's feet! But, let us return to letters.)

Women in their letters like to stray from the main issue. St.

Theresa of Jesus wrote letters full of parenthetic insertions about anything that happened at the moment, just as a hospital nurse, on her way to a patient in the ward, pauses here and there to straighten a ruffled blanket or a cluttered night table.

For that reason, women write better letters than men. Men are intent only on expressing specific ideas in as literary a style as possible. Women write letters as they should be written—freely, spontaneously, full of disconnected items, distractions, and trifles, because to them a letter is equivalent to a chat. Women tell "things" better. This is why Madame de Sévigné's letters reflected so faithfully the blithe chaos and gay confusion of life.

With splendid realism woman places things before ideas, exactly the opposite of what man does. Men write letters as though they were lectures to be read by a vast invisible audience. Women, on the contrary, flit gaily from topic to topic, like happy birds in a sunlit cage, chatting solely for the benefit of their listener and to some extent to hear themselves, like a canary well pleased with its own golden warbling.

A woman's style in writing, as in speaking, is volubly versatile, not rigidly architectonic like the male's. Her syntax is often surrealistic, her spelling Picassian, her style Daliesque in its baroqueness, her reasoning jumpy and incomplete but sparkling with wit and humor. Two of the greatest letter writers, St. Theresa and Madame de Sévigné, often jumbled their sentences and took all kinds of grammatical liberties. But women's outward volubility cloaks an inner constancy that is common to them all. Between Hippocrates, Rembrandt, Balzac, Lincoln, and Gregory Peck there is a much greater difference as human beings than there is between Sappho, Isabella the Catholic, the Marquise de Pompadour, Madame Curie, and Zsa Zsa Gabor.

Women's common denominator is that they are true to themselves, to their sex, and to their sense of social life. Even the fickleness of fashion is liberty for woman (though a liberty that sometimes enslaves her to the new styles). Nevertheless, there is less difference in the epistolary style of women down the centuries, whatever their era and country or their social and human quality may have been, than in that of men.

It cannot be denied that the great creations in art and history have been made by men. Woman's greatest creations have been in mysticism and in love, not in the arts or politics, except in acting as inspiration to great men. Recently women have started to win fresh laurels in literature, especially in Europe, where the younger women are succeeding with books that are like love letters, in which happen only things that seem trivial to men but that are really the essence of life itself. The purpose of the things they tell is to reveal their impact on love and their reflection in the female soul. This is what happens with the novels of Françoise Sagan and Christine de Rochemond, which are merely long letters about love and suffering written by perpetually adolescent souls.

Woman is a creature of love. That is why she is so superior to man in her letters, since in them she employs all the tricks of the crafty player, embracing these as part of the battle. But woman is also closer to the magical and the elemental, to the plant and the animal. She is much more "species" and less "individual" than man. The female sex is a freemasonry. Women prefer to be mastered rather than to be convinced. They love mystery. That is why a sick countrywoman will prefer a written prescription of magic symbolic significance to a simple pill.

We praise man by calling him cultured or famous. Woman we compare to lovely things—the palm tree or the gazelle, the rose or the nightingale—because poetically she belongs in that intuitive and mysterious, elemental and instinctive world that is also the world of the saint, the mystic, the hero, and the poet. There is in woman a Pavlovian unity between facts and ideas, life and emotion, which contrasts with man's Cartesian duality. That is why women's letters, with their frivolous trifles woven out of moonbeams and mending thread, tell much more than men's letters with their symphonic prose.

A woman writes letters the way she lives, without distant objectives or planned programs, carrying her ethics and her ideals within herself, without placing her life, as man does, at the service of an ideal or a goal. A woman in love places her life at the service of her loved one, just as man dedicates his to the tremendous task of being a man. The biological motive of woman's life is love, just as the underlying motive of man's life is work.

Biologically, woman was created to be man's companion and the bearer of children, and only secondarily for work. Woman is as she is. She is loquacious because her being overflows with her thoughts. And when she talks or writes it is the concrete, specific, individual case that interests her, not the abstract idea that interests the male, for she loves things and not ideas.

Woman prattles in her letters, and therein lies the charm of her letters. The perfect woman in this sense is the geisha, who chatters charmingly and whose verbal letters give the male a sensation of being admired for his superiority and of being in a corner of Paradise unmarred by the serpents of problems.

In this sense woman is "historic," because she lives in the present and becomes a part of history only by being a part of the biography of the man she loves. What counts with her is the present. Perhaps that is why Milton, rather rudely, labeled her "this fair defect of nature." But through her function of safeguarding the survival of the species, woman protects mankind in *time,* just as by his deeds and achievements, man protects it in *space.* In such a sense, we owe woman our eternal gratitude, because through love of her we attain salvation in the future, just as through worship of her beauty we are ennobled in the present.

VII. the marvels of man

THE MASK AND THE MIRROR

a face bewitched Paris fifty years ago—the face of a young girl who put an end to her life in the still, green waters of the Seine. Her death mask at the Paris morgue gripped the hearts of Parisians. The adolescent countenance, already marked by suffering, glowed with gentle resignation, and the young lips appeared to smile as if in death the child had at last found peace and contentment. Paris poetically called her *L'Inconnue du Seine.*

In the past the human face held a great fascination for both physicians and artists. "The countenance proclaims the heart and inclination," said Sir Thomas Browne. Artists sought to immortalize the beauty of the human face, while physicians avidly studied it—the Hippocratic facies, the scrofulous facies, the leonine face, the myopathic facies—in search of the inner processes of disease.

But early in the present century, Picasso, with his "Les Demoiselles d'Avignon," started a trend in art that would culminate in the automatic massacre of that mirror of the soul—the human face, while physicians began to lose interest in the patient's face as a whole and concentrated instead on its parts. "Modern" artists conscientiously dismembered the face and put it together again, turning into multispiked geometry the sweet harmony of its curves; while physicians, under the impact of the advances in laboratory research, concentrated on ocular, otoscopic, rhinoscopic, and other explorations, and gradually forsook the clinical observation of the whole face, which down the centuries so fascinated Greek *periodeutai,* Arabian hakims, and Renaissance physiks alike. Dismemberment of the spatial scheme of the face and loss of interest in the face occurred simultaneously in art and medicine.

From *MD,* the MEDICAL NEWSMAGAZINE, *3*:11, March, 1959.

Perhaps there were reasons for such events. Perhaps the face was being overornamented. How severely taxed a nineteenth-century Frenchman's face must have felt under the burden it was forced to carry! In addition to its usual parts, it had to withstand a mustache the size of a fox's tail, sideburns several inches long, a goatee, spectacles or a monocle, wrinkles, and birthmarks. It must have felt like an overcrowded attic. The female face was subjected to an equally sad fate. Cosmetics feuded bitterly with personality and original charm. Perhaps the artist sought to find in a single feature what the whole face could no longer reveal. Instead of beauty of the whole, the mystery imprisoned in each part became the challenge. And the artist who concentrated his interest on one facial feature—eyes, mustache—was but reflecting the attitude of the physician, who himself turned his attention to the partial reports made by the specialist and the laboratory.

Fortunately, there seems to be a revival of interest in the face as a whole, be it mirror or mask. We no longer believe that the face is a mirror of the soul. This new interest that is being evidenced in both art and medicine is centered not on the form of the face but on its *expression,* not on the face as a window but on the world that lies beyond it.

This change in interest from the purely anatomical to the psycho-physiological in the human face had its beginning in art in the Baroque, as exemplified by Il Tintoretto and El Greco. A good example was the change in interest from the eye, an organ, to the look, a function. Greek sculptors left just a hole between the eyelids, for they felt that if the eye was beautiful the look was not. Only in the Baroque did the look begin to have more importance than the eye. The best exponent of this point was Goya, in whose paintings the pictorial anatomy of the eye was relegated to the background by *the look* conveyed by the eye. The yearning to capture the *expression* not just of the eye but of the whole face is now also infiltrating medicine.

Today it is recognized that no objective scientific description can provide as clear an idea of what ails a patient as his own words can. Hence the advisability of using the patient's own words when writing a clinical case history. Similarly, nothing in the face of a patient can guide a clinician as much as his *expression.*

Let us, then, learn once again to look at the human face with the same avid curiosity as our ancient predecessors. Let us be fascinated above all by its expression, that priceless clue to character and, even more important to us, disease. For just as the young face of *L'Inconnue du Seine* vividly recorded her tragedy, so may the face of man record the greatness of his life and the misery of his pain.

236

THE MIRACLE TOOL

Once in Tangier, that stab of light in the back of the Mediterranean, a Moorish shepherd boy revealed to me the secret of the hand. Coming out of my hotel one morning, I saw him, his hand outstretched, holding a blossom that he absent-mindedly waved at the lambs in his care. When I returned to the hotel that evening, he still sat there in the same indolent yet arrogant pose, like a sultan out of the *Arabian Nights,* while his weary flock lay dozing in the violet dusk. His hand, though now empty, was still outstretched, as if waiting for heaven to drop into it a silver star. The hand for that young Moor was a poetic instrument with which, while engaged in his contemplative task, he plucked flowers by day and begged at night for alms from heaven.

To us physicians the hand is of great interest because of all it reveals about a person's condition, particularly his endocrine state. Since Aristotle, man has been called intelligent because he has a hand. It might be more correct to say that because of the intelligence directing it, the hand is a wonderful organ that has turned man from *homo sapiens* into *homo faber.* The gesture of the hand dynamically sums up our personality. The meaning of "gesture"—a word cognate with "geste," meaning exploit—is especially embodied in the hand, which is the most expressive vehicle for the individual gestures of emotion— the lover's passionate hand, the twitching hand of the angry man, the suppliant hand of the mystic, the fluttering hand of the dancer—and for collective gestures—the upraised open hand or the clenched fist,

From *MD,* the MEDICAL NEWSMAGAZINE, 4:11, March, 1960.

symbolic salutes of the totalitarian regimes. The physicians of yore had good reason to maintain that the tongue was the agent of the brain, and the hand of the heart, to which it was united by special veins. This was why the wedding ring, symbolic of the sickness of love having found a happy consummation or a definite remedy, should be placed on the ring finger of the left hand.

Despite its anatomical imperfection, the human hand is a very beautiful thing and represents a sovereign advance in the biological evolution of this organ by way of the horse's hoof and the hand of the ape. Although the parts of the hand—bones, muscles, synovial membranes, tendons, and articulations—are rudimentary and irregular in direction and size, the hand as a whole is of an exquisite and delicate structure. Contrasting sharply with the highly developed, strong, and grasping thumb (that all-powerful and cruel digit with which the Roman emperors granted life or death at amphitheatres) and the bold, aggressive index finger (digit of instruction in the teacher, of inquiry in the pupil, of direction and decision in everyone), we have: the weak, clumsy middle finger, which, though it is prolonged by the third metacarpal bone and the forearm, is an extension of the shaft of the arm and lacks mobility; the even clumsier helpless ring finger, held imprisoned and powerless between the middle finger and the little finger; and last, the dwarfish, spindly little finger, a thwarted puny imitation of the thumb. Notwithstanding such imperfections, the hand is the most wonderful tool man possesses, a fact symbolized in the first gesture of the newborn babe and the last gesture of the dying man—the hand fluttering in the air.

A simple handshake with a patient or a quick glance at his hands can reveal many things to the physician. Hands can betray congenital heart diseases, subacute bacterial endocarditis, telangiectasis, hyperpigmentation, and embolism. In particular, hands reveal the endocrine condition of a person. We may cite, for instance, the "winter" hand described by Gregorio Marañón—hypogenital, acrocyanotic, cold, moist, and swollen, as if it had been kept a long time in water and had never quite dried, betraying in both sexes a pluriglandular insufficiency syndrome; the "summer" hand—delicate, aristocratic, warm and dry or warmly perspiring—of the hyperthyroid person; the broad hand of the acromegalic; the "cook's" hand of the hypothyroid; the "angelic" hand of the thymicolymphatic person; the Mongolian hand; the childish hand. The hand can indeed enable us to cast the endocrinal horoscope of a patient.

In literature, art, and history, we encounter every sort of hand: the gentle hands of Christ, like luminous lilies nailed on the Cross; the hands of Pontius Pilate, from which water could not wash off his criminal abulia; the dovelike hands in Botticelli's canvases; the blood-stained hands of Lady Macbeth; the healing hands of the Renaissance monarchs; the loving passionate hands of Chloë, Juliet, Messalina, and Cleopatra; the brave, noble hands of Don Quixote; the creative hands of Leonardo da Vinci, Vesalius, El Greco, Pasteur, Beethoven, and Harvey Cushing; the inspired hands of Alicia Markova, Paderewski, Pablo Casals, and Edith Sitwell. Especially we note the hands of the physician, who, from Hippocrates to Osler, has devoted them to exploring his patient, to investigating in the laboratory, and to teaching in the lecture hall.

But perhaps nothing so much as applause reveals the magic power of the hands to convert emotion into action. In applauding to show admiration, the human being opens his arms as if to give a hug, brings his hands together again to make a clapping sound, and separates them once more to set free the invisible magic bird of applause, that winged messenger from the heart of man.

THE EYE AND THE GLANCE

I f you want to "collect" *eyes,* you need only enter any museum and
look at all the paintings and statuary. But if it is the *glance* you
are interested in, nowhere will you find better examples than in
Rembrandt's paintings at the Rijksmuseum or in Goya's works at the
Museo del Prado.

For both Rembrandt, the magician of light, and Goya, the wizard
of shadows, gave up painting the eye and its anatomy to concentrate
on its physiological function, seeking not so much to portray the
human eye as to capture with their brushes all the splendor of its
glance.

For the specialists of today, and particularly for neurologists, the
eye is an exquisite coffer filled with subtle diagnostic signs. For
ophthalmologists it has become, moreover, a theatre for the most
extraordinary surgical operations, in which, as in certain episodes of
the Bible, is enacted the sublime miracle of light.

The history of ophthalmology is a unique chapter in the history of
medicine because of the superstition, myth, and legend surrounding
the eye from the dawn of history. While other sense organs, such as
the nose, tongue, or ears, were studied by physicians down the centuries, first empirically and later scientifically, the eye, the most vital
of all to man because of the importance of its function and the mystery of its nature, remained a *terra* not only *incognita* but also *mystica.*
The eye was not explored for fear of offending the gods, of whose
omnipresence the eye itself was a symbol. Hence, the history of

From *MD,* the MEDICAL NEWSMAGAZINE, 5:9, March, 1961.

ophthalmology is the history of a gigantic conflict between mystic prejudice and practical necessity, a conflict settled only in comparatively recent times by the scientific exploration of the eye. It is also the history of the attitudes of society not only toward the eye but also toward the visual function, reflected in the religions, art, and culture of each period, attitudes so strong that they hampered our knowledge of this organ until the Renaissance, when the "visual" replaced the "auditive" attitude in medicine.

It is enlightening to follow the evolution of the eye in art and its correlation with progress in ophthalmology. In every period in history, the artist's attitude in portraying the eye reflected and often anticipated the medical attitude on this subject. Each of these two attitudes, in their turn, sprang from the cultural, religious, and social atmosphere of each period. The human eye was regarded and portrayed as a symbol in mythology, an anatomical part in ancient Greece, an allegory in medieval art, an architectonic part in Renaissance art, an optical instrument in baroque art, and a functional organ in the Age of Enlightenment. From this last period sprang the streams of thought that led to the current concept of the "cerebral eye," now studied in ophthalmology and depicted in modern art as an organ expressive of the human mind and emotions.

The ophthalmology of prehistoric man was limited probably to the application of clay and vegetable poultices to soothe and protect eyes that had been scratched or injured by claws, thorns, or stones, and to wash away sight-dimming secretions and matter. This crude ocular traumatology was paralleled by the rarity with which the eye was shown in prehistoric paintings, doubtless owing to fear of the magical disasters that might result from portrayal on cave walls of the mysterious organ, which at night winked down by the thousands with a menacing fiery glint from the distant heavens.

A new attitude in art arose in the Mesopotamian, Chaldean, and Egyptian civilizations. The eye then was depicted salient and open, with the lids chiseled to an equal curvature, there being no prolongation of the upper eyelid in Mesopotamian bas reliefs or in the cruel eyes shown in Assyrian art.

In ancient Egypt, except in the time of Akhenaton, the eye was shown naturalistically in sculptures, with a straight edge to the lower lids, the axis between the two corners of the eye stretched horizontally, and the eyes were set close to the nose. In statues the iris was tangential to the upper eyelid, and the glance was fixed and hard, in contrast to its languid and wandering appearance in Egyptian paintings.

The most exemplary portrayal of the eye in ancient Egypt was the Eye of Horus, which made its appearance more than five thousand years ago. According to legend, Horus, son of the goddess Isis, as an infant was attacked and blinded by the demon Set, but recovered his sight when his mother invoked the aid of Thoth, god of learning. Therefore, the Egyptians implored the hawk-headed god Horus to cure their ills, accompanying their pleas with the plucking of lyres made from medicinal woods.

Depicted in Egyptian iconography as an *R* with an eye painted inside the top circle, the eye of Horus became a healing symbol, and *utchats,* or amulets of gold, copper, wood, or wax representing it, were used as protection against ocular infections and sore eyes. Later, Horus was supplanted by other gods, since fashion has ruled even in the popularity of gods. In the Middle Ages the Eye of Horus reappeared in the form of a sign similar to the figure 4, which physicians and alchemists wrote on their prescriptions to invoke divine aid, thus resuscitating the Roman custom of writing the sign of Jupiter for similar purposes.

The ℞ sign was introduced by the physician Krinas in the time of Nero as a graphic symbol that the physician—and Christianity—was subject to the power of the state. In the Middle Ages, in a typical swing of history's pendulum, the Church, in its struggle against medieval paganism in countries like Spain, compelled physicians to use the initials of the *Responsum Raphaelis* instead of the heathen sign for Jupiter. Thus, little by little, the sign of Horus became confused with that of Jupiter and turned into the ℞, which is still used today in the upper left-hand corner of prescriptions.

Egypt's glaring sun and the sandstorms that forever fill its air with a floating infinity of silica and mica grains—tiny mirrors that give the Egyptian air that magic luminescence—were among the factors responsible for the large number of eye diseases in that country. Exposure to the glaring sun, heat, wind, and dust provoked a hyperemia of the bulbar conjunctiva, and, just as the skin reacts to such a climate by turning freckled or tanned, the eye developed a delicate web of dilated blood vessels that made it more susceptible to morbid processes.

The frequency, in ancient times just as now, of trachoma and other eye conditions in Egypt spurred specialization in ophthalmology. Again, to prevent the ocular deformation that occurs at death, the Egyptians filled the eye sockets of the dead with linen compresses on which was painted the iris, and then covered the whole thing with the eyelids, or they filled the sockets—as in the mummy of Ramses I—with tiny onions, whose magic properties were of additional value.

This intimate association of the eye with religious symbolism hampered the scientific study of the sight organ for thousands of years. However, people living in areas of the globe—such as the Middle

East, cradle of civilization—exposed to furious and unending sand-storms, which brought on ocular irritations often followed by infections, were compelled to seek some remedy against the atrocious penalty of blindness. This is why in ancient Egypt servile submission to the dogmatism of magic medicine contrasted sharply with the empirical development and study of medications for curing eye affections.

Even so, the frequent mention of blind people in the songs and legends of ancient Egypt bears witness to the appalling prevalence of blindness among Oriental peoples. Often these blind beggars became immortal bards, as if their loss of the precious gift of being able to contemplate the wondrous world around them was compensated by the power to contemplate and sing of the wondrous world within them—a world in which was reflected, as in a magic mirror, the vast tapestry of the outside world as seen through eyes deprived of light but filled with a sublime poesy.

The ancient civilizations came and went. Centuries passed. Until one day, some 2500 years ago, in sun-drenched Greece and its adjacent islands, a handful of men, philosopher-physicians, posed transcendental questions on man and nature that would thereafter guide mankind on the path to civilization and establish the dignity of man. In art a noble type of statuary developed, which portrayed the Greek gods like men and the men like gods. Intended for a people that liked to keep moving all the time, Greek art concentrated on sculpture, a dynamic three-dimensional art form that requires the spectator to walk around it to better appreciate it. In contrast, medieval art was primarily two-dimensional and static, intended for crowds that stood still and agape in front of a stained glass window, an altar screen, an icon, or a mural fresco.

It was the custom of Greek sculptors to leave out the pupil and trace only the eyelids, suggesting the glance only by the shading of the eyelids. Sometimes, in busts of emperors, they indicated the transparency of the cornea by making a hole in place of the iris and filling it with solid material to reflect the light. Greek artists depicted the eye as an anatomical part but only as seen from the outside, its internal structure being to them somewhat of a mystery. The wise Aristotle, however, although like the Greek artists he too did not correlate the eye with the human body, already denied that the vision was produced by rays emanating from the eye and impinging on the objects seen. The Stagirite, however, studied only the eyes of animals, mainly fish. When the Greek Ptolemies authorized vivisection at the School of Alexandria—to the horror of the Egyptians, who reveled in zoolatry, worshipping cats, sacred bulls, scarabs, and crocodiles in their mighty temples—the eye was finally dissected and described as much as it was possible without the aid of a microscope, and its parts were given names still used today. The retina, for instance, was compared by Herophilus to a net, because of its resemblance to the fishing nets used by the Greeks. It was then that the error—perpetuated for centuries by Galen—originated to the effect that the optic nerves were hollow and that vision was due to fine rays, like gossamer threads or delicate tentacles, which made an object visible on contact. This concept of the eye as a mere anatomical organ caused optical progress to be confined solely to catoptrics or the study of reflection, and little attention was paid to dioptrics or the refraction of light through transparent bodies.

As a symbol of strength and luminosity, clarity and power, the eye embodied divinity in Greek mythology. Plato used to say that we "look" with concepts; he also said that an idea is a "point of perspective." In mythological iconography, according to Cirlot, the magic powers of the eye were stressed by means of three processes: *displacement,* or placing the eyes in other than anatomically normal positions (heterotopic eyes in the mythological images of Pan or on the wings of Romanesque angels); *diminution,* or reducing the number of eyes (the one-eyed Polyphemus and Cyclops); and *augmentation,* or increasing the number of eyes (the hundred-eyed Argus of Greek mythology).

To these processes should be added the conversion of the eye into a protective magic talisman, such as the eyes painted on Greek galleys and, later, the Oriental eye amulets and eyes painted on the faïence orbs used by Indochinese religious sects.

Cirlot also drew a contrast in the three attitudes adopted by man upon facing the Infinite to inquire about his fate: the symbol of the *wall,* representing a feeling of impotency before the Infinite, for instance, the Wailing Wall of the Hebrews in Jerusalem; the symbol of the *window,* representing a feeling of possible but restricted human activity, for instance, the perforated jade disks of the Chinese; and the symbol of the eye talismans, which is not an impossibility like the first symbol, nor an opening offering escape, like the second, but an answering *mirror* in which man, looking into it as into his own eye, can find within himself the answer to his anguished query.

Ceasing to be an anatomical representation, the eye became allegorical in Byzantine paintings, which depict the basileis with expressionless eyes that look only straight forward or sideways, while in the ancient Christian Gnostic images the eye became a symbol of God, and in Arabic and Persian paintings it became an allegory of the wisdom or power of caliphs, viziers, and physicians. Under the compulsion of the ocular scourges inflicted by their deserts, the Arabs, victims of "Egyptian ophthalmia," or trachoma, and of other sight afflictions, excelled in practical ophthalmology. Although their religion forbade dissection of the eye, they made progress in its clinical and surgical treatment. *The Arabian Nights,* whose tales bear witness to the great medical wisdom of the Arabs in the ninth century, abound in blind characters, sometimes kindly and unfortunate, sometimes crafty and cruel, who file through its pages like a tragic chorus.

The Arabs left us several masterly treatises in ophthalmology, the oldest drawing of the human eye, and the magnificent work on optics by Alhazen, who anticipated Leonardo da Vinci and Giambattista della Porta in comparing the eye to the camera obscura.

In that very visual world of allegory of the Middle Ages, artists were interested more in the eye as an allegory—of God, as well as of the powers of darkness in the allegories of Satanism—than as an anatomical organ, and they presented a slightly protuberant eye, immersed in concentration, meditation, and mystery. Thus Giotto, to express mental concentration and somber sorrow, lengthened the lid to form a triangle. In their turn, the virgins and saints of Botticelli, Fra Filippo Lippi, Ghirlandajo, and Il Perugino had eyes set wide apart, very symmetrical and straight, with only the edge of the upper eyelid curved and with a diagonal crease from the inner corner to the cheekbone, which lent the face serenity, just as the long arch of the brows gave it an air of naiveté.

Art was no longer collective in the late Middle Ages, when, as the glance became of greater interest than the eye itself, optics advanced more than did clinical ophthalmology, though, of course, advice was given on ocular hygiene. The *Regimen sanitatis Salernitanum* contained a recommendation to wash the hands after meals, since "Tis wholesome, cleanly, and relieves your eyes." * This was possibly a survival from the Talmudic tradition, since on taking salt after a meal it was customary to avoid contact between the hands and the eyes during the postprandial prayer.

In spite of the prevailing ignorance about the eye, a visual hunger eventually led to the discovery of reading glasses and the beginning of the optical industry.

The theoretical science of perspective in turn was born, according to Sarton, with Filippo Brunelleschi, who invented the first optical instrument after the invention of spectacles. His instrument, called a *perspicillum* (perspective glass or telescope), was a wooden tablet on which was painted a fine colored miniature of the Cathedral Square in Florence as seen from a point three feet inside the main door of the cathedral. He covered the sky in the picture with a polished silver plate,

---

* Lotio post mensam, tibi confert munera bina
  Mundificat palmas et lumina reddit acuta
  Si fore vis sanus, ablue saepe manus.

The Eye and the Glance

so that the real air and sky of Florence were reflected with the moving clouds on the silver plate. In the front of the painting, where the line of sight met the painted scene, Brunelleschi bored a hole, the size of the pupil of the eye, going right through the wood. Then, by placing a mirror at arm's length opposite the painted tablet, if one looked through the hole from behind the tablet at its reflection in the mirror, the picture was seen exactly from its right point of perspective and seemed to be "the proper truth and not an image." Centuries later this apparatus was reversed to allow the light to enter through the hole and project the outside scene on a waxed screen in the camera obscura, but credit is due to Brunelleschi for having paved the way to this important discovery.

The passionate interest during the Renaissance in architecture, not only of buildings but also of the human body, considered as a *fabrica* by Vesalius, was reflected in the architectonic conception of the eye. In the pictures of the period the eye already appeared endowed with a glance, but the artist was still more concerned with its outer structure, just as Vesalius was more interested in building up a "fabrica" than in setting it in motion. The eye as painted by the Renaissance artists remained static, but it was architectonic and correlated with the rest of the face.

With Leonardo da Vinci a new visual attitude in art and science commenced, the *saper vedere* that laid bare the mysteries of the human eye, its anatomy, its physiology, and, above all, that led to the correlation of form and function, or the eye and the glance.

For Leonardo the eye was "the window of the soul"—as he described it in his *Codex Atlanticus*—which was why he studied, dissected, and sketched it with so much care. Leonardo—whose anatomy was still Galenic, just as his physiology was Aristotelian—did not give the crystalline its correct position in the eye, a point on which even Vesalius was mistaken. This was not done until the time of Felix Platter. The reason for such error was that Leonardo studied only the eyes of myopic bulls, fixing them in whites of egg and coagulating them by boiling. While he was sectioning the crystalline lens, whose hardness made cutting difficult, it probably moved so that Leonardo never found it in its right place. Nor was Leonardo able to explain how the human brain created an upright image from the inverted visual image.

Leonardo's knowledge of optics and his *saper vedere* were applied to the marvelous portrait of the gelatinous-like Mona Lisa, whom Leonardo painted in two halves: the right half Madonna-like, contemplative, serene, judicious; the other half smiling but sly. To obtain that effect he made the eyelids more elongated and ovoid on the smiling side than on the placid side of the face, leaving it to the onlooker to effect in his mind the synthesis of the portrait, in whose smile flutters an inner world of mysterious magic and bewitching charm.

It was especially in the Baroque Age that the glance was granted full artistic recognition in the paintings of El Greco, Velázquez, Zurbarán, and Rembrandt, who made of the eye a magician that gave light and expression to the face. This tendency to appreciate the glance more than the eye found a parallel in the attitude of physicians. William Harvey, the outstanding investigator of the Baroque, was called "the ocular philosopher" by Sir Thomas Browne. This attitude, inspired by Leonardo's *saper vedere,* that is, the desire to see the world and its peoples not symbolically or allegorically but as they really are, led, through interest in studying the visual function, to a better knowledge of the eye. Leonardo and the painters of the Renaissance and the Baroque thus awakened a fresh interest in the act of seeing, in knowing how to look at things, turning sight into the most valuable instrument for exploring the world.

The romantic yearning of the Age of Enlightenment stimulated investigation of the mysteries of the visual infinity of the human eye. We have mentioned elsewhere that while Vermeer in Delft was painting the minutest details of Dutch interiors in his exquisite miniatures, only a few blocks away Leeuwenhoek, in a similar desire to examine the minute, was studying the crystalline and the retina in his home-made lenses.

The greatest figure in the Enlightenment, the prodigious Goethe— who said in his *Poetry and Truth* that "Medicine occupies the whole man because it is concerned with man as a whole"—studied light and color all his life. In his hour of death his last words were symbolically a demand for "Light! More light!" This "ocular" psychology of Goethe explains why his memoirs, novels, and visions so abundantly used visual imagery. To put himself to sleep, Goethe would "see" in his mind a seed gradually growing into a plant. His admiration for the eye was expressed in his phrase, ". . . *gegen das Auge ist das Ohr ein stummer Sinn."* ("Compared with the eye, the ear is a mute faculty.")

Goethe based the science of chromatics on the study of turbidity, color being his favorite subject of study, ranging from observation of the phenomenon that if immediately after admiring a red rose on a bright, sunny day one shifts the eyes to a white background, the image of the rose is reproduced in green, to the analysis of the secret of the colors of the autumn moon, which takes on orange and crimson tints when seen through a mist. With Goethe, investigation into the function of the ocular organ considered as an optical instrument reached its peak. It is symbolical that this global and "encyclopedic" perspective of ophthalmology was developed at the same time as Diderot and the other Encyclopedists were introducing "encyclopedic" concepts in politics.

Such was the road followed by the present wondrous science of modern optics—from the initial naturalistic external observations to Brunelleschi's artistic device, to the work of della Porta, Leonardo, Galileo on lenses, Leeuwenhoek, and Goethe on the theory of colors, to our great modern achievements.

Modern ophthalmology can claim a whole arsenal of triumphs: internal repair and dissection of the eye; analysis of its function; interpretation of ocular signs; anti-infectious ocular chemotherapy, of great value in saving human eyesight; biochemical ocular research; the remarkable developments in modern ocular surgery; intracapsular cataract extraction; diathermocoagulation for retinal detachment; corneal grafts; contact lenses; and the conquest of ophthalmia neonatorum. All these victories have made ophthalmology one of the cleanest and most perfect specialties, in which, though physical instrumentation is a vital factor, still more important are the hands and brain of the man handling the instruments.

It would be interesting, first, to analyze the correlation between art and ophthalmology in modern times; second, to study the parallelism between the impressionists' attempt to capture light in their pictures, sometimes splitting it up into tiny luminous dots (as in Seurat's pointillism), and the coinciding interest of ophthalmologists in the vision of light and color; and third, to analyze the resemblance between the surrealist attitudes of Ernst, Magritte, and Dali—who have used the eye so much as a powerful magic symbol (returning thus to the original eye symbolism of mythology) and as an organ expressive of human thought and emotion, that is to say, of what goes on in the brain—and the modern concept of a cyclopean "cerebral eye" formed by the visual centers and their correlation to the eyes. This concept had already been anticipated by Descartes when he tried to chase the elusive butterfly of the relationship between body and mind.

We began by speaking of the "glances" in Goya's paintings. Goya was a painter of glances. His secret, as analyzed by a Spanish oculist, consisted in painting the iris two millimeters larger than life, thus increasing the expression in the glance by contrasting the enormous iris with the white background of the sclerotic against which the iris stands out. Be that as it may, in the same way that art has proceeded successively from portrayal of the eye as a "bulge," to portrayal of its light, and finally to portrayal of the "idea" and the feeling expressed by the eye, so also has scientific study of the eye progressed from physical observation to ocular optics to the psychoneurological study of the "cerebral eye."

Ophthalmological study of the eye is now focused on its glance—function—rather than on its anatomy. This triumph of the glance is exemplified in the progress made with contact lenses, which besides correcting vision can alter the appearance of the glance, a valuable thing in photography, television, movies, and art. To the artist—even to an iconoclast like Picasso, who has disintegrated and displaced the ocular organ (and every iconoclast is a believer at heart, since if he did not believe in the religious merit of saintly things he would not try to destroy them)—the eye is a tiny cathedral of the human being, a cathedral through whose stained glass windows—the pupils of the eye—the light of God enters into man, and the light of man's soul shines out on the world.

VIII. the philosophy of medicine

DOCTORS MUST TELL

No other profession uses communication as much as medicine does. Throughout history physicians have depended on words to communicate with their colleagues, teachers, pupils, and patients. In the beginning all communication was oral. The physician gleaned the gold of his teachers' knowledge only by listening carefully, and then, by word of mouth, he himself transmitted his knowledge to both the healthy and the ailing. When writing was invented, the horizon of communication widened. At first, physicians wrote huge books—the *Canon* of Avicenna or the *Fabrica* of Vesalius—intended to preserve the sum of their knowledge for posterity. Later they wrote small popular treatises, such as the *Regimen sanitatis Salernitanum,* for the benefit of the public. As the printing arts progressed and the exercise and teaching of medicine became formalized, the practice developed of writing texts for schools and to inform others of whatever knowledge had been acquired, though Morgagni, for instance, in the eighteenth century, still resorted to "letters to a friend" to divulge all the knowledge he had acquired while dissecting corpses of soldiers, princesses, and harlots in a hospital in Florence.

The advent of medical journals expedited the progress of medical communication. There was no longer any need to write long volumes to say short things. The medical paper became the banner for scientific progress. In our times scientific journals have greatly widened medical communication. The physician communicates with his col-

From *MD,* the MEDICAL NEWSMAGAZINE, *3*:11, October, 1959.

leagues and pupils by means of lectures, lessons, papers, textbooks, theses, seminar or panel discussions, symposia, and talks at hospitals or professional societies; and with the public by means of newspaper columns, public lectures, radio or television programs, and popular medical books.

No other profession needs to communicate with other human beings, patients or others, or to divulge its methods and mysteries, so much as the medical profession. We never hear of lawyers publishing popular articles on how to prepare legal documents, or of engineers telling the public how to construct a bridge. But today surgeons willingly disclose to all and sundry the intricacies ad infinitum of an operation, and psychiatrists do the same with the involved processes of personality, and internists will gladly reveal the technicalities of a cardiac diagnosis. Long long ago, the Magi in Chaldea, the priests in Memphis, the theologists in Byzantium, and the scholars in Salerno— all took great pains to shroud their ministrations in forbidding robes that emphasized the hieratic and esoteric nature of their profession. Today what was once the most sacred and most forbidding of professions stands stripped of all the old subterfuges and within reach of all intelligent minds intrigued by health and disease.

Paradoxically, despite the physicians' willingness to strip their profession of all mystery and to cease being "men who call a headache by a Greek-sounding name and use Latin to communicate with the druggist," medicine has retained an aura of mystery; while the physician himself has retained the aureole that is bound to surround a man who can listen to the secrets of the chests of his fellow beings, who can lay bare the fund of their eyes with a pencil of silvery light, who by tapping their knees can trigger the Sagittarius of the reflexes, who, knocking with his fingers on the abdominal wall, can decipher its enigmas, who has the right to ask esoteric questions—in fact, who holds in his hands the secret of life and death. Such an aureole, wisely used, is still one of the clues to success in healing of the physician and to his towering stature in modern society.

The present eagerness of the physician to tell people what he knows is a reflection of today's intense preoccupation with health. Never as in our times, in which human life is so universally threatened, has humanity been so anxious to be informed on medical matters, as if it felt that such knowledge would increase its defenses against death. And never before has the physician been so interested in helping the public to understand medicine and in sharing his knowledge and experiences with his colleagues. In the England of the Enlightenment, physicians still refused to share their secret remedies unless they were handsomely remunerated. In our time, Fleming promptly shared his discovery of penicillin with all physicians; Freud willingly disclosed his new method of warding off the demons of neuroses; and Ramón y Cajal deciphered the mystery of the neuron for the benefit of all without distinction.

In this respect we have made great strides. The new arts of communication are improving and facilitating, every day more, the relationship between physicians themselves and between physicians and the people. When we realize that it is possible today to televise a brain operation or colored microphotographs, to amplify the cardiac beat so that a full auditorium may hear it, to observe the invisible world of viruses with an electron microscope, to diffuse electronically the essence of medical knowledge in all the languages of the world, to project from cosmic space the sounds of the thorax of a dog— when we realize all this, we feel proud to be physicians in the twentieth century. We are proud indeed that our profession, once the most mysterious, dogmatic, and hieratic, is now intent upon telling the whole world in simple, clear language its secrets, its failures, and its dreams.

MAN, AS NATURE AND AS HISTORY

medicine, as well as its history, is steadily becoming medical anthropology. The main purpose of the history of medicine is no longer to present a chronology of events, but to depict the evolution of the image of man in health and in disease as recorded in the medical works of the past. Similarly, perusal of the clinical case *history,* on which clinical medicine will always be based, makes one realize that the physician's main concern is man, as a unit and as a whole.

The medical historian today must investigate the forces that guided Vesalius' hand as he wrote the *Fabrica,* or that made Pasteur explore the world of the invisible with his microscope. The physician's task today is not only to know the nature of a disease, but also to study the *whole* patient, to decipher the pathologic episode of his ailment and integrate it into the historical trajectory of his biography.

Like Molière's hero who without knowing it talked in prose, we physicians, without realizing it, often practice "biographic" medicine, even in those cases where all we are looking for is the specific treatment for a disease. Often, besides applying a remedy and studying the patient's reaction, we must also keep watch on his biologic constitution, his environment, his genetics, and his behavior. This means that we must to some extent disengage our eyes and hands from the diseased body in order to have a better perspective of the *nature* of the sick man's organism and of his life *history,* as the best means of treating his disease and restoring him to health. This explains the increasing interest in medical anthropology, the science that studies man in health and disease in correlation with environmental, cultural, and social factors.

From *MD,* the MEDICAL NEWSMAGAZINE, 5:11, November, 1961.

Thus considered, medical anthropology includes the study of paleo-pathology or the diseases of prehistoric man, which shed a revealing light on those of his heir: modern man. It also studies primitive medicine among contemporary primitive peoples, that is to say, *isolated* peoples who have no cultural contacts, who are truly islands in time, human culture plates or living sociologic laboratories in which health and disease may be studied under conditions like those that existed before the dawn of civilization.

Medical anthropology likewise includes the study of health and disease in relation to cultural, social, and economic factors, and to the historical evolution of peoples.

Of the great trends of modern medicine—clinical medicine, medical anthropology, psychosomatic and psychologic medicine—medical anthropology offers the best possibilities for furthering medicine's main goal, which is not to create a physically and morally perfect man, but to keep him healthy and therefore happy.

The basic principle of medical anthropology is a simple one. Man responds as a *whole* to every difficult situation, whether it be emotional conflict, social stress, environmental change, or disease. In that "moment of truth" when he faces a threat, man mobilizes his soma and his psyche to help him in his struggle against the perils that threaten the survival of his whole person as an integrated unit.

The physician therefore must minister to the *whole* person and must possess the maximum knowledge of man as a psychophysical whole and as a historical entity, since that is the only way in which he can fathom the "biographical configuration" of each individual disease. This concept, brilliantly developed by the German clinician Victor von Weizsäcker in his biographic medicine—which accepts three kinds of diseases: neuroses, bioses, and esclerosis—was first expounded by Thomas Sydenham when he classified diseases into acute (biologic), which he attributed to divine causes, and chronic (biographic), which he ascribed to man himself.

It is easily realized that each disease belongs more to one class than to the other. A neurosis is a "biographic" affection, resulting largely from the patient's way of life, while a uterine fibroma is a "biologic" affection. Nevertheless, a neurosis may also have to do with the patient's biology, just as a fibroma may also be related to the biography of a woman who wants children but cannot bear any. In any case, the revival in our time by Karl Jaspers of the classification of diseases into "biologic" and "biographic" helps us to understand why disease is a "biographic enterprise," and why the physician requires as humanistic an education as possible in order to understand such an enterprise.

For human disease does not disappear with therapy; it merely *shifts to a new stronghold.* This concept, which encouraged the belief of classic physicians in the virtue of the "golden flux" of hemorrhoids against cerebral congestions, has endured and was supported by Dr. Besançon's theory that the best protection against major diseases is to suffer a mild chronic affection that will keep the body's defenses on the alert.

Thus, the formidable offensive with antibiotics against infections has driven disease into fresh combat areas. People live longer, but now they must face the mounting attack of cardiovascular and degenerative diseases. The physician with his new weapons is cornering the wild beast of disease, but the latter still has fresh lairs from which to launch its attacks.

The important thing to do, then, is to steer medicine toward the *whole* man—his *nature,* his body, and his *history,* his life—in order to understand better his diseases. Pertinent in this sense is Rudolf Virchow's opinion (restated by George Rosen) that epidemic disease is a manifestation of sociocultural maladjustment, and that epidemics are a sign of vast socioeconomic upheavals in the life of man which affect the history of mankind.

Knowledge of man means also knowledge of those generations that preceded us. About thirty years ago, Professor L. Bolk of Amsterdam expounded before the Freiburg Anatomic Society a challenging theory on the origin of man. To him, the determinant factor in man's primary characteristics is not his attainment of the upright walking position and erect gait. Man's "humanization," he suggested, does not arise from his standing upright; rather, man stands upright because his form became "humanized." Man's primary somatic characters— orthognathism, lack of body hair, loss of skin pigmentation, shape of his auditive muscles, weight of brain, structure of hand, foot, and pelvis, variations in teeth—are, when studied in the light of the ontogeny of primates, "fetal states or situations" that became permanent in man but were surpassed in the primates!

That means that what was merely a transitional stage in the evolution of the ape became permanent in man. The fetus of the lower apes and the newborn of the anthropoid look human not because apes come from a stock similar to man, but because man retains the fetal type until the end of his biological evolution. Man's evolution was probably preservative and the ape's propulsive, man being "a primate fetus that attained sexual maturity," a being that underwent "fetalization," that is, a lag in his evolution.

This lag may have been due to that architect of the body, the endocrine system. Dr. Bolk adduced that in endocrinopathies, body hair and skin pigmentation reappear, the mandibles and frontal bones increase in bulk, and the cranium becomes misshapen, as though the endocrine system were a brake that the disease had released. The endocrine system ("endocrinon," he called it) may have governed the historical evolution of the soma or bodily form, the relationship between genes and species being similar to that between the "endocrinon" and the individual, the first controlling the genesis and preservation of the species, the second controlling the genesis and preservation of the form of the individual.

Bolk's theory was fascinating in its boldness. Years after I first heard of it, I realized that this theory re-echoed the one advanced by Dietrich Georg Kieser in the romantic first half of the nineteenth century. Kieser considered disease as a "molluskization" of the human being, or regression to "an animal and vegetative state" approaching that of the toad and the reptile.

In opposition to Bolk's theory, I recall the anthropologic doctrine of one of my teachers in Madrid, Dr. Roberto Nóvoa Santos, who defined "animal," including man, as "an energetic stationary system . . . comprising a series of reactional possibilities, able therefore to respond adequately to entirely novel situations or to the pressure of indirect and casual necessities."

According to Dr. Nóvoa Santos, the key to the structure of man lies in how he attained the erect posture, which he attributed to a *pathologic* mutation that led to the orthostatic position. That mutation could have been the congenital dislocation of the hip, frequently found in prehistoric remains. Since that time, man, an upright-walking animal, may have suffered pathologic as well as meliorative mutations. Hence, man is neither a fallen angel nor a perfected beast.

Man may have been an erect mutant who became humanized by his strife against his environment. His spiritual faculties for creating myths and legends enabled man to elude nature. Animals remained in the bosom of nature; but man was the only creature able to face nature, to elude her through the magic window of his mind, and eventually to tame her to his own use. Man is consequently the outcome of a pathologic mutant regenerated through his spirit and endowed with a consciousness that flows with images and symbols but is not entirely dependent on its content.

Through his mind, man may be corporeally a part of nature, but his spirit is in perpetual revolt against nature. Noteworthy characteristics of man would be his conflict between his will to live and his thanatic impulse, or desire to die, as a respite from the fatigue accumulated in his life span, and his ability to perceive physical time through his biologic time by subordinating time to spatial perception.

The two great gifts of the human being would be intelligence in man and fertility in woman. Through his creative intelligence man sustains and preserves himself as an individual; through her fertility, the female protects and preserves the species. This means that the male survives *in space* through his intelligence, just as the female survives *in time* through her fertility.

Knowledge of these and other theories is of value to the physician. The physician's object of study is man. And since man's somato-psychic unity is in constant motion through time and space, the physician must study man in these conditions, as a whole and in motion, his organism and his history, his nature and his biography. Only then can the physician respond to the patient's complaint, not only with instrumental explorations, but also with a knowledge of that *individual peculiarity* that personalizes a patient's disease and differentiates it from the same disease in other patients.

Medicine as a science has studied the diseased person in a fragmentary way and responds to his complaint with a detailed exploration, but as an art it has studied him as a whole and suffering person and responds with the physician's first question to the patient, which initiates his clinical case history. Rational therapy is concerned with dispelling the objective signs of disease; psychosomatic medicine, with making the patient well and happy. Medical anthropology tries besides to make him feel useful to society.

This anthropologic criterion has been the one followed for centuries by that noble institution now in peril of disappearing—the family doctor. For he knows not only his patients' ailments but also their families, homes, occupations, and economic and social problems, and he applies all that precious knowledge, gleaned from simple observation, to treating his patient as a *whole* and to integrating his sickness into the course of his life history.

The key to medicine is the relationship between physician and patient, which in every period of history has varied in accordance with the prevailing social, cultural, and environmental forces. In our modern cities, this relationship is growing increasingly impersonal.

Of greater human depth and historical duration is the application of medical anthropology to medicine. Only by using medical anthropology can that "emanation of divinity," as Paracelsus called the physician, study and treat the whole man, his nature, and his history.

The conflict between the earthy, space-bound, time-limited, biological structure of man and the spaceless and timeless aspirations of his mind, the subject of medical anthropology, is symbolically dramatized on our cover by the great Spanish painter, Teodoro Miciano: in his dreams, Don Quixote, leaving the scorched dusty plains of La Mancha, soars up into the blue of the night, reaching for the distant stars.

IX. Religio medici

TO BE A DOCTOR

My course on the history of medicine had ended. Facing me were a hundred and twenty-eight young men and women. There were pale faces and swarthy faces, students with dark, blond, or red hair, but throughout the entire group the same restless light shone in their young eyes, as if they had captured a spark from the sun. These freshmen of mine asked me to tell them what it means "to be a doctor," and I ended my course with this explanation:

Ever since the day you first said those magic words, "I want to be a doctor," you have been wrapped in the colorful fabric of the history of medicine, a fabric woven from the ideals, wisdom, endeavors, and achievements of our glorious predecessors in medicine.

You have just embarked on a fascinating voyage leading to the harbor of one of the most dynamic professions. Year after year new windows will keep opening before your eyes, revealing the multi-faceted landscape of medical art and science.

But medicine today is so complex that no human mind can possibly absorb it all, as was possible a few centuries ago. Only by using the history of medicine as a gigantic frame to contain what you learn is it possible to integrate the numerous fragments of medical theory and practice that will be taught you in your student years. Only through the history of medicine can one appreciate that to be a doctor, in the true sense of the word, is to be not only a wise man but, above all, a good man. To be a doctor is, in other words, to be a whole man, who fulfills his task as a scientist with professional quality and integrity; as a human being, with a kind heart and high

From *MD*, the MEDICAL NEWSMAGAZINE, 4:13, November, 1960.

ideals; and as a member of society, with honesty and efficiency.

Contemporary medicine is founded on a series of events that resulted from the thoughts and deeds of a few men in the course of history. History is made by men, and the greatest among the makers of history is the physician because of the effects of his ministry on all other human beings.

Man is the only creature able to make tools with which to make other tools, and of all the tools made by him words are the most important. The fabric of medicine is woven with words that express the ideas from which they sprang. The original meaning of the three words—physician, medic, doctor—that describe our profession is highly illuminating. The word "physician" derives from the Greek *physis,* or nature, denoting that the physician has his roots in an understanding of the nature of things; the word "medic" comes from *mederi,* to heal, and the prefix *med* means to meditate or think, so that medic is equivalent to thinker and healer; the word "doctor" originally meant master, instructor. Thus, semantically, our profession involves learning, knowing, healing, and teaching.

In its turn, the word "medicine" not only means what medical men do (many of the great figures in medical history, such as Pasteur and Leeuwenhoek, were not physicians), but also denotes a *social* science that uses the methods of the natural sciences to attain four objectives: to promote health, to restore health, to prevent disease, and to rehabilitate the patient.

Every day, more and more, medicine becomes, above all, the prevention of disease and the promotion of health. For only by knowing the healthy man can we cure him when he falls ill. Knowledge of the healthy man is obtained by studying our fellow beings, both the healthy and the diseased, not only in the mirror of classical and modern medical literature but also in current newspapers. You will then learn that poverty is still the main social cause of disease, just as it was in archaic times.

The history of medicine epitomizes the history of civilization. The history of man has passed through three great stages: man learned to master nature by yielding to her laws; he learned to live in society by establishing the first communities; he acquired consciousness of his human dignity and of his ability to forge his own destiny, which in turn enabled him to acquire greatness.

The physician in his threefold capacity, as a professional, as a member of society, and as a human being, has throughout history helped man in his physical, mental, and social ascent. As a professional man in particular, the physician has always acted as a healer, using magic, faith, empiricism, or rational resources; as a knower, for he knows the secrets of nature and of the human being; as a preventer, for he can arrest disease by forestalling its inroads before they develop; and as an organizer, for he can guide society in fighting the historicosocial process called disease. To heal, to know, to prevent, to organize—these will be your four future spheres of professional activity, embraced in the expression "to be a doctor."

To be a doctor, then, means much more than to dispense pills or to patch up or repair torn flesh and shattered minds. To be a doctor is to be an intermediary between man and God.

You have chosen the most fascinating and dynamic profession there is, a profession with the highest potential for greatness, since the physician's daily work is wrapped up in the subtle web of history. Your labors are linked with those of your colleagues who preceded you in history and those who are now working all over the world. It is this spiritual unity with our colleagues of all periods and of all countries that has made medicine so universal and eternal. For this reason we must study and try to imitate the lives of the great doctors of history. Their lives, blazing with greatness, teach us that our profession is the only one that still speaks of its duties in this world of today, in which almost everyone else speaks only of his rights.

An ideal of service permeates all our activities: service especially to the patient, as a fellow creature isolated on the island of his suffering, whom only you can restore to the mainland of health. For that purpose you must know thoroughly not only the diseased but also the healthy.

Your own contributions to medicine can begin even in the golden years of student life. There is no need to wait for your medical degree to start making medical history. Many physicians while still students made historic contributions to medical science: Vesalius, Stensen, Laënnec, Remak, Freud, Best, men who believed in themselves and were dedicated to the profession you have chosen for your own.

From now on your professional conduct must adhere to the moral code of medicine that began with the Hippocratic oath. Despite its negative aspect in prohibiting a number of activities, the Hippocratic oath was not a law but a precept self-imposed by physicians who accepted an ideal of devotion and service enjoined by their moral conscience. Five types of ethical duties must guide your life: duties to your teachers, to society, to your patients, to your colleagues, and to yourselves.

You have duties to your teachers, because they, the parents of your mind, are the most important people in your life next to your own parents. I do not mean only your university professors, but any physician from whom you learn anything—his science, art, ethics, self-denial, or example—that may become a source of inspiration in your professional life. You must honor your masters with devotion and friendship, for friendship is man's noblest sentiment, greater even than love.

Your duty to society is to be idealists, not hedonists: as physicians, to accept your profession as a service to mankind, not as a source of profit; as investigators, to seek the knowledge that will benefit your fellow beings; as clinicians, to alleviate pain and heal the sick; as teachers, to share and spread your knowledge and always because you are imbued with an ideal of service and not the ambition for gain. Thus will you maintain the dignity of our profession as a social science applied to the welfare of mankind.

Your duty to your patients will be to act toward them as you would wish them to act toward you: with kindness, with courtesy, with honesty. You must learn when and how to withhold the truth from your patients, if by not telling them all the facts of the case you can relieve or console them, for you can cure them sometimes, and you can give them relief often, but hope you can give them *always*. Remember that a laboratory report is not an irrevocable sentence. A hematological determination, a roentgenogram, an electroencephalogram may supply vital information on the organic working of the body, but it is even more vital never to forget that, behind all such reports and data, there is a human being in pain and anguish, to whom you must offer something more than an antibiotic, an injection, or a surgical aid; you must, with your attitude, your words, and your actions, inspire confidence and faith and give understanding and consolation.

To your colleagues you have the obligations of civilized men sharing a great and noble task and fighting for a common cause in a great crusade. Medicine lives and is nourished by the great social prestige it enjoys. Hence, never speak ill of a colleague, since to do so would be the same as speaking evil of medicine and therefore of your own selves. If you have something good to say about a fellow physician, say it everywhere; if you have not, then keep silent. You belong to a team of gallant professionals of all races and eras, bound together across the ages and continents by a glorious ideal.

Finally, you will have obligations to yourselves. Every man in his youth forms an ideal profile of himself or of what he wants to be. He envisions, while young, an ideal program of things to do in life. The rest of his life is spent trying to fill in that profile with achievements. Some fail to reach fulfillment, and later it is tragic to see that ideal profile, of which they dreamed during their youth, in ruins, with the stumps of things begun but never completed. But in the majority of cases, that ideal silhouette created in youthful days really represents our true selves. You must live to be worthy of that silhouette. Your life, your work, and your personality as a physician must be such that your ideal profile of yourself will be filled in with brilliant achievements.

Learn to live perceptively, using that key to wisdom that comes from seeing everything with a total perspective and in view of eternity. Learn through science to correlate things in space, through history, to correlate events in time, and combine all this knowledge esthetically through the beauty of art.

You are embarking on a noble career in which there is no room for amateurs or dilettanti, a career in which we must all aspire to be masters of whatever we undertake, for the mistakes of medical carpenters and prescribers' apprentices can have tragic results.

Remember that the important thing in life is to be great, not big, a *great* man, not a big man. Let your actions be great, but preserve your personal modesty and humility. What counts in a man and in a physician is his greatness. By greatness I mean grandeur in the things we do and simplicity in the way we do them, doing things that influence the lives of many people, but preserving always the greatest personal simplicity. For greatness *is* simplicity. Know how to feel yourself an important part of the deeds of history. Try to find out as soon as you can what your ideal self is. Try to be what you truly are; otherwise you will be nothing. Man's dignity rests in his ability to choose his destiny. You have chosen the best destiny of all, a life of dedicated service and dynamic activity. If you work with faith and without dismay, all your dreams will come true.

In your future work you will be in good company. The great physicians of history, the glorious figures of the past, will always be near you. When you perform a dissection, a red-bearded young man with flashing eyes, Andreas Vesalius, will be peering over your shoulder; when you make a physiological experiment, the melancholy, pensive eyes of William Harvey will be watching you; when you teach medicine, the venerable figure of William Osler with his Apollonian head will come and sit like a medical Goethe beside you; and when you approach the sickbed, the shades of Hippocrates, Sydenham, and Fleming will gather round to counsel you.

The Greeks created the legend that Delphi, site of the famous oracle, was the center of the world, because if two eagles were to fly from any two points of the globe, sooner or later they would meet in Delphi. We now know that the two eagles of science and medicine do not fly only in space but also in time, and their wings hover over the illustrious shadows of the investigators, clinicians, educators, pioneers, rebels, and martyrs of the history of medicine. The meeting place of those two eagles lies not in space but in time, in the future, and in the mind and the heart of every one of you who answered destiny's call to greatness when you decided "to be a doctor."

THE YOUNG PRINCES

about seven thousand medical students—the young princes in the kingdom of medicine—will be graduated this year from American colleges. With this annual explosion of youth, the rosebush of medicine will blossom afresh in full brilliance and fragrance. This is a good moment to consider the role of the student in the history of medicine and the role of the history of medicine in the student's education.

If there are two figures in medicine whose social status has changed in the course of the centuries, they are the surgeon and the student. In the case of the student, the social antagonism he aroused in the past had its source in the revenge he took against the rigors of student life. In the Middle Ages, poor students whose families were unable to support them often had to beg on street corners. Fortunately in those days, as in many Eastern countries even today, begging was not a shameful act but a devotional one.

Many students lived in gloomy cubbyholes, with naked, mildewed walls, small paneless windows, and straw-covered floors. Always cold and hungry, these poor students fed every morning on the hope of getting, by fair means or foul, a piece of sausage or boiled tripe. They drank warm beer, often in the company of their teachers on the eve of examinations, which both parties attended the next day with a royal hang-over! They reveled in street brawling and were the terror of the towns they lived in, so much so that as night fell, the townspeople would lock up their houses, trembling for the survival of their old wines and the virtue of their young daughters.

From *MD*, the MEDICAL NEWSMAGAZINE, 5:11, May, 1961.

Classes began at five in the morning, and the students, who had risen at four, numb with cold and without breakfast, had to stand for hours or sit on the freezing hard floor during lectures, which sometimes lasted fourteen hours a day with only a short break for lunch. Afterward, back in their dismal cold rooms, they would study for hours on end by the flickering light of a candle. Even so, the thirst for knowledge was so strong that students flocked in thousands to the universities and stood for hours in the public squares of Paris or Padua, Bologna or Oxford to listen to the learned discourses of Albertus Magnus, Pietro d'Abano, Taddeo Alderotti, Arnold of Villanova, or other eminent teachers of the age.

Much time passed before the medical profession gained—in the eighteenth century—social status, crowned with respect and privilege, and the medical student won the consideration and comfort that his studies merited. In any event, the "official" irruption of the medical student into the history of medicine came comparatively late. Although, as Galen relates, medical students in imperial Rome were often mere children, sons of physicians, who practiced dissection under the watchful eye of their father, and in medieval times also they began their studies at an early age, the medical student, from the mere nature of his occupation, was considered a man in miniature rather than a child.

Students practiced a thousand wiles at every turn in their fight against hunger, employing bold and ingenious artifices. One need only read the masterpieces of the Spanish picaresque novel to learn some of the stratagems to which hunger pushed them. The great seventeenth-century satirist Francisco de Quevedo tells of the trick played by a famished student who passed a yard where a woman was feeding her plump chickens handfuls of corn. The unwary woman kept crying, *"pío, pío,"* the word used in Spanish-speaking countries to call chickens, just as we use "kitty" to call a cat. The student, with a perfectly straight face, promptly informed the startled woman that to use a pope's name (Pius, in Spanish, *Pío*) for calling chickens was a sacrilege, which the Inquisition would punish at the stake, and that the chickens thus called were condemned as profane. Whereupon, with the consent of the terrified woman, the wily student carried off under his cloak the "excommunicated" chickens, which, after they were deliciously roasted, wound up in his own hungry belly and in that of his equally ravenous fellow students.

Despite their workaday problems, many students have made important contributions to medicine during their college years. Among other things, this proves that scientific discovery does not wait on age and may be achieved as well by the adolescent as by the aged, and that the student need only know how to "invent his own duties," beyond those that are imposed by his curriculum, for him to make history.

In his admirable, aptly entitled *Young Endeavour,* Professor William Gibson describes the great medical discoveries and contributions made by students during the past four centuries. The list is impressive and enlightening. A few examples are: Vesalius' pregraduation discoveries in anatomy; Lorenzo Bellini's discovery as a student of the renal tubules in a stag; Henry Gray's study of the comparative anatomy of the optic nerves while at St. George's Hospital Medical School in London; Joseph Lister's student papers on the contractile tissue of the iris; Ramón y Cajal's studies in his youth on bones, which incidentally were stolen from cemeteries; the two thousand thumbnail biographies written by Albrecht von Haller at the age of eight and the Greek dictionary with Chaldean and Egyptian equivalents he prepared when ten years old; John Shaw Billings' modern concept of a medical reference library born while he was performing "that melancholy duty," preparing his doctoral thesis; William Harvey's observations on chicken embryos, made with his master Fabricius ab Aquapendente in Padua; Ehrlich's pregraduation *Archives of Microscopic Anatomy* outlining his theory of histological affinity; Niels Stensen's discovery as a student of the parotid duct bearing his name; Claude Bernard's studies of gastric juice; Ivan Pavlov's studies on the nerves of the pancreas and pancreatic fistula; Paul Langerhans' studies on microscopic anatomy of the pancreas; Pierre Marie's discovery of the sign of tremor in the hand and digits in thyroid diseases; Laënnec's studies on peritonitis and visceral membranes; William Osler's first paper on the microscopy of some algae he found in a barrel one Christmas Eve; the self-immolation of the Peruvian student Daniel Carrión when he inoculated himself with blood from a patient with verruga peruana in order to prove its affinity to Oroya fever; Sigmund Freud's studies on the nervous system of the lower invertebrates; Jean Pecquet's discovery of the thoracic duct; Max von Pettenkofer's identification of arsenic with a Marsh apparatus; and the discovery of insulin by Charles H. Best with Frederick Banting; and many others. Numerous indeed are the discoveries that have been made by medical students.

Having shown the two sides of the medal, the glory and the misery of the medical student in history, let us now consider what the student should have the right to demand in his medical education.

Every student of medicine has the right to learn his profession as a response to the innermost call of his vocation. In this process he will acquire a means of earning a living, and also a greater knowledge of man and the universe and a means of developing his personality as a human being. Medical education undertakes to provide him with

270

a vast amount of knowledge that will help him develop his profession with ability. Unfortunately, such knowledge often makes of him a specialist instead of a physician, a technician instead of a scientist, an expert instead of a man. And I believe that *the student* should influence his teachers, even as they influence him, by demanding what will be most useful to him in his future professional life.

Obviously the concept of what will be "most useful" to him is a relative one. I would say the most important thing is that both the student and the teacher recognize that it is more important to be a *professional,* that is to say, a man endowed with a general knowledge of his profession and a specialized knowledge of its techniques, than to be a mere medical technologist or artisan. Originally only theology, medicine, and law were recognized as "professions," that is to say, the three branches of human knowledge that since prehistoric times have tried to minister to inexplicable moral afflictions, physical diseases, and lawsuits and disputes. Of these three professions, medicine down the ages has kept its singleness of purpose unchanged in the hands of physicians—those men endowed, according to Homer, with "knowledge beyond that of all other men."

As the centuries have passed, a stricter criterion has been established in the selection of students of medicine, and the relationship between student and teacher has become increasingly closer. Not yet, however, has a philosophy of medical education been established on the basis that the important thing is not just to instruct the student but to *educate* him, that medical instruction, based on the study of its technology, must be replaced by medical *education.* In other words, knowledge of the philosophy and history of medicine must precede knowledge of its technology.

Indeed, the brave Kentucky physician, Daniel Drake, of whom William Osler said, "In many ways [he] is the most unique figure in the history of American Medicine. . . ." himself asserted that "literature and science are not the same; but a physician should acquire both, and the cultivation of the former should precede that of the latter." And in our own time, a voice that can hardly be accused of cultural dilettantism, that of the eminent chemist Conant, has said, "In terms of general education, poetry and philosophy are of vastly more importance than science." To that I would add the study of the history, art, philosophy, and literature of all peoples as a means of knowing mankind better. Literature, like poetry, reflects man's dreams, thoughts, and visions, but history records the deeds and actions of mankind as a whole. "History is a clinical study of man in society," as Sir Richard Livingstone said. And since medicine is merging more and more each day with medical anthropology—the study of the image of man in health and disease considered in both space and time, that is, in his country and society and in his passage through historical time—medical anthropology should also be added to the student's basic education.

Yet today too many specialists and technologists without any basic scientific preparation are being created. This might eventually turn medicine from a profession into a technology and degrade the noble medical education into a mere vocational training. But that is not so important as the molding of *men,* men who later, if they so wish, can become specialists. For in our profession the general practitioner preceded the specialist for many centuries.

Nothing is better than the history of medicine for instilling into the medical student a high sense of his professional mission, history taught not for the purpose of making the student a historian on a small scale, but of making him a better physician by making him a better man. For the history of medicine is medicine, but above all it is history. In other words, it is a study of man in society, of his supreme greatness and his tragic errors, and it teaches the concatenation of ideas through the ages, the living panorama of the human mind in full creativity, the relative value of truth and error in science, the relativity of human knowledge, the duty of "equanimity."

Taught not as a musty recital of names and dates but as a living tapestry of human figures brought back to life by the magic of the teacher's and the student's enthusiasm, the history of medicine creates a historical conscience in the student within which he can frame the scattered, fragmentary learning acquired in the classroom.

Of course, when the student takes his medical degree, it will matter little whether he knows the date when Vesalius' *Fabrica* was published or when Harvey announced his famous discovery, but the accumulated centuries-long experience of his predecessors will be a priceless spiritual guide for his thoughts and for his hands in the practice of his profession. It will give him moral fortitude, wisdom, understanding, and tolerance toward his patients, his colleagues, and his teachers, toward himself and toward society. With the history of medicine, that loom of rich individual experiences on which the multicolored fabric of the past is woven, the student can clothe the shivering nudity of his technological accomplishments and give them warmth and color.

What, therefore, must the university teach students?

From my teacher, Dr. Gregorio Marañón, I learned that the university must create in the student that "university spirit" that seeks the truth rather than scientific erudition, shows tolerance, cultivates scientific curiosity, respects investigation techniques, and is eager "to invent duties" beyond those imposed by the curriculum. Only then will the student respond to his vocation—that inner voice that calls us to a particular profession—through love of duty and efficiency in doing. The university must also teach the student not just to be a sportsman obsessed by the "chase for high marks," which, after all, are not of much value in professional life, but to create new tasks for himself, to be guided by sincere inclinations rather than by mere aptitude. The teacher's mission is to diagnose inclinations rather than to determine aptitudes. In doing so, he may discover a future medical genius, who sometimes happens to be a mediocre student, perhaps because his genius already makes him rebel against standard academic teaching.

The teacher must encourage the student's own originality and imagination, setting himself as the example to be followed by continuing to be himself a student who is always learning and not a dogmatic teacher.

No great teacher has ever liked to repeat his courses word by word, preferring instead to create something original each year, stimulated by the young minds in his care. Hence all great teachers, remembering the agonies of their student years, have always opposed the present educational system, which, particularly in Europe, is often barbarously medieval in its demands on the student. I myself, educated in Europe and having graduated in medicine in Europe on the highest academic plane, say yet that the high marks I got and the university honors conferred on me left me with only the desire to campaign for a change in that system of medical education for the benefit of the student.

This too is why I believe that every teacher achieves his best educational work not from his professorial chair, however eminent he may be, but through his free and independent work, that work accomplished in the chair of everyday life, where the teacher through his words, his pen, his thought, and, above all, his example exerts his influence not only on students and colleagues, but also on those who read his writings or enjoy from afar the intellectual fruits of his labor.

All this means that the history of medicine, interpreted as a living and dynamic history of dreams, enthusiasms, efforts and achievements, failures and miseries, and as a passionate chronicle of the eternal quest for medical truth, must be the compass to guide student life from its beginning. I also believe that this history must be interpretative, not just descriptive; that is, it must correlate facts and ideas, the past and the present, as a means of anticipating the future. It must also be a romantic epic and a quixotic and idealistic crusade.

The student in our profession becomes more important every day as a catalyst for the school of medicine as well as a future man of medicine. In this day and age, when everyone flaunts his rights, the student has the opportunity to dedicate himself solely to his *duties*—

those imposed by the university and those he himself invents—that is to say, the duties to be a whole man, a good citizen, an expert in his profession, and, above all, to be faithful to those tasks that stimulate in him the vision of history as a spur to his own dreams. If he understands his mission this way, the student—that young prince of our profession—may hold in his hands the power to become the strongest and brightest thread in the fabric of medicine.

THE LEGACY OF ST. LUKE

medicus pius res miranda! "A pious physician is to be admired!" So spoke Pope Pius VII in 1805 in Paris, after the crowning of Napoleon Bonaparte, when he received the homage of a 23-year-old physician who had delivered his doctoral thesis a few months before. The physician was René Hyacinthe Théophile Laënnec, who lived in those stirring days of the Corsican eagle. Despite the philosophic breezes laden with the atheistic breath of Voltaire and Diderot, young Laënnec was a devout Catholic.

The physician in the intimacy of his conscience has often had to face the conflict between his pragmatic education and his spiritual inclination to feel religious awe in front of the marvels of the human body and particularly of the mind, that apparent reflection of a higher intelligence. It is therefore fitting at this time, when the world, threatened by a nuclear apocalypse, prays to God in hundreds of different tongues, to review the relations between religion and medicine as mirrored in the historical evolution of the healing miracle.

Nowadays we no longer study history as a cold chronology of events. We are as interested in *how* and *why* it happened as in *what* happened. We wish to understand history in depth—as a process of spiritual biology that reaches down into the subsoil from which historical events sprang. Everything else stems from this authentic meaning of history, which can be grasped only by realizing that the historical deed is merely the epidermal outgrowth of the subterranean process represented by the spirit in the evolution of history.

From *MD*, the MEDICAL NEWSMAGAZINE, 5:11, December, 1961.

Applying this criterion to the evolution of medicine in its relationship with religion, we can resort to the same "law of dependencies" that Taine borrowed from biology and applied to art. According to this law, there is in every zoologic species—in our case, in every historical process—one fundamental symptomatic fact, around which all the rest gather and take shape. This fundamental fact—dentition in mammals, or form in art—is a vital key to historical dynamics in the history of medicine. Of such nature, in the comparative study of religion and medicine, is the healing miracle and, even more than the miracle as an anecdote, the subterranean current that originated the miracle in each historical period.

To say "miracle" is to say an event whose cause is unknown in essence and mechanism and whose nature is unusual. The word "miracle" comes from the Latin *mirari,* to wonder, and for a miracle to be so considered—as laid down by Thomas Aquinas in his *Questiones Disputatio*—it was required that its cause be unknown and that its effects be in contraposition to those normally obtained. In medicine, any cure attained by a mysterious procedure, the result of which surpassed those obtained by normal methods and was often even contrary to the result that was logically expected, was called a "miracle."

With the first great civilizations of Mesopotamia and Egypt, the healing miracle performed by mystic forces made its appearance. The primitive witch doctor tried to govern disease through magic rituals that sought to enlist demoniac forces, whereas Mesopotamian and Egyptian priests besought the intercession of their deities through prayer. Supplicant religion replaced dictatorial magic, and the priest, instead of standing upright and commanding the demons to leave his patient in peace, knelt before his gods to beg for his patient's cure.

Just as all the elements of a landscape—mountains, lakes, forests —seem tinged with the chromatic tones of the sky overhead, so also do all the deeds that form the scenery of a historical epoch seem tinged with the glow from its horizon. In Greece, medicine flourished under the sign of a dual constellation. The Greek philosophers, whose intellectual courage freed man from the shackles of magic, ushered in a new empirico-rational system of medicine; but ancient fears and hopes endured in sunny myths, which crystallized into the psychotherapeutic cult of Aesculapius, disciple of the kind Centaur Chiron.

The Greek philosophers did not altogether spurn the magico-mystic tendencies that inspired the healing miracle. Hippocrates ranked his faith in the therapeutic value of Corybantic chants next to his humoral pathology; Galen believed in astrology, and in the temples of Apollo, with the incubatory dreams at the foot of the god's golden statue, the healing miracle flourished.

The golden age of the religious healing miracle was reached with the advent of Christianity, which established its power of healing as a basis for medicine. Christ through His word performed many healing miracles. His apostles shared this divine gift. None of them is as important to us as St. Luke, the Evangelist, whom St. Paul in his *Epistle to the Colossians* called "the beloved physician."

In the fourth century, Eusebius supported St. Paul's assertion that St. Luke was a physician. Luke himself made no mention of his occupation, perhaps because the medical profession did not yet enjoy the prestige it was to acquire after Galen. Son of a Greek slave liberated by a Roman family, Luke came from Antioch, where he had practiced medicine. He took up medicine impelled by his passionate desire to help the poor and by his revulsion against slave dealers, who even denied their charges treatment for their ailments.

Fired by his social views, St. Luke believed in a kingdom of God that began on earth. His sociologic zeal is evident in his *Gospel* in which he appears as the champion of charity against superstition. His book was like a banner for the oppressed in the Roman Empire. A remarkable painter and a distinguished wood carver, St. Luke was also the best writer in the New Testament. Sir William Ramsay called him *"the greatest historian who has ever lived, save only Thucydides."* In his gospel Luke preached his *religio medici,* his compassion for the suffering, and expressed his faith in the triumph over body and soul of the divine art of healing. St Luke cites seven healing miracles unmentioned in the other gospels: the raising of the widow's son at Nain, the healing of the woman "possessed by the spirit of disease," of the man who "had the dropsy," of the ten lepers, of Malchus' ear, of Lazarus' sores, and of the Good Samaritan on the road to Jericho. But in the marvelous adventure that was St. Luke's life, the most dramatic event was his meeting with St. Paul.

The two apostles met for the first time at Antioch in 44, when Paul went to consult Luke as a physician. The second occasion was in the year 50 at Troas, the prosperous Aegean port at the mouth of the Hellespont, where Luke possibly practiced among merchants and mariners. Apparently the two apostles met on their departure from Corinth.

When Christianity became the official religion of the Roman state, Christians were allowed to become physicians. Religion and medicine were united for some time. Classic medical texts were used as guides for treating patients, and religious hospitals were built. With the advance of the concept that the sick person was a being chosen by God to suffer the divine trial of disease, and with the founding of the kingdom of God on earth at Byzantium, where the best hospital was the Church, the best physician the priest, the best medicine prayer, and the supreme Healer God, the religious miracle became the supreme form of medical therapy.

Then the Roman Empire began to totter, and on the death of Theodosius, Nordic barbarians finally invaded the empire. While martial storms lashed the world, medieval man, whose existence wavered between the cross and the sword, distorted Hellenic culture through the lenses of zealotry. Monks, in the quiet of their cloisters, guarded the ancient medical heritage, and science became monastic and medicine became bookish. Thus mystic esoterism came to permeate the Latin science that, behind the carved stones of great cathedrals and charter houses, hives of industrious friars culled from ancient Galenic texts.

In France, churches dedicated to the Virgin as healer of the sick were raised everywhere, and saints who "specialized" in healing particular diseases, from St. Sebastian, healer of the plague, to St. Lucia, guardian of the eyes, were worshiped.

From this unwholesome morass of superstition, pseudo-sciences then sprouted like evil blossoms and even physicians practiced theurgic medicine. Arnold of Villanova treated hemorrhages with spells; Nicholas of Salerno treated dropsy with prayer; Agilon treated epilepsy with readings from the Gospels. Magic once again became the basis of the healing miracle. Every person became an entity linked by invisible threads to the stars and demons. Miracle-working deteriorated into quackery and, while erotic degradation contrasted sharply with the romanticism of the troubadours and the knights-errant, symbolized in the *Roman de la Rose,* the cult for curative fetishes increased.

More than to divine causes, a miracle was ascribed to the miracle worker himself and his fetishes. The miracle was based on zodiacal links or on alchemic symbolism, that is, on the bond of faith established between the sick person and the healing relic or magic talisman. The women of the Lyons diocese worshiped at the tomb of a greyhound called St. Guignefort. Mythical relics, such as a feather from the wings of the archangel Gabriel, were worshiped. Temples were crowded with votive offerings of a markedly heathen flavor, and many an offering became a sacred healing relic and was entrusted to the mighty stone-and-crystal walls of a cathedral.

When Giotto's slim, pallid Virgins gave way to Rubens' and Titian's golden-fleshed, opulent Madonnas, the return to the simplicity of the Gospels began. People abandoned their relics and fetishes, their pilgrimages to the cathedrals, and their worship of the Virgin Mary— the greatest spiritual force in the building of cathedrals in the Middle Ages—and of miracle-working saints. They returned to healing through prayers to God. The shapeless chaos of medieval medicine changed into the solid-ribbed structure of the Renaissance and the

278

Reformation, and medicine gradually became a science of measurements. The physician began to change from a miracle-working thaumaturge into a scientist. Against this new sweeping wave the last defenders of healing by quackery—Casanova, Cagliostro, Saint-Germain, Graham, Mesmer—fought a losing rearguard battle.

Paradoxically, as happens in every period of historical crisis, the twentieth century opened with a revival of "miracle-working." Clairvoyants, astrologers, and palmists revived their pseudo-sciences, and the cult of quack remedies and medieval polypharmacy reappeared. "Scientific" medicine also adopted quasi-mystical systems, such as autosuggestion, chromotherapy, and acupuncture.

As in medieval times, when disintegration of the world encouraged a wave of mysticism, the present-day crisis makes man hunger for miracles. It is time now that the conflict between science and religion be resolved. Medicine is learning to consider the patient not as a system of wheels and levers but as a being in anguish who expects his salvation from that "servant of the living God"—the physician.

We physicians should take to ourselves the words of an unknown surgeon: "We are not working for the sake of statistics. Even though the operative surgeon saves only one patient in a thousand, his words, 'Thank you, brother, you have saved my life,' are worth much more than millions of written figures."

As Paracelsus said, the physician springs from God. He should therefore cultivate that relationship of faith with the patient in which resided the key to the healing miracle, which was accomplished through the physician's voice and hands and the patient's faith. For these are the things that ultimately direct the healing drug, the mending scalpel, or the reassuring psychotherapy.

The physician cannot simply break his patient down into cells and atoms in his laboratory. He must, with his perceptive mind, consider both the patient's life history and his spirit. Healing is a sacred act, requiring pure hands and as pure a heart. The physician must be an artist in his science, for his alliance with art will open within him a fount of healing forces for the good of his patients and for his own good.

The conflict between religion and medicine, which caused so much woe to Hoffmann in the eighteenth century, was resolved in the nineteenth by Laënnec, who was a man of science when facing disease—lesions—and a man of faith when facing the patient—a suffering human being. That is to say, before the facts, he was a scientist; before his fellowmen, he was a religious man.

Such, then, is the spiritual legacy bequeathed to us by St. Luke, who besides being a good man was also a physician and a painter and, as such, a patron of both arts. In happy conjunction, medicine, religion, and art are combined in the portrait, all celestial lights and human shadows, of the beloved physician St. Luke, painted four hundred years ago, in the imperial city of Toledo, by a mystic artist whom the Spaniards, who already revered him in his own day, called El Greco.

index

INDEX

Abano, Pietro d', 146–147
Abelard, Peter, 142, 146
Addison, Thomas, 171
Adler, Alfred, 176
Aesculapius, 46–50, 79, 121; staff of, 49–51, 64 n
Aëtius of Amida, 43, 133
Agathon, 73
Agilon, 278
Akhenaton, 118
Albertus Magnus, 131, 146, 148
Albucasis, 140
Alcmaeon of Croton, 123
Alderotti, Taddeo, 145
Aldington, Richard, 32
d'Alembert, J., 162
Alexander of Tralles, 43, 133
Alhazen, 245
All Men are Enemies, 32
All Quiet on the Western Front, 29
Al-Tabari, 138
Alvarez, Walter, 53, 54
Alvárez de Chanca, Diego, 200
Anatomy: in Baroque age, 155–156, 158
  in Enlightenment, 164
  in Nineteenth Century, 170
  in Renaissance, 149–150, 152–153
Anaximenes, 42, 123
Ancient Egypt, medicine in, 117–121
Andernach, J. G. von, 151
Anesthesia, discovery of, 171
Animism, 163
Antibiotics: discovery of, 87–95
  history and, 88
  problems with, 92–93
  prophylaxis and, 93
  research in, 88, 91
  therapy with, 92–94
Antisepsis, 173, 174
Anthropology, in medicine, 256–260
Antoninus Pius, 127
Apollo, 47, 123; arrows of, 53
Arch of Triumph, 29
Archigenes, 127
Archimedes, 91, 124

Architecture, medieval, 144
Aretaeus of Cappadocia, 127
Aristotle, 61, 125, 243
Arnold of Villanova, 131, 145, 146, 278
Arrows, in symbolism, 53
Art: in Ancient Greece, 124
  in Baroque Age, 156–157
  of Byzantium, 133
  Egyptian, 118
  in Enlightenment, 161–162
  eye in, 240–249
  face in, 235–236
  hand in, 238–239
  medieval, 147
  Mesopotamian, 116
  in Moslem Empire, 139
  in Nineteenth Century, 168, 169–170
  of primitive man, 44
  Renaissance, 152–153, 154
  symbols in, 41, 43–44
  in Twentieth Century, 43–44, 176
Asclepiades of Bithynia, 127
Aselli, Gasparo, 156
Asepsis, 173
Ashurbanipal, 115
Asiatics (The), 27
Asoka, Emperor, 121
Ataraxia, symbolic meaning of, 61–62, 66 n
Athenaeus of Attalia, 127
Atom, symbolic meaning of, 59, 61
Auenbrugger, Leopold, 164
Avenzoar, 139, 140
Averroës, 140
Avicenna, 138, 152

Bacon, Sir Francis, 157
Bacon, Roger, 146
Baglivi, Giorgio, 158
Baikie, William Balfour, 200
Balboa, Vasco Núñez de, 193
Balmis, Francisco Xavier de, 166, 201–203
Banting, Sir Frederick, 270
Bantug, José P., 203
Baroja, Pío, 28; quoted, 192–193
Barthez, J., 163
Bartholomaeus Anglicus, 146

Prehistoric medicine, 111–114
Pre-Raphaelites, 169
Priestley, Joseph, 163
Primitive man, art of, 44
Printing, invention of, 150
Prokosch, Frederic, 27
Prophylaxis
    antibiotics and, 93
Psychiatry: in Enlightenment, 165
    in Nineteenth Century, 173
    Renaissance, 153–154
    symbols in, 41
    in Twentieth Century, 179–180
Ptolemy I Soter, 124
Public health: in Enlightenment, 165
    Roman contributions to, 128
Pyrrho, 61
Pythagoras, 119, 123

Quevedo, Francisco Gómez de, 269
Quiet (The) American, 28

Rabelais, François, 32
Ramón y Cajal, Santiago, 18, 83, 101, 198, 203, 255, 270
Ramsay, Sir William, 277
Raphaelien, H. M., 68
Reade, Charles, 20–21
Récamier, Madame de, 169
Redi, F., 158
Reed, Walter, 173
Reid, 163
Religion: iron in, 53–54
    medicine and, 275–280
Remak, R., 170
Remarque, Erich Maria, 29
Rembrandt, van Rijn, 157, 240, 247
Renan, Ernest, quoted, 83, 84
Renaudot, Théophraste, 157
Renoir, Pierre Auguste, 169
Research: in antibiotics, 88, 91
    in medicine, 80–84, 88. 91
    in Twentieth Century, 177
Restlessness (The) of Shanti Andia, 192–193
Reynolds, Jack, 31, 169
Rhazes, 138
Richard Coeur de Lion, 140
Rimbaud, Arthur, 63 n
Ringer, 91

Riolan, Jean, 156
Rochemond, Christine de, 230
Rock (The) Pool, 33
Roentgen, Wilhelm, 44, 91, 172
Rokitansky, Baron Karl von, 170
Rolland, Romain, 19, 22
Romance (The) of Leonardo da Vinci, 20, 21
Romanticism, 166
Rosen, George, 258
Rousseau, Henri, 161, 162, 165, 166
Roux, 87
Rubens, Peter Paul, 157
Rufus of Ephesus, 127
Rugs, symbols in Oriental, 68–70
Rush, Benjamin, 166, 174

Sagan, Françoise, 230
St. Germain, Comte de, 165
Salerno, school at, 144–145
Salvany y Lleopart, Francisco, 166, 202
Sanctorius, 158
Sands (The) of Karakorum, 28
Santos, Nóvoa, 259
Sargon, 115
Sarton, George, 245
Scarpa, A., 164
Scheele, K., 163
Scheu-Riesz, Helen, 228
Schelling, Friedrich von, 168
Schiller, Johann von, 168
Schleiden, M. J., 170
Schönlein, L., 170
Schwann, Theodor, 170
Science: challenges in, 74
    in Enlightenment, 162–166
    experimentation and, 80–81
    mythology of, 78–81
    symbols in, 41
    in Twentieth Century, 176–177
    words and, 17–18, 94–95
Scot, Michael, 146
Scott, Sir Walter, 22
Scribanus, 91
Sea, magic of, 192–197
Sebastian, St., 53
Semmelweis, Ignaz Philipp, 173
Seneca, 61
Sertürner, 87
Servant, The, 33
Servetus, Michael, 151, 155

Ullman, James Ramsey, 28
Unamuno, Miguel de, 227
Unanue, J. Hipólito, 202
United States: in Enlightenment, 166
Nineteenth Century medicine in, 174
Universal (The) Gospel, 22
Universities: medieval, 144–146
in Renaissance, 150–151

Vaccination: Balmis and introduction of, 201–202
discovery of, 165–166
Vagabond Trilogy, 31
Van Helmont, Baptista, 158
Van Swieten, Gerard, 164
Velázquez, 157, 247
Vergil, 19
Verlaine, Paul, 63 n
Vermeer, Jan, 10, 43, 156, 247
Verrocchio, Andrea del, 43
Vesalius, Andreas, 11, 43, 95, 129, 149–150, 152, 153, 154, 246, 270
Vicar (The) of Wakefield, 21–22
Vilallonga, José Luis de, 33
Vile Bodies, 30
Virchow, Rudolf 172, 258
Viscount of Bragelonne, 20
Vitalism, 163
Vivekananda, 19
Vives, Juan Luis, 75, 151, 152, 154
Voltaire, 22, 161, 162

Wagner, Richard, 63 n
Walden, 22
Watt, James, 162, 168
Warren, John Collins, Jr., 171
Watermarks, 63 n, 64 n
Watteau, 162
Waugh, Evelyn, 30
Weizäcker, Victor von, 257
Wells, Horace, 171
West, Jessamyn, quoted, 227
Weyer, Johann, 51, 153–154
Wilkins, George, 228
William of Saliceto, 145
Willis, Thomas, 158
Wilson, Lambert, 159
Winslow, 164
Wirsung, Georg, 157
Witches: medical history and, 48
symbols of, 64 n–65 n
Withering, W., 165
Wolfe, Thomas, 32
Wolff, Kaspar Friedrich, 164
Woman (A) from Bangkok, 31
Women, letter writing and, 226–231
Wooten, Thomas, 159
Words: importance of, 15–16
magic of, 12–13, 17–18
and science, 94–95
World Health Organization, 180
World Medical Association, 180
World (The) of Suzy Wong, 31

Yperman, Jan, 146

Zola, Émile, 43, 172
Zurbarán, Francisco, 157, 247
Zweig, Stefan, 33

ABOUT THE AUTHOR

Born in Cartagena, Spain, Dr. Félix Martí-Ibáñez received his Doctorate in Medicine from the Medical School of the University of Madrid. He then practiced psychiatry in Barcelona and lectured throughout Spain on psychology, medical history, art, and literature. During this period, he also edited several medical and literary journals and wrote two novels and several books on the history of medicine and psychology.

In 1937 he was appointed General Director of Public Health and Social Services of Catalonia, and later, Under-Secretary of Public Health and Social Service for Spain. He officially represented Spain in 1938 at the World Peace Congresses held in Geneva and New York.

Returning to the United States in 1939, the author held positions as Medical Director with three leading pharmaceutical concerns. He participated in the International Congresses of History of Medicine, History of Science, Psychology, and Psychiatry, held in Amsterdam, Paris, Stockholm, Nice, and Zurich. He has also lectured extensively throughout the Western Hemisphere, Europe, Japan, and the Philippines.

Dr. Martí-Ibáñez undertook the publication of several medical journals in 1950 and founded the publishing house of MD Publications, Inc., and in 1957 he created and launched the Medical Newsmagazine *MD,* of which he is the Editor-in-Chief and publisher.

In 1956 the New York Medical College, Flower and Fifth Avenue Hospitals appointed the author Professor and Chairman of the Department of the History of Medicine.

The Order of Carlos J. Finlay was presented to the author in 1955 by the National Academy of Sciences of Cuba in recognition of his educational work in medicine. He is also an honorary member of the outstanding history of medicine societies throughout the world, as well as a member of fifteen American, European and the Near East medical, historical, and literary associations.

Medicohistorical papers by the author have been published in journals throughout the world. He is also the author of the section on the History of Medicine in the latest edition of the *Encyclopedia Americana.* Articles and short stories of his have appeared in *Town and Country, Esquire, Gentry, Art & Architecture,* and fantasy story magazines, and he contributes a column to Latin American newspapers.

Dr. Martí-Ibáñez is now completing a pentalogy on the history of medicine of which this is the fourth book. The first two books in this series, *Centaur: Essays on the History of Medical Ideas* and *Men, Molds, and History,* were published in 1958. *A Prelude to Medical History* appeared in 1961. The fifth volume, *The Fabric of Medicine,* will follow.

Among his current literary endeavors are a book of fantasy stories, *All the Wonders We Seek; Waltz,* a collection of short stories; *A Sword from Toledo,* a historical novel on the times of Vesalius; and *Journey Around Myself,* a recounting of his trip around the world.

A NOTE ON THE TYPE AND DESIGN

The text of this book has been set in Linotype Times Roman, derived from Times New Roman, which was designed in 1932 for the newspaper The Times *of London by Stanley Morison, the well-known typographic adviser to the Monotype Corporation, Ltd. This design was cut simultaneously by both the English Linotype and Monotype companies as an interchangeable face.*

The chapter titles in this book are set in Garamond Bold, a derivative of Garamont, traditionally ascribed to Claude Garamont, the sixteenth-century punch-cutter.

The initial letter of each chapter is in the American Uncial type face, designed by Victor Hammer, distinguished American artist and typographer. The result of thirty years of study and experimentation, American Uncial is derived from German Uncial.

This book was composed, printed, and bound by Rand McNally & Co., Book Manufacturing Division, Chicago, Illinois.

The typography, binding, and jacket designs are by Ted Bergman.